A Chance to Remember – My Life in Medicine

A Chance to Remember – My Life in Medicine

Professor Sir Thomas Symington
BSc, MD, DSc (Hon), FRCPath, FRCP (Glas),
FRSC, FRS (Ed)

M͟C

© Professor Sir T. Symington, 2003

First published in 2003 by
The Memoir Club
Whitworth Hall
Spennymoor
County Durham

British Library Cataloguing-in-Publication data
A catalogue record for this book is available from the British Library

ISBN 1 84104 058 4

The descriptions of events, incidents and characters featured in this book
are true and correct according to the recollections of the author

Printed in the UK by The Cromwell Press, Trowbridge, Wilts

Contents

Illustrations

Figures

To Esther and Alan, and to Robin whose stay with us was too short

Introduction

I HAD BEEN RETIRED ten years when my sight became impaired. I had
cataracts and required surgery. The operation, I am pleased to say, was a
success. The result was dramatic, and my sight completely restored. During
the period of recovery, I had time to think about the past and remember
many events that had happened. It was then I decided to write my memoirs,
which in time, I hoped, would interest my grandchildren and their descendants.
I wanted them to know their forbears as persons and not names which, in
time, weather would erase from their tombstones.

It was not long before I began to appreciate the loss of valuable secretarial
assistance, which for many years I had taken for granted. Accordingly, *The
Concise Oxford Dictionary* and an old school grammar book were my constant
companions as I embarked on this new venture.

There were relevant scientific and medical publications I could consult and
from special sources learn about my ancestor William Symington who, in 1801,
built the *Charlotte Dundas*, the world's first practical steamship. I was able to
piece together information on the beginning, in 1633, of the moorland Ayrshire
parish of Muirkirk, where I was born. The standard of living of the people
was poor and scurvy not uncommon in the population. The church wielded
considerable power and this lasted until the middle of the nineteenth century.

The rural landscape of this small parish changed abruptly in the last years
of the eighteenth century when vast deposits of coal, iron ore and limestone,
worth £140 million, were discovered on the outskirts of the village. Coal mines
were sunk, blast furnaces built and soon iron was being produced and
transported in quantity to the expanding towns and cities of Scotland. Slag
from the blast furnaces was used by John Loudon McAdam to construct the
hundred yards of road he made from the furnaces to the gas works. Indeed
this was the first road McAdam constructed, and it was in the Furnace Road
Public School, built on land adjacent to the road, that six university professors
and numerous arts, science, and medical graduates of my generation received
their elementary education.

I never kept a diary and was pleased to find I had a clear recall of interesting and important events in my life. Indeed, in time, I began to enjoy these periods of recollection, and there was one particular incident I remembered, which was to shape my career. In 1933 I had completed the first year of a science course at Glasgow University and in the autumn of that year I attended a lecture in biochemistry which was delivered by a young man who had graduated in the subject. I knew nothing about biochemistry, but his lecture excited me, and his enthusiasm for the subject was so infectious. When I returned to the university I altered my course to study biochemistry and graduated in it in 1936; and to extend the scope of this subject, I took the advice of my professor, enrolled in medicine and graduated in 1941. It was during this course I met and later married my wife, Margaret, who graduated with me in medicine.

I found the course long and tiring and neither the lectures I attended, nor the staff I met, kindled my enthusiasm to specialise in any branch of medicine. Nevertheless I could remember with amusement the undergraduate course in midwifery, when it was compulsory to deliver fifteen babies. This was done in the patient's home, usually in the slum districts of Glasgow. The patients had no doctor of their own and delivery was carried out by two medical or nurse students. Most of us enjoyed the experience and everyone had stories to tell. My first delivery was carried out on the second evening of the German air raids on Glasgow, and it was an experience I would remember. But it was the kindness and gratitude shown by the poor people and their relatives for the little help we gave, that touched me and made me decide, on qualification, to spend some two years in general practice. This was a worthwhile experience I would never regret.

In those days tuberculosis was a disease dreaded by everyone. My paternal grandfather and an uncle had died of tuberculosis and in general practice I came across many forms of the illness, for it affected young children and adolescents, as well as old men and women. If I was to learn more about tuberculosis I would need to look for a post in a sanatorium. I was fortunate to be appointed to East Fortune Sanatorium as assistant to Dr Charles Cameron, who was an outstanding physician. During the six months I spent with him I saw all forms of tuberculosis and learned how to deal with them.

Now it was time to make use of my training in science; a chance remark was made to my wife by a well-respected medical officer of health, that a career in pathology would allow me to do this. I obtained an appointment as an assistant to Professor John Blacklock in the University Department of Pathology at Glasgow Royal Infirmary. He was an authority on tuberculosis, and a fine teacher; under his supervision I would receive an excellent training in pathology.

Graduation photograph of the author in Medicine, 1941.

Pathology is defined as 'the science of bodily diseases' and understandably the meaning of the word has changed as more has been learned about
the nature and cause of different diseases. From the time of Hippocrates

Graduation photograph of Margaret in Medicine, 1941.

in the fifth century BC, until the middle of the eighteenth century, disease was believed to result from an abnormal balance of the four bodily humours. Accordingly, treatment of patients by purgatives, emetics, enemas and bloodletting was intended to restore the balance of those humours. Humoral pathology seemed an appropriate term by which to refer to disease processes. During this period human autopsies were illegal and knowledge of the appearance of human organs was based on reports of dissections of pigs and monkeys by Galen, whose books were widely acclaimed, and whose descriptions accepted until the fifteenth century. When human dissections became possible Vesalius correctly recognised the structure of the human body and created *anatomy* as we know it today. When human autopsies were performed, abnormalities were discovered in many of the organs and the term *morbid anatomy* used to describe them. Even at the beginning of the nineteenth century those abnormal changes in organs were attributed to an imbalance of bodily humours and treatment of patients by purgatives and bleeding still used.

In the middle of the nineteenth century anatomists and pathologists in Germany learned to prepare and stain thin slices of normal and diseased organs and examine them under the newly developed compound microscope. They found all organs were composed of cells which were altered in appearance by disease. Humoral pathology was replaced now by *cellular pathology* and in time pathologists described the cellular or morphological appearance of human organs in every disease. Nevertheless cellular pathology was a descriptive discipline and as Rudolf Virchow declared in his Presidential address to the German Pathological Society in 1898, 'We must strive to understand what is happening during a morbid process and not be content merely with the existent condition.' The discovery of bacteria as a cause of infectious disease established *bacteriology* as a branch of pathology. When chemical changes were found in the blood and body fluids in some illnesses *clinical chemistry* or *chemical pathology* was assured a place within the ambit of pathology.

When I joined Professor Blacklock's department of pathology in 1943 there were divisions of morbid anatomy or cellular pathology, bacteriology and chemical pathology, and he insisted I receive training in all three. Since that time pathology has expanded in medical schools and hospitals to include departments of haematology, immunology, cytology and forensic pathology, which is the special branch of pathology dealing with such things as murder and rape.

I appreciated the need to become proficient in diagnostic or cellular pathology, but my training in chemistry made it possible for me to try and find out what was happening in both normal and diseased cells. The opportunity to do this came unexpectedly when the professor called me into his room and pointed to two jars on a table. Each jar contained a black adrenal gland tumour. The patients from whom they had been removed had died after the operation. The tumours, he told me, were phaeochromocytomas and when handled by the surgeon during operation, they released massive amounts of adrenaline into the blood, and the shock produced had killed the patient.

Wedding photograph of Margaret, 19 March 1943.

This was my introduction to adrenal gland research which would occupy more than twenty-five years of my professional life. It would take me to research laboratories in the United States, Canada and Europe, where I would make life-long friends in science and medicine. As time passed I would introduce those with adrenal interests to some of the problems I encountered in adrenal pathology.

My adrenal research was sufficiently advanced to be submitted to the University of Glasgow for the degree of Doctor of Medicine (MD) when, in November 1947, I was called up to the army. After initial army training I was posted to Malaya, with the rank of Major, in charge of pathology and stationed at the British Military Hospital in Kuala Lumpur. I was in post only a few weeks when the communist uprising took place and work in the laboratory soon increased. I had to undertake the preparation of culture media and transfusion fluids which, until then, had been shipped from the United Kingdom. As the number of army units in Malaya increased, I arranged to blood group every soldier in the army camps around Kuala Lumpur and had no problem supplying blood and transfusion fluids for the casualties of the ambushes which, in time, increased in frequency.

Tropical medicine, I found, was very gratifying, since the laboratory played a key role in diagnosis, and the patients invariably recovered with treatment. The military hospital was situated close to the world-famous Institute of Medical Research directed by Dr Raymond Lewthwaite whose studies on the disease scrub typhus, and its cure by chloromycetin, would receive world acclaim. I was present in Malaya when the American Typhus Research Team carried out trials with chloromycetin, and was involved with the army patients who had contracted the illness and were treated successfully with the new drug. In addition to Dr Lewthwaite, I had regular discussions with the bacteriologist, Dr Richard Greene and with Dr John Field, the eminent malariologist whose book *The Thick Film Technique for Malaria Diagnosis* was written and illustrated when he was a prisoner of war in Changi jail in Singapore. This distinguished trio was a source of inspiration and I could rely on their help with any problem I encountered. I would look back with pleasure on my army experience in Malaya, the people I met and worked with, and the influence some would have on my future.

I was still in the army when Professor Blacklock left Glasgow to take the Chair of Pathology in St Bartholomew's Medical School in London. Professor G. L. Montgomery was appointed to the Glasgow Chair and to my delight appointed me *in absentia* to a vacant senior lecturer post in his department. When I returned to Glasgow Royal Infirmary in January 1950, exciting new changes had taken place in medicine. Aneurin Bevan had introduced the National Health Service, hospitals were no longer dependent on voluntary subscriptions and salaries so improved that I could afford to go full time and not have recourse to private practice.

It was Bevan's intention to raise the standard of treatment of patients in corporate or poor law hospitals to that found in university teaching hospitals. This was achieved in Glasgow by making the committee of management of each of the five teaching hospitals responsible for patient care in all local government hospitals in the area of the city allocated to them. Furthermore, the endowments of teaching hospitals were placed under the control of the committee of management and used to improve the facilities of all hospitals under their control. The five teaching hospitals and their management committees were given in addition the responsibility to develop the medical services of the counties which came within the Western Regional Hospital Board. Thus Glasgow Royal Infirmary became responsible for developing the medical services in hospitals in Lanarkshire, as well as those allocated to them in Glasgow. The Principal of the University, Sir Hector Hetherington and the Chairman of the Western Regional Hospital Board, Dr Alexander Bowman, worked closely to make the Glasgow health service a success.

Under Professor Montgomery, endowment funds became available to extend and improve facilities and provide scientific equipment for the department of pathology. Money for research came from successive applications to the Scottish Hospitals Endowment Research Trust (SHERT) which was founded by a committee under Sir Sydney Smith. £250,000 was taken from the endowments of each large teaching hospital in Scotland to create the trust, which was advised by an Advisory Committee for Medical Research (ACMR) consisting of senior scientists and clinicians from the Scottish medical schools.

My adrenal research prospered in this new environment and with a grant from SHERT, Sir Alistair Currie and I carried out a study on the effect of severe stress on human pituitary and adrenal glands. During this period the enlightened board of Glasgow Royal Infirmary funded travel grants. This encouraged senior medical and nursing staff to travel abroad and see the new advances in medicine and nursing, some of which were introduced into the hospital on their return. I had been awarded one of the travel grants and was in the process of arranging a three-month visit to basic science and clinical departments in the United States and Canada when Professor Montgomery accepted an invitation to the Regius Chair of Pathology in Edinburgh. I was thirty-nine when, in the summer of 1954 I applied for and was appointed to the St Mungo Notman Chair of Pathology at Glasgow Royal Infirmary, Sir Roy Cameron and Dr Lewthwaite acting as my external referees.

The appointment delayed my visit to North America until the autumn of 1955, when I spent three months visiting departments where adrenal research was in progress. I attended the Laurentian Hormone Conference, which on this occasion was held in Estes Park, Colorado, and had the good fortune to meet most of the scientists whose departments I had arranged to visit. My room-mate on that occasion was Arnold Lazarow, Professor of Anatomy at the Medical School in Minneapolis. I had not intended to go there, but changed my itinerary to visit him and was not disappointed. His research on diabetes was impressive and the study of insulin production by single pancreatic islet cells of fish was years ahead of its time. I arranged for one of my assistants to work in his department, and Lazarow's death at an early age was a great loss to medical science.

It was during my visit to Minneapolis I met Professor David Glick whose adrenal research would have a profound effect on my own studies. He was Head of the Division of Histo, and Cyto,chemistry in the medical school and had developed a technique to produce serial 6μ sections from different levels or zones of the adrenal gland. He refined well,established chemical techniques and developed new ones to determine the concentration of chemical sub, stances and enzymes in the sections whose position in the adrenal gland he could identify histologically. During this visit I began to realise my human adrenal studies lacked quantitation and this I rectified by sending assistants to work with Glick and introduce his techniques on their return to Glasgow. My friendship with David and his family progressed with the passage of time. When he moved to Stanford University, California, he invited me with my family, to spend a sabbatical year with him, and some years later he came to my department in Glasgow as the Macfarlane Visiting Professor.

Adrenal research was making steady progress world wide by the 1960s. A large variety of steroid hormones had been synthesised and their chemical structure determined. Chemical and later more sensitive radioimmune assays were developed to determine the concentration of those hormones in body fluids. The enzymes involved in steroid biosynthesis were identified and their site in cell organelles located.

Senior steroid chemists had joined our adrenal group which was well supported by grants from the Cancer Research Campaign (CRC), Medical Research Council (MRC) and the National Institute of Health in the United States. Our morphological and chemical studies were conducted exclusively on human adrenal glands removed surgically from patients as part of the treatment for breast cancer. The results obtained over the years provided a clearer picture of the normal structure of the human adrenal gland and a better understanding of the role in steroid hormone production played by the cells of different zones of the adrenal cortex (See Figures 1–4, pp. 339–42). No longer need we be content to describe the complicated histological appearance of the adrenal cortex in disease, now we could understand and explain it. Out studies were presented at meetings in this country and abroad, and in 1961 with financial support from the Principal of the University, an International Conference on the Adrenal Cortex was held in Glasgow.

It was pleasant to remember the colleagues who were present in the department when I returned from the army. Some were research,minded and had been to the United States on a travel grant, others took advantage of the arrangements I had made and spent a year in a basic science department in America. Each had developed his own research and in the late 1950s, four left the department to take up senior posts in England; in time all were appointed to Chairs of Pathology in this country. Their departure and that of other colleagues to National Health Service consultant appointments, left vacancies which were filled by a new dynamic group of young medical men. All of them had been students in my undergraduate course of pathology and some, like myself, had taken an honours degree in science. They worked in my research group during university vacations and I supported them from my research grants. Some came to pathology as part of a training for a career in medicine or surgery and a few remained to make a career in academic pathology. In addition to their research activities, everyone received a training in morbid anatomy and all took part in undergraduate teaching. When I left Glasgow in 1970, many of the academic group were ready to move, and it is particularly gratifying to me and to the two senior members of staff with whom they worked, that eleven of that dynamic group have been appointed to Chairs of Pathology in this country, Canada and the United States. While I will always remember the 1960s for the stimulating influence of the group, other important events took place, some of which would determine the final years of my professional life.

In 1962 the Porritt Report on Medical Aid to Developing Countries decided it would be better to train most of the graduates in their own country and receive financial and technical aid to do so. I was a member of the delegation from Glasgow University that spent two weeks in East Africa to assess the medical needs of Uganda, Kenya and Tanzania. Our recommendation that Glasgow should help to establish a medical school in Nairobi was accepted, and for ten years, senior and junior medical, nursing and technical staff were seconded to Nairobi. A fine new hospital with excellent laboratories was built, and a senior member of my staff appointed to the Foundation Chair of Pathology. A smaller medical school was developed in Dar-es-Salaam and over a period of six years I seconded three of my young colleagues. They ran the laboratory services and taught pathology in the medical school. Three young African graduates were selected and came to Glasgow to train in pathology. In time they returned to take over the department in Tanzania.

In 1965, I was appointed Visiting Professor of Pathology at Stanford University and during the year I was there, used the excellent facilities of the Lane library to check references and begin writing my book *The Functional Pathology of the Human Adrenal Gland.*

I could reflect on the valuable experience gained in the late 1960s, when I was a member of the scientific committee of the Cancer Research Campaign (CRC) and Medical Research Council (MRC). I learned that preparation of an application for grant support is time-consuming and should be submitted in such a way that the assessors have no difficulty understanding what research the applicant has done, what he/she wishes to do and what staff and finance are required to undertake the study. When this assessment is made in association with a site visit to the applicant's department to discuss the project, a better appreciation is obtained of the value of the proposal. I found this to be so when I was a member of the CRC/MRC committee which visited the Institute of Cancer Research, London, in the summer of 1969.

The Institute has an interesting history and like most people, I was not familiar with its composition or the nature and location of its constituent departments. When the world's first cancer hospital, the Royal Marsden Hospital, was built in Fulham Road in 1865 it had a small department of pathology and cancer research. However in 1911 a new Cancer Hospital Research Institute was built in the grounds of the cancer hospital and the first Institute Director, Dr Alexander Paine, appointed. Although he attracted excellent scientific staff to the Institute, he was dismissed in 1920 for some unknown reason. His successor, Dr Alexander Leitch, was interested in chemical carcinogens and in 1922 brought Dr Ernest Kennaway to the Institute as chemical pathologist. When Leitch died in 1931, Kennaway was made Director and under his control the Institute received world acclaim when its chemists synthesised the first pure chemical substance to produce cancer when applied to the skin of mice. In 1939 the Institute moved out of the hospital to occupy more extensive quarters in the red brick building which had been the Freemason's Hospital in Fulham Road. This move was made possible by the benefaction of Sir Alfred Chester Beatty whose name is now incorporated in the title. The inscription in gold letters across the face of the building reads *Chester Beatty Research Institute* and to show its origin from the Marsden hospital are the words *Cancer Hospital (Free)*. In the jubilee year of the opening of the Cancer Hospital Research Institute in 1911, an extension was made into an adjacent building to provide further accommodation and laboratories for the increasing number of research scientists attracted to the Chester Beatty. This is the name by which the Institute is known now in the world of medical science.

In time the Chester Beatty Institute acquired an experimental station at Pollards Wood, Chalfont St Giles, Buckinghamshire, where research on biological mutation, tracer biochemistry, nucleic acid and protein chemistry was to be done. Later a germ-free animal colony was built and housed in a modern building. The Chester Beatty Institute was dispersed further when new laboratories were built at Sutton, Surrey, to house a department of tumour immunology. When Kennaway retired in 1946, Sir Alexander Haddow was made Director of the Chester Beatty and under his stewardship, chemotherapy was added to surgery and radiotherapy in the treatment of patients with cancer. The Chester Beatty, with its large staff of synthetic chemists, was ideally suited to play the role in the development of chemotherapy drugs. The introduction of this form of therapy increased the need to have physicians who could carry out clinical trials on the drugs. In 1962 a small clinical research department was created with a clinical director in charge. The development of the Chester Beatty Institute on three sites made effective control of research more difficult and led to considerable reduplication of effort.

While the Chester Beatty was the largest section, the Institute of Cancer Research had large academic units in radiotherapy and physics each under the control of a director who in addition, had clinical responsibilities in the Royal Marsden Hospital. Initially both departments were located in the hospital in Fulham Road, but the equipment required to treat patients was becoming more sophisticated and expensive to run and space for expansion at the Royal Marsden in Fulham Road was limited. Due to the drive and enthusiasm of Professor Sir David Smithers, academic departments of radiotherapy and physics and a radiology unit were established in new accommodation in a large open site in the country at Sutton, Surrey, where Sir David built, with Government funds, a modern hospital with one hundred and fifty beds. This allowed space for some redevelopment of radiotherapy in the hospital at Fulham Road which still retained a radiology and physics department as well as pathology and biochemistry which had remained when the Chester Beatty Institute was formed in 1939.

Over the years, research was undertaken to study the effects of radiation on normal and malignant cells, how radiation affected the delicate mechanism which controls the cell cycle during cell division. In time a department of biophysics, under a director, was formed and occupied a building at Sutton.

In the autumn of 1969 the University of London declared a moratorium on all academic promotions and appointments to departments in the Institute; and a committee of senior academic and lay members of the Institute, under Sir Edward Hale, was set up to examine staffing and administration of departments within it. The Hale Committee recommended there should be appointed an overall Director of the Institute, who would have administrative responsibility for all Institute departments. This was accepted by the Committee of Management of the Institute. In addition, a committee of senior Institute scientists recommended a staff redundancy programme which involved the dismissal of twenty-five scientists. This, understandably, led to great upheaval in the Institute.

In the middle of December I was invited to meet Lord Halsbury, who informed me I had been recommended for the post of first overall Director of the Institute of Cancer Research. After discussing the problems, he agreed

I should have time to think things over and talk only to my wife and the Principal of Glasgow University, Sir Charles Wilson.

Unfortunately Sir Charles was out of the country so I could not have the benefit of his advice. I was dependent on the reaction of my family to the decision I would make. Most of the young medical colleagues I had brought to the department at Glasgow Royal Infirmary were ready to move to senior appointments. My adrenal research could be continued in London, and my book *The Functional Pathology of the Adrenal Gland* had been published. The few senior colleagues I would leave behind had their own research interests, and the professor who would be appointed in my place would be free to introduce his own line of research, and have sufficient vacancies to introduce new young staff. While there was no compelling reason for me to remain, it would not be easy to leave the department where I had spent twenty-seven happy years.

I had discussed my involvement in the East Africa Medical School with Lord Halsbury who saw no objection to me continuing with it. Indeed, he felt it would be possible to second scientists from the Institute to help with the venture. My main concern was the reaction of my family to the move, since we had built our retirement home in Glasgow. We discussed the problems I would have to deal with in the Institute and while everyone agreed it was a daunting task, in the end it was agreed I should accept the challenge.

When I took up the appointment in the summer of 1970, I found many small isolated groups in the Institute and a considerable amount of reduplication of research. There was an obvious need to create a proper divisional structure, appoint someone to head each division, and incorporate all small units into the appropriate division so that all research could be co-ordinated. The staff redundancies, with their adverse publicity for the Institute, affected the mood of the staff. I decided to delay any decision on divisional reorganisation. Instead, I allowed each scientist to prepare and submit a grant submission to justify their research and win financial support for themselves and staff.

All grant applications were submitted by September 1970 and I received the report of the MRC/CRC grants committee in January 1971. The result was alarming. They approved only £400,000 of the £1 million requested, but agreed to allocate the £1 million until 1977. In the intervening years it would be my responsibility to reorganise the research work of the Institute so that the yearly allocation could be justified and even exceeded by 1977. The grants committee allocated only thirty tenured posts to the Institute and in addition to those scientists whose research was approved and supported, there were forty-five senior scientists who considered they had tenure although their research was unsupported. They were now supernumerary to the establishment.

Now it was time to create institute divisions to which everyone would be attached and appoint someone in charge of each division. I allocated the tenured posts according to the size of the division, larger ones received two or three posts, smaller divisions, one post. The forty-five scientists who were supernumerary to the establishment were allocated to divisions and the head of each division given the responsibility to involve them in the research of the division and win financial support for them in future grant submissions.

All forty-five were well-qualified and highly competent scientists who, not unnaturally, had lost their creativity and found it difficult to win support on their own. When they were retrained and redeployed to become part of a new research group under a younger creative scientist, their previous research experience soon made them valuable members of the new group. They were treated with dignity and they responded. When each division was created, new applications for grant support were submitted, and by the end of 1975 only three of the original forty-five scientists were unsupported.

Once the divisional structure was in order and the retraining and redeployment programme progressing, the next step was to attract into the Institute young scientists who, in time, would be the leaders of the Institute. I was about to make a start on this when, late one evening in the autumn of 1971, I received a call from Mr Dick Kent, House Governor of the Royal Marsden Hospital. Apparently two young businessmen had walked into his office and said they represented Mr Daniel K. Ludwig, one of the richest men in the United States. He wished to set up an Institute in conjunction with the Royal Marsden Hospital and the Institute of Cancer Research. When they asked me what money I wanted to set up this combined effort, I felt sure they had escaped from a lunatic asylum. However, I explained I needed enough finance to bring young scientists into the Institute and create an academic Division of Medicine under a professor who would help cement the link between the Royal Marsden Hospital and the Institute of Cancer Research. I would need $1 million over the next five years. They phoned New York and spoke to Mr Ludwig who agreed to my request. This was how the Ludwig Institute for Cancer Research began and how I became its first director.

In time the finances of the Institute of Cancer Research improved, the divisions were winning financial support, voluntary or public subscriptions were increasing and by 1976, the Institute was able to provide the finance to build the Ludwig Institute laboratories in the grounds of the Royal Marsden Hospital at Sutton. Ludwig, in all its ventures, would not provide any finance for bricks and mortar, so I rented the buildings to the Ludwig Institute at £90,000 yearly and over the ten-year period Ludwig agreed to be in London, was able to recoup the money spent by the Institute of Cancer Research.

When the forerunner of the Institute of Cancer Research was built in 1911, it was sited in the grounds of the hospital. In 1939 it moved a few hundred yards along Fulham Road and its link with the hospital became very tenuous. When I began the retraining and redeployment programme of senior scientists, it appeared to me that many Institute scientists could provide the expertise needed by clinicians to improve their clinical research. Initially there was resistance to this, but in the end both groups accepted and in time enjoyed the collaborative studies that were established.

As time passed, I met the Directors of many Cancer Research Institutes in the United States, France, Germany, Russia, Poland and Hungary, and visited their Institutes on a number of occasions. My association with Dr Gerald Murphy of Roswell Park Memorial Institute, Buffalo, and Dr Lee Clark of MD Anderson, Houston was very rewarding, and from them I learned of the negotiations which preceded the signing of the Cancer Act 1971 by President Nixon. A vast sum of money was allocated to cancer research in the United States, and to create comprehensive cancer centres in the medical schools of that country. In Russia I learned from Professor Blokhin how his massive new cancer centre in Moscow was financed by a process called a sybbotnik, when every citizen in the then USSR worked for nothing one Saturday in the year, the money raised being used for a certain project.

Things were beginning to run smoothly in the Institute and my wife and I arranged to spend Christmas 1975 with our son Robin and his wife Sandra in Nairobi where he was in business. Our flight had been booked when we received a cable that Robin was ill and returning to Britain. Sadly he had developed cancer and in spite of treatment at the Royal Marsden Hospital, he died sixteen months later. He was only thirty years of age and his illness and death at such an early stage in his life had a profound effect on us. Most Institute problems had been resolved. There was a proper pyramidal structure. Each division had financial support, and the relationship with the hospital was good. I had not the same enthusiasm for the job and in September 1977 resigned as Director of the Institute and retired to Troon in Scotland.

When a patient develops cancer, the doctor's effort is directed to *cure* the condition. It was during my association with the Royal Marsden Hospital and St Christopher's Hospice in London that I appreciated a time would come when *cure* in some instances was unlikely, and efforts had to be directed towards *care* of the patient during the terminal phase of the illness. My wife and I became more conscious of this when we became involved personally. Now we were able to understand more clearly the need for suitable measures to control the pain and distressing symptoms which occur during the terminal phase of the illness. Although we never required bereavement counselling, we could appreciate the value of such a service when the end came.

During my first year of retirement I was surprised to find cancer referred to as 'The Big C'. People were frightened to talk about it. Most knew nothing about its cause, and many had a bad experience with close relatives during the terminal phase of the illness. All would have received benefit from bereavement counselling. It was this experience that convinced Margaret and me there was a need to establish a hospice in Ayrshire and we could work together to achieve this. Initially there was an adverse public reaction to a hospice, which many people regarded as a place shut away in the woods, where patients with cancer went to die. Over a period of years we talked at meetings of church guilds, rural institutes, rotary clubs and schools, until we convinced the public that the hospice was a place of special caring, where patients could spend their last few days with relatives, in a caring atmosphere, free from pain, to die with dignity.

I was not surprised at the enthusiastic support we received from the nursing community, since they had the responsibility of dealing with the problems of terminal care. However, I did not bargain for the hostility and opposition of most general practitioners, hospital doctors and members of the Area Health Board. Nevertheless, after many years, and with the enthusiastic support of representatives of Age Concern, Ayrshire, an Ayrshire Hospice Project was started and within two years sufficient funds were raised to build the Ayrshire Hospice which has been a great success.

I was at the stage of completing this manuscript when in 1989 the Government published its White Paper on the Health Service. It caused me to reflect on the years I had spent in medicine, the changes I had seen and the part doctors played to make the service applauded throughout the world. Undoubtedly times were changing. The Health Service was the largest employer of labour in the country, and very expensive to run. There was a need to control and justify expense, and I could see the need to employ general managers in the hospital services to achieve this. What did disturb me was to find the influence of doctors on decision making curtailed and hospitals controlled by non-medical general managers. It could be argued that doctors were free to carry out the work for which they were trained, and they were equipped with the most expensive diagnostic and surgical instruments to do so. Naturally, reduction on the size of waiting lists and the length of time a patient requires to be in hospital must be considered by administrators with fiscal responsibilities. Keyhole surgery will shorten the time a patient needs to be in hospital and cut the cost to the service. In time this form of treatment will be extended to deal with cancer, and while this form of therapy might reduce a patient's time in hospital and be justified if the tumour is localised, how can the surgeon determine if the patient has metastasis? There must be a proper assessment of this and other forms of therapy and I am quite convinced that the internal audit committees which have been created will find it difficult to deal with those and other problems.

The more I have pondered the new developments and proposals for the Health Service, the more convinced I have become of the need to appoint a *Medical Director* to every hospital eligible for Trust status. This man or woman should be in the fifty to fifty-five age group and be an experienced clinician, respected by clinical colleagues. The divisional structure which exists in hospitals at present should be retained and the medical director should act as chairman of a divisional group. He/she would be in a position to know what is happening to the clinical services in the hospital and to deal with problems as they arise. The Government should create a series of external audit committees which would visit each clinical, nursing, administrative and catering service in the hospital once every five years and determine what each service has done, what they want to do, and what staff and finance they need and can justify. If the present arrangement of a *General Manager* is extended by the appointment of a *Medical Director* and the introduction of a quinquennial site visit to every service in the hospital, a Health Service can be developed in which money follows the patient and not, as at present, the patient follows the money. In present circumstances it is doubtful if this will ever be achieved. We can only hope it will.

CHAPTER 1

William Symington and the World's First Practical Steamship

IT WAS CUSTOMARY at Cumnock Academy, the secondary school I attended in Ayrshire, Scotland, for pupils in the English class to learn and recite the whole of a poem by the great English and Scottish poets. The amount we learned, each period, depended on the time the English master took to read the morning paper; after which he would dictate an appreciation of one of the great authors and poets, and this we would study at home and use for the university entrance examinations in English literature. Today this type of teaching would find little acceptance by modern educationalists, yet after a period of more than sixty years I remember much of what I learned and derive pleasure when I find myself in circumstances where it is apt to quote some lines from those poems or in an evening when I open my *Oxford Book of English Verse* and turn, instinctively and with more understanding, to the poems I learned so laboriously in my youth.

> Five years have passed, five summers,
> With the length of five long winters.

This introduction to Wordsworth's 'Tintern Abbey' is, I feel, quite apposite for it represents the period of time I was in London as Director of the Institute for Cancer Research. For the first few years my summers and winters were quite arduous, and it was some time before a light would appear at the end of the tunnel and I could hope to fulfil my mission. The transfer to London, I thought, might be traumatic for the family, but to my delight they coped very well. My wife, Margaret, had settled in our new home in Surrey and was happy to work once more as a doctor, in the geriatric unit in Cuddington hospital. This was a happy place, with pleasant medical, nursing and ancillary colleagues, where the patients were well cared for. Our daughter, Esther, who

1

had studied beauty therapy in Sloane Square, became interested in cosmetic camouflaging and went to the United States where she met a young American soldier, Bob Le Borgne, and in the Spring of 1975 they were married in the Mexican border town of El Paso. Our second son Alan had completed a degree at Cambridge, and was in his final year in medicine at St George's Hospital in London. Robin, our elder son had remained in Glasgow and married Sandra in September 1970. He appeared to have recovered from the many illnesses he had suffered over the years; had completed his training, with Stenhouse, as an insurance broker and in the autumn of 1974 we had seen them off to Nairobi to work there with Minet of London. Everything seemed fine, his years of illness were behind him and he looked forward to his new life with great expectancy.

The evening before they flew to Africa the boys were capering with each other when Robin injured his groin. He said nothing to me, and next evening he and Sandra flew to Africa where he worked hard, enjoyed the country and the game parks and took cine films of the animals in their natural surroundings. At the age of twenty-eight he was well settled and making a success of his career in this beautiful country. I knew Kenya well, had helped to create and develop the magnificent new Medical School in Nairobi and a smaller one in Dar-es-Salaam in Tanzania; and had visited both countries on many occasions. Margaret had never been to either country and we looked forward to spending Christmas 1975 with Robin and Sandra in Nairobi, visiting the hospitals once more and some of the game parks and have New Year with them at a hotel in Mombasa on the Indian Ocean. They had arranged everything for us and I had bought the flight tickets to Nairobi, but,

> The best laid schemes o' mice and men,
> Gang aft agley [wrong]
> An lea's us nought but grief an' pain
> For promised joy.

Next day, in early October, we received a telegram: Robin was ill and would be on the plane from Nairobi and we were to meet him at London Airport.

The pain he felt the night before he left for Nairobi, was in the testis, not the groin, and during the year he had been away he had experienced attacks of excruciating pain. The family doctor he consulted in Nairobi treated him for hook worm. He had gone with Sandra, on vacation, to the Seychelles where he had another severe attack, but on this occasion he was seen by an Irish surgeon who said he required immediate surgery. If this was so, Robin decided he was coming back to the Royal Marsden Hospital, which was linked with the Institute of Cancer Research, and the Irish surgeon agreed. My wife and I met him at the airport and we went directly to hospital where he was examined by Dr Tim McElwain, one of the medical consultants and Dr Michael Peckham, Professor of Radiotherapy. They sent him to St Bartholomew's Hospital where the swelling was removed and dispatched for histological examination to Dr Roger Pugh with whom I had had a close association for more than twenty years. We were both members of the British Testicular Tumour Panel, Roger was the secretary and a world authority on the subject, and for the last ten years I had been chairman of the panel. That evening my telephone rang, it was Roger.

'Tom,' he said, 'I'm sorry to tell you it's a malignant teratoma and one of the worst I've seen.'

I couldn't answer him, I knew how serious it was and understood why Robin had had such attacks of severe pain; this occurs when the tumour is growing and there is a haemorrhage into the growth. If only I had asked him about the initial injury to his groin the evening before he flew to Nairobi our chances might have been so much better; but would he have agreed to stay? I doubted it.

I told Margaret the painful and distressing news and on the way to see him in hospital we kept wondering how we would break it to him; we needn't have worried. He was sitting up in bed when we entered the ward and before we could speak he said, 'I've seen the surgeon and he has told me I've got cancer. I'm getting home tomorrow and have to go to the Surrey branch of the Marsden for tests.' Then looking at us he continued, 'I want you to phone Sandra in Nairobi and I want you both to promise to look after her if I don't make it.'

In all the illnesses he had experienced he had borne them with courage and this one was to be no different.

Next day he went to the radiology department of the hospital and when I saw him a radio-opaque dye had been injected between the toes of the foot corresponding to the side from which the tumour had been removed.

'What's this for?' he asked me. I explained that the dye would pass up the lymphatic or drainage system of the leg and into the abdomen, then the chest and an x-ray would help the radiologist to outline the tumour in the lymphatics and determine the extent of the spread and the treatment that should be needed. The dye, I explained, would remain in the lymphatics for up to two years and subsequent x-rays would show how effective the treatment was. Indeed the tumour had spread into the abdomen where there was a swelling about the size of a hen's egg, but nothing was visible in the chest, although small deposits of tumour could still be there. The clinicians decided to treat the abdominal tumour by radiotherapy and after some weeks when this tumour had been dealt with he would receive chemotherapy for any tumours which must be present but were too small to be seen on x-ray. Cancer, I explained to him, was like an iceberg, most of the tumour can't be seen, and even when treatment reduces the size of the tumour it must be continued in the hope of getting rid of that part of the iceberg under the water.

Robin took a great interest in what was going on, asked many questions and as time passed he developed a great relationship with his doctors. He could see, on the x-rays, that the swelling in the abdomen was getting smaller and eventually disappeared. This gave him great confidence and he was ready and eager to start chemotherapy. Dr McElwain used to say to me, chemotherapy is like walking a therapeutic tightrope between killing the tumour and killing the patient, since the chemical agent used is lethal to many normal body cells as well as those of the tumour. Robin knew that, in time, his hair would fall out after chemotherapy and so, before treatment started, he was fitted with a toupee which would match the colour of his hair. He stood up well to the treatment, and one day when I collected him at the hospital, where he had gone for a blood count, he said, 'I feel good, what about a game of golf at Walton Heath?' I knew he would become ill in a few days' time, as the treatment took effect, and it was with some apprehension that I agreed. He played extremely well and was very happy.

'Do you realise,' he said on the way home, 'this is the first time I've been able to beat you at golf? Maybe I should have more of this treatment.'

His feeling of well-being was short lived, he became ill, felt very tired and slowly his hair began to fall out; but this phase passed quickly and with his blond toupee he looked well when we all attended the Christmas dance at Cuddington hospital where he had become very popular with the staff.

Christmas that year was celebrated in Surrey and not in Nairobi, as planned. Nonetheless it was a pleasant one, I was confident we were succeeding and this feeling was reflected in Robin's approach to treatment. The next chemotherapy was early in the New Year and this was followed by attacks of abdominal pain when he had to spend a week in hospital. One evening when we called to see him I noticed milk stains on the floor of his room. He began to laugh when I asked what had apparently happened; he was on a milk diet for the abdominal condition and a black nurse, who was new to the unit and did not know him, came into the room carrying a large jug of milk. 'Gee Robin,' she said, 'you've got gorgeous hair, I like it,' and in a flash he took off the toupee and threw it at her saying, 'You can have it, nurse.' The poor girl got such a shock, the jug dropped from her hands and crashed to the floor.

The outlook was looking good after two further treatments, the x-rays revealed no evidence of tumours in either chest or abdomen. Naturally he was keen to return to Africa and I was very apprehensive when he was allowed to go towards the end of March 1976. I arranged for one of the doctors in the medical school in Nairobi to look after him and felt happier when Dr Trevor Powles, one of the Marsden and Institute consultants, said he would spend a few days with Robin and Sandra at their home in Nairobi on his return from a visit to South Africa. Robin knew Trevor well and I felt relieved with this arrangement but sadly, an x-ray taken at the hospital in Nairobi showed tumour had reappeared in the chest and Robin would need to return home for further treatment. He had been away less than a month. More chemotherapy, with newer drugs, was given and once more the tumour disappeared and he was able to go to his brother's wedding in July of that year. The new drugs were very powerful and he was required to be in the barrier nursing unit at the hospital as a protection against infection. He showed great interest in what was going on in this unit, and for the first time he told me,

'I wish I had done medicine.'

'But,' I said, 'what you are doing is a great help to people. Since you have become interested in law, you can help me with a legal case with which I'm involved.'

He was interested and I explained the problem. A very wealthy, titled army colonel had received an injury during the allied invasion of France in 1944. A piece of shrapnel had entered his left buttock, injured the sciatic nerve, ruptured the rectum which required immediate surgery, and finally lodged in the wall of the caecum (bowel) on the right side of the body. The injury to the sciatic nerve left him with a flail leg, and for the rest of his life he dragged the outside of his foot along the ground. On numerous occasions the area became inflamed and infected and over the years he had episodes of blood poisoning when bacteria were cultured from the blood. Twenty-five years after the injury he developed cancer of the caecum where the shrapnel had lodged and he died two years later. On the death certificate was written: cancer of the caecum, secondary tumour, injury to the sciatic nerve and septicaemia (blood poisoning). Around 1953, the government introduced an estate duty act which would exempt from duty the estate of any soldier who died as a result of a war injury, and in this case the duty would amount to millions of pounds. This excited Robin's business instinct and every time we visited him in hospital I had to report on what I was doing.

'Could the cancer be caused in any way by the shrapnel which had lodged in the bowel?' he asked me.

I searched the literature and found references to patients in the First World War who developed skin cancers in limbs following shrapnel wounds but in all those patients there had been longstanding discharges from the wounds. I consulted a number of experimental papers where tumours of the bowel had been produced in animals by injury to the caecum, but the results of those studies did not apply in our case. One evening as we were discussing this intriguing problem, Robin suddenly looked at me and said, 'Dad, you will only win the case if you can show there is no break in continuity between the injury and the death of the patient; and from what you say it would appear you cannot prove conclusively that the shrapnel which had lodged in the bowel did cause the cancer.'

'Wait,' I said to him, 'there is no need to invoke cancer, the death certificate shows blood poisoning which had been confirmed, on a number of occasions, by positive blood cultures. This could certainly be attributed to shrapnel injury to the sciatic nerve, with subsequent development of the infected foot and attacks of blood poisoning.'

Robin agreed there was no break in continuity between the injury and the final blood poisoning which appeared on the death certificate and was a contributing factor to the patient's death. This was the recommendation I made to the lawyers. Although the case was won, Robin never knew the important contribution he had made; he died before the result was announced.

At the time of Alan's wedding to Celia Brassington, in the summer, Robin looked well but I was concerned about the cough which was troublesome, although x-ray still showed no evidence of any lesion in the chest. There were reports by clinicians in Finland that the drug interferon had been used, with some success, on cancer patients. When the director of a large firm making the drug offered me some, I discussed the offer with McElwain and Peckham who decided, in the end, to try the drug and Robin returned to the barrier nursing unit for treatment. At that time interferon was very impure and he became pyrexic and so ill that treatment was stopped and he returned home. In spite of further deterioration he was able to carry on work for his company and at no time did he believe he would not recover. One Sunday evening, late in autumn, he was working in the study when he turned to his mother, rubbed his eyes and remarked, 'I think there is something wrong with my eyes, I'm needing new glasses as I can't see properly.'

We looked at each other and I knew we were thinking the same thing: the tumour had spread to the brain and was affecting the part involved with vision. He was due to attend the hospital next day for a check-up and Margaret, with no apparent sense of the concern we both felt, quietly remarked, 'I think you should tell the Professor about your eyes when you see him tomorrow.'

A brain scan showed the presence of tumour deposits, as we had feared, and while we were worried about the terrifying outcome with severe pain and headaches, Robin was not perturbed, the Marsden consultants would deal with the tumours as they had done with those elsewhere. He had radiation to the tumour and cortisone which gave him a sense of well-being and at the end of treatment the tumour had gone and his sight returned to normal.

Christmas 1976 came, we had a quiet family gathering, he tried to eat the helping of turkey but it was with difficulty and little enjoyment; the New Years came but with little hope. Towards the end of the month a swelling appeared in his neck and reluctantly my colleagues dealt with it but this was not to be for much longer. It was Friday evening in the first week in February when Margaret and I went to the hospital to see him. His room was empty, he was, sister said, having a chest x-ray and we waited until he returned to the room in a wheelchair. I had never seen him like this before, he looked ill, his face was drawn and the cheery smile and pleasant welcome at seeing us was absent, his eyes were fixed on the floor of the room. Slowly he raised his head and with an appealing look spoke slowly to me.

'They are not giving me any more treatment, is this the end?'

It was the worst moment of my life. I did not know what to say, as my eyes filled with tears. I heard Margaret say, 'Come on son, you're feeling tired, Sandra and I will help you into bed and you'll feel better.'

Sandra sat in the reclining chair at his bedside and Margaret asked her to show Robin the baby jacket she was knitting for our daughter's baby which was expected in April.

'Do you like it?' she asked Robin as he picked it up.

'Yes,' he replied.

'Maybe it will be a boy and he will be named Robbie after you,' his mother said.

'Yes,' he replied, 'that will be nice.' He was back to his old self. At that point sister came in and gave him an injection and he was sleeping peacefully when we left. Sandra remained and slept fitfully in the chair at his bedside.

When needed it was Margaret who had taken control of the situation, and it was then I began to appreciate what Sir William Osler meant when he talked about equanimity, and the need for imperturbability in surgeons and physicians. 'Imperturbability,' he wrote, 'means coolness and presence of mind under all circumstances, calmness amid storm, clearness of judgement in moments of peril. The doctor who is without it rapidly loses the confidence of the patients.' That evening I felt very disheartened. I felt he had believed in me and I had failed him and it was Margaret who had shown that quality of equanimity. She had not been as upset as I would have expected and that evening as we sat at home, I asked her why. Her answer was direct. 'I had been prepared for this sixteen months ago. When Robin had the first chemotherapy I met Tim and asked him what to expect. Brutally, I thought at the time, and without a moment's hesitation, he replied, "I give him eighteen months." I cried that night but I did not tell you. Robin needed your support and your belief he could win through. You gave him the will to fight and the type of support, I have learned, that every cancer patient should receive no matter how hopeless the outlook may appear.'

We returned to hospital next morning and remained there all day; Robin was well sedated and had no pain and from time to time he would waken and say, 'You're still there.' It was early Sunday morning when sister suggested we should go home and have a rest.

'We'll see he has a good night's sleep,' she said. We slept fitfully, always waiting for the phone to ring, but it never did and we were back in the hospital about eight o'clock next morning.

He had, said Sandra, wakened at six o'clock and asked for us and since then had not been conscious. As the day wore on his breathing became laboured and he was placed on an oxygen mask. Soon the dreaded gurgling, the death rattle which is so alarming to relatives, appeared. Margaret looked at me and left the room to return in a few minutes with the young resident doctor.

'I think he needs some hyoscine,' she said quietly, as we left with sister to have a cup of tea in her room.

When I returned on my own the disturbing noise was gone and he was breathing quietly. I had to appear before an industrial tribunal on the following Tuesday, for sex discrimination, and tried to read over some papers I had brought with me. I had rejected an application for promotion by one of the lady scientists whose research was no longer financed by the grant-giving bodies who supported the Institute. It had been a difficult decision for me to make since she was an excellent scientist, but the research she had been doing for many years was no longer considered relevant, and her salary and any promotion would have to come from Institute reserves built from public donations. I thought of the many men and women who collected money for cancer research. They believed they were making a contribution to the work of doctors and scientists who were trying to understand the cause and find a cure for this distressing illness that had claimed the life of some members of their own family. I could understand their views with greater clarity, as I saw my own son leaving us, and I too could only hope that my colleagues had learned something from Robin's illness that would, with continued financial support for the Marsden Hospital and the Institute of Cancer Research, help them to save the lives of young men of his age who developed this form of cancer in the future.

It had been a worrying time and we had slept fitfully during the last few days. As happens frequently in those circumstances, my mind began to wander and I found myself looking back on life and thinking of two men who had influenced my early life and whose names Robin had been given. The year was 1918 and my father James was only 29 years old when he died during the influenza epidemic which raged throughout the country in that year. I was three years old and too young to appreciate what was happening, or to remember how devastated my mother felt by his loss. The trauma of sorrow lessens, but never disappears and in time as I grew older, she would talk to me about the young man to whom she was devoted and who had been taken from her so early in their marriage, three months before my sister, Ina, was born. She talked about their life together, the happy times, the family holidays at the sea, his interests and the future he had planned for me. Like most youngsters in the village he left school at twelve to work in the Kames Colliery in Muirkirk. In the evenings he attended the continuation classes where he met and studied under my mother's brother Robert Steven (Uncle Bob) who had taken the diploma in mining engineering and in time became the chief mining lecturer for the County of Ayrshire. He was called into the army in 1916 and was serving in France at the time my father died. He returned to his teaching post at the end of the war and, being unmarried and very attached to my father and mother, accepted responsibility for her young family.

In time, my mother began to live again, she was kept busy with two young children to care for and was hostess to Uncle Bob's many students who took mining posts in this country and abroad, and always came to see him during their vacations in this country.

'If I had all the coal dug in my lounge during those visits,' she would say to their wives, 'we would have enough fuel for the rest of our lives.'

Indeed life for me was very pleasant in those early days; there was Grampa Steven, a number of aunts and uncles, my mother and especially Uncle Bob.

One of my earliest recollections was the closure of the gates of the ironworks blast furnaces in 1923. They had been in constant production since 1789 and the affluence of the village in the nineteenth century had been centred on them; now all that remained was the Kames Colliery and in 1921 the miners in Muirkirk, like those in the rest of the country, were on strike. I have clear recollections of the strike when soup kitchens were set up. My uncle raised money from his friends to help the miners and induced those students in his class to continue their studies. Later I learned he contributed part of his salary to help finance the soup kitchens. Miners' representatives went to football matches in Glasgow, and at half-time went round the track with large bed sheets into which the spectators threw coins. Uncle Bob was a keen football supporter and from an early age took me to football matches where I saw the collections being taken.

The soup kitchens always intrigued me and, although mother helped in them, she would tell me they were run for the miners' families who were

The author's mother, Margaret Steven Symington, in her wedding dress.

short of food and if I went to the soup kitchens I could be depriving children who had to depend on them. Nevertheless the food in those kitchens and the spirit of friendship which existed among the miners' families was so attractive that I felt deprived if I could not go there with my school friends, who in turn knew they were always welcome in our home. Uncle Bob helped to make those tragic days more tolerable for the families and I well remember the sports gala day he arranged, and provided the prizes for the races and the football five-a-side tournament. In retrospect I can understand why he chose teaching as his profession rather than become a mine manager or mine inspector. People meant a great deal to him and he derived great satisfaction from helping them.

'If young miners are going to improve their lot in life,' he said to me, 'they must receive an education,' and he was providing this opportunity not only to the youth of Muirkirk, but through the evening continuation classes organised by the Ayrshire Education Authority to all the young miners in the county.

After a day's work in the mine and a two hour sleep, they would attend the local school at five o'clock when he would give them two hours of mathematics, science and technical drawing. Each evening from Monday to Friday he taught in schools in different villages in Ayrshire and on Saturday all his students attended the Technical School in Kilmarnock. Monday evening he was at Muirkirk and when the class was over all the students went to the local cinema, where I joined them, to follow a serial I remember called *The Lost World.* On Saturday his students travelled by train to Kilmarnock, met at Rugby Park to see the football match, and after a simple meal, at five o'clock on Saturday evening those young men attended mining engineering classes at the Technical School until eight o'clock, then caught the last train from Glasgow to their homes.

In retrospect I could understand why he was so popular and respected by those young men; he gave them hope and encouragement and taught them you only take out of life what you put into it; in time they would reap a harvest from their efforts. Many became mine managers or mines' inspectors in this country and abroad, one became the Professor of Mining at Glasgow University and a number, like Uncle Bob himself, took the diploma of the Royal Technical College in Glasgow. But he taught them other things.

There were, he said, other worlds to explore, and introduced them to the worlds of music, art and literature. He was an avid reader, with Dickens, Hardy and Shaw particular favourites, and today some of my treasured possessions are his leather bound copies of books by those authors. I, too, benefited from my contact with his students. On vacation from University I would attend some of his classes and on occasions he would allow me to conduct those in mathematics and science. His experience of living conditions in the mining community, the inhuman and dangerous conditions under which miners had to work and his period in the army made him conscious of the need to improve the lot of the working man and he attempted to do this through education. The coal mines to me in those days were places of great danger. Scarcely a family at one time or another had escaped without some form of pit accident, which would be heralded by the wailing noise of the pit siren. This brought wives and families rushing to the pit head to hear the nature of the accident and who was involved. The miners worked either day, afternoon or night shift and during winter months some of them saw the light of day only at weekends. There were no washing facilities at the mines and the miners returned home tired and hungry, their faces, bodies and hair black with coal dust, and their pit clothes often soaked and muddy from the wet conditions in which they worked. A large wooden tub was placed on the floor of the kitchen and filled with hot water from kettles boiled over the kitchen fire. This was the miner's only form of ablution; his head, face, arms and chest were washed daily and on Friday his wife or mother would scrub his back.

The lot of the miner's wife was not any easier, after dinner she had to wash the pit clothes, dry them before the fire and have them ready for the next day. Wives and mothers of men on the morning or early shift would rise by three-thirty or four in the morning to ensure the pit clothes were dry and ready for use, and prepare the 'piece' or slices of bread, butter and jam or cheese the miner would carry in a special tin box, along with a flask of tea. This meal he would take during a short work break. What a difference it must have made to the women as well as the men when pit-head baths and canteens were introduced and the miner could go to work dressed like a civilised person!

The house where we lived on the Glasgow Road, Muirkirk, had been the original manse of the United Free Church and it was here that my uncle's students, past and present, would be regular visitors. One of them, Johnny, became a shaftsman at the Kames Colliery and his job was to go down the mine, on top of the cage, examine the shaft and carry out any repairs that needed to be done.

'I think it's about time I took you down the mine to see for yourself what goes on,' he said to me during one of his visits. I experienced an eerie feeling when I entered the cage, the gates at the top had closed and we were on our way down in total darkness. I was conscious of the rushing dank air being displaced by the cage as we descended to the pit bottom which by contrast was illuminated brightly. I was given a miner's cap to which was attached a carbide lamp, which my friend lit, and a beam of light shot into the darkness as we made our way underground. Hutches filled with coal were being pulled by ponies to the pit bottom where they were loaded onto the cage and brought to the surface. I had seen some of these ponies in the fields around the pit, normally they were stabled at the pit bottom and only brought to the surface when major underground repairs were being carried out or when the miners were on strike. My friend pointed to the wood props and beams which supported the roof as he took me to the coal face where miners were loading coal onto the conveyor belts which emptied it into hutches. Apparently shot-firers drilled holes into the coal seam, and filled them with sticks of dynamite which were lit as the miners withdrew to a safe distance. It was the coal, dislodged in the explosion that I saw being loaded on to the conveyor belt. My friend explained that some coal seams were very thick and easy to work while others were only eighteen inches. Sometimes the miners would bore through hard headings of rock and the air, from explosions, would be thick with stone dust which the miners inhaled. It was this silica dust which caused silicosis, the intractable and fatal lung disease which was so common in men who had spent a lifetime in the pits.

As we walked back to the pit bottom I could feel, on my face, the fresh air coming to the coal face from a ventilation shaft and understood why ventilation was a subject taught to mining students. I mentioned to my friend how I had helped to set up an experiment in uncle's science class, to show the explosive danger of over-ventilation in a pit where the miners used an open flame lamp and there was a great deal of dry coal dust in the atmosphere. He was interested to hear about the experiment and asked me to tell him about it. A steel tube six feet long and two inches in diameter was mounted on a tripod. The tube narrowed to a quarter of an inch at one end and this was connected by thick rubber tubing to a cylinder of compressed air. Finely powdered coal dust was packed into a covered pocket at the narrow end and a spark from an electric battery passed across the lumen of the tube. When the compressed air cylinder was opened, the rush of air dispersed clouds of coal dust over the spark and a loud explosion resulted. I used to put a small stone in the steel tube and the explosion would propel the stone out like a ball from a cannon.

'Yes,' said my friend, 'coal dust explosions do occur in some mines, but there are other hazards for the miner.' He explained how over the centuries coal can give rise to both combustible and non-combustible gases which can be equally lethal. The combustible gas in fire damp is chiefly methane and in mines where fire damp occurs, the miners use safety lamps in which the flame is protected so that it will not ignite the gases. Where non-combustible gases are encountered there may be pockets of black damp and in them the oxygen is replaced by carbon dioxide, which will extinguish the miner's lamp.

Since the gas is colourless and odourless, anyone entering a pocket of black damp will be rendered unconscious. Another colourless and odourless gas is carbon monoxide which can combine with the haemoglobin in the patient's blood and replace oxygen with fatal results. At one time canaries, which are very sensitive to this gas, were used to detect its presence.

As we continued to the pit bottom he mentioned other hazards that face the miner — a cave-in of the roof, coal filled hutches being derailed, and flooding. It was important for the students to understand mining surveying, since over the century of coal mining in the area, old mines had been abandoned and many had filled with water. It was necessary for management to know where the old mines were and how near the approaching coal face could go to them without causing an in-rush of water. In addition to teaching students who were destined to become mine managers and inspectors, my friend reminded me that my uncle held classes for miners who wished to take the examination and be designated as firemen. It was their job to go round the mine in the morning and make sure that conditions were satisfactory for the day-shift to start work. Unfortunately in those days not all the recommendations made by government inspectors were followed and it was a great day for the miner when the mines were nationalised and attention paid to the safety recommendations of the inspectors.

My father had two brothers and a sister and my grandparents were religious and members of the Plymouth Brethren. Grandfather Symington, after whom I was named, died a few months before my father, from pulmonary tuberculosis. Indeed as the years passed and Grandma Symington approached her 80th year all her family had died, yet throughout those years she showed no bitterness and no recriminations. She was a wonderful organiser and always had people doing things for her before they realised it. I visited her regularly in the days before I went to University and during vacations and from time to time she would talk to me about William Symington, my great-great-great-grandfather, who built the *Charlotte Dundas*, the world's first practical steamship. She had a number of papers and letters about him and said that when I was old enough to be interested, she would let me have them. I was a resident in hospital when she died, and after the funeral I discovered her housekeeper had burned the papers. I wish I had paid more attention, in those early days, to what she was saying and had asked for the papers and letters; now I have had to learn about him from biographies and articles.

The original Newcomen steam model was an atmospheric engine open at one end, and in the James Watt version both ends were enclosed. In the middle of the eighteenth century Watt's steam engine was used to pump water out of the lead mines at Wanlockhead, in Lanarkshire, where Symington worked. He was born in the adjacent mining village of Leadhills in 1764, attended the local parish school and became an engineer at the mine, where he helped to install a Watt engine. Since this engine, he argued, was enclosed there was no need for it to be vertical; it could lie horizontally and in this position could be used to drive wheels. Accordingly, in 1786, when only twenty-two years of age, he built a model steam driven carriage which he demonstrated at Edinburgh University 'to the approbation of the best mathematicians in Scotland'. His invention was more than fifty years ahead of its time and it is quite a coincidence that John Loudon McAdam, the road builder from Maybole should, in 1831, the year Symington died, build his first experimental road outside the village of Muirkirk.

Symington's involvement in steam navigation can be traced to his association with James Taylor who was said to be a fellow student at Edinburgh University. Since there are no records that Symington was enrolled either in Glasgow or Edinburgh University, it is more likely that Taylor heard about the steam carriage or saw the model on a visit to his elder brother George with whom Symington worked. Indeed in 1779 when he was only fifteen years of age, Symington and George Taylor installed a Bolton and Watt engine in the mine at Leadhills. Later Symington designed a smaller and more efficient modification of the Watt engine. The records of the Carron Ironworks Company at Grangemouth in 1786, the year he demonstrated his steam carriage, shows they supplied Symington with a consignment of machinery which led in 1787 to his patent for a steam engine in which 'he achieved rotary motion by chains and ratchet wheels to improve the performance of the Watt engine'. This did not endear him to Watt, but he prospered and became the engineer in charge of machinery at Wanlockhead lead mines and adviser to the Carron Company when they had requests to manufacture a variety of engines for different purposes, such as a fire engine.

In the meantime James Taylor, who was tutor to the younger sons of Patrick Miller, introduced Symington to this Edinburgh banker who was a shareholder in the Carron Company. Miller had an estate in Dumfriesshire, and had been actively involved in the company's production of war cannons. He was now interested to install steam navigation into the boat he had built on Dalswinton Loch on his Dumfriesshire estate. While both men had close association with the Carron Company it is surprising they should, in 1787, commission an Edinburgh brass founder to build the steam engine to power Miller's boat on Dalswinton Loch. The boat had twin hulls, between which two paddle wheels were set, and it was powered by a small two-cylinder steam engine with a tall smoke pipe. Although it was crude the method used for propulsion was effective, but the engine was underpowered for the size of the boat and was able to generate less than half horse-power. Nevertheless, while only partially successful, the trials on that day in October 1788 demonstrated that steam navigation was possible and a more powerful engine needed. It is regrettable that the engine used at Dalswinton Loch did not survive; it was taken from the boat and left in Miller's house for many years, then sold as scrap metal. Some parts were removed and lost and in 1853 what remained was rescued by Benner Woodcroft who had the engine rebuilt and displayed in the Science Museum in London. Sadly little of the original material from the old engine remains, and it is only from drawings by Nasmyth and Symington that we know what his first marine engine looked like.

Symington's relationship with the Carron Ironworks Company was good.

'Any money Mr Symington may want he shall be cheerfully supplied with,' they wrote and in June 1789 he extended his experiments with steam to the Carron river where he had a larger set of engines made with 18-inch cylinders fitted to a vessel. The trials were successful for the engines but the paddle wheels broke up and new stronger ones had to be fitted. A subsequent trial, in the presence of witnesses, was declared a success, but Miller was dissatisfied, asked Watt for his opinion, and when he disapproved, Miller withdrew his support and the project languished.

In spite of this disappointment, Symington's relationship with the Carron Ironworks remained good. During the next ten years they received many orders for engine work through him and their promise to supply him with funds was made good. His second chance to build a steam-powered vessel came in 1801 when Lord Dundas, Governor of the Forth and Clyde Canal, was interested in the possibility of using steam vessels to hasten the passage of ships through the canal which had been completed. This would spare them the long and dangerous journey round Cape Wrath on the north coast of Scotland.

Symington built the engines for the first boat which was named the *Charlotte Dundas* after Lord Dundas's eldest daughter. Although he undertook trials on the Carron river and towed several sloops on the River Forth, the engines were not sufficiently powerful to make a suitable canal tug. Secretly Lord Dundas commissioned a second boat, also called the *Charlotte Dundas* and this was the only vessel designed exclusively by Symington. It was provided with a single paddle wheel that turned in an enclosed slot in the stern. It was quite a large vessel, 58 ft long with an 18 ft beam, and contained the most powerful marine engine Symington had yet built, a single horizontal cylinder, which drove the paddle wheel through gears and a crankshaft. On 29 March the *Charlotte Dundas* pulled two sloops each of 50 tons against a strong headwind the 18.5 miles' length of the canal to Port Dundas in just over nine hours. The canal owners were not impressed, the wash from the boat they said, without any justification, would destroy the banks of the canal, and they gave instructions that bills incurred for building this *Charlotte Dundas* were not to be paid. The rejection by the canal authorities to what must have appeared a resounding success was tempered by an order from the Duke of Bridgewater to build eight ships for the Manchester ship canal. Sadly Bridgewater died, his order was cancelled and Symington abandoned further work on steam propulsion. He returned to work as an engineer, built horizontal and vertical engines for the mining industry and died of fever in London in 1831. Nine years after the *Charlotte Dundas* trials, Henry Bell's ship, *The Comet*, was launched successfully on the River Clyde.

The *Charlotte Dundas*, on which Symington had expended so much thought and effort and achieved so much, was moored on the canal bank and the engines were removed. Later it was refitted and for fifty years was used as a dredger. The ship described as 'the world's first successful power-driven vessel and first commercially successful paddle steamer' was allowed to rot ignominiously in a berth on the canal and in 1860 the canal company added further to their shame by selling it for £5.00.

Little did Symington realise that one day his creation, the *Charlotte Dundas*, would be acclaimed as one of the landmarks in maritime history along with the Queens of the Atlantic, the nuclear-powered submarine and the hovercraft, nor that 'history would regard his technical achievements worthy of the place already accorded him by Scottish engineers, in the triumvirate of mechanical engineers beside James Watt and William Murdoch'. What I feel would please him even more would be to find that the *Charlotte Dundas* did rise like a phoenix from the ashes. Recently the government introduced a longer period for their youth training programme, and Falkirk District Council decided to celebrate the 200th anniversary, in 1989, of the first steamship fitted for practical use on the Forth and Clyde canal at Grangemouth. A three-quarter size replica of the *Charlotte Dundas* was built professionally with the help of thirty-three young people; in doing so they acquired a wide range of skills in woodwork and general engineering and rescued for posterity a rich legacy in marine engineering.

The village of Muirkirk is about 12 miles from Leadhills; and both would have an established place in the history of industrial archaeology. I was, for many years, a member of the local ramblers club and learned a great deal of the past history of the village from three old miners during those rambles. I say old, for that is how they appeared to me, yet I doubt if they could have been more than 50, and they certainly had no problem with the hikes. All were avid readers and Bob's special interest was local history and industrial archaeology. Willie was an expert botanist with an enquiring mind, and Andy a quiet pipe-smoking man of Irish descent, was the only Catholic in the group, but not a devout one. He had been to the evening mining classes and acquired the manager's diploma but never took a post as manager. The three would talk and argue about things but they never became personal and always remained good friends. During the ramble one of them would give a talk and the younger members of the club listened with great interest for what they said carried conviction.

I heard how the village got its name, the influence of the reformation of 1559 on the life of the people, the cruel repression of the covenanters by the clergy and military during the reign of Charles II (1660–89) and the effect on the village of the discovery there of massive deposits of iron ore, coal, and limestone towards the end of the eighteenth century. Later I would learn how the Reformation and reformers like John Knox planned education in Scotland and of their determination to have a school in every parish and village. Bob told us the village was thought to have its origin in the 'Moor Kirk of Kyle' a small barn-shaped church with thatched roof built in 1631 in the Kyle district of Ayrshire. Initially the village was in the parish of Mauchline and in 1633 Muirkirk parish was created which included the village of Glenbuck; John, Earl of Loudon, was made patron.

'What,' asked Willie, 'was the patron and what was his duty in the parish?'

Bob explained that following the dissolution of the old church, much of its wealth went to the land and property owners who were called heritors. They paid taxes for the upkeep of the Church buildings, built and administered new schools and were responsible for the minister's and schoolmaster's salaries. The chief heritor in the parish was given the title of patron and he could, if he wished, appoint the minister or leave it to the other heritors or the kirk session to make the appointment.

'Bob,' I said, 'some heritors were more public-spirited than others and they built schools in their parish, but in Muirkirk it took more than 140 years before the heritors and kirk session built a school.'

'That's true,' said Bob. Then he went on to explain how the reformers believed that laymen should be more involved in Church matters and a Presbyterian system of Church Government was developed.

'Where does the kirk session fit into this?' asked Willie.

'The kirk session, consisting of minister and elders, is the governing body of the congregation and above that is the Presbytery which is made up of ministers and an elder from each church within the district. The highest body of the Presbyterian Church,' explained Bob, 'is the General Assembly.'

Now we had quite a gathering listening to Bob's talk and encouraged by their show of interest he continued.

'In the first *Book of Discipline*, John Knox waged a campaign against moral weakness and this was vigorously pursued by the clergy throughout Scotland. Sadly it became the hallmark of the new Church for almost three hundred years. In the village of Muirkirk the minister and kirk session, as elsewhere, used their power over the population to issue strict codes of conduct which were applied vigorously to supervise moral behaviour. Swearing, fighting, drunkenness, failure to attend Church or working on Sundays were crimes and the punishment meted out could vary from a fine to castigation by the minister.'

The younger members of the club listened attentively as Bob went on, 'The complete lack of Christian charity was seen in the humiliating punish/ ment meted out to those unfortunate men and women who committed the more serious sexual offence of promiscuity. Some, dressed in sackcloth, stood before the congregation on Sunday and were reviled by the minister. More persistent offenders had an iron collar placed round their neck, were seated chained to the wall at the church door and were humiliated before the congregation as they entered the Church between bell ringing. We were all taught at school that Sunday was a day of rest and worship. In the early days of the village, after Church the head of the family was expected to lead them in bible reading and study, and teach the story of the bible to their children who had regular tests from members of the kirk session. As the population grew the rules were rigidly enforced.'

When the Earl of Loudon was made patron, I learned, he brought to the village labourers who built dykes and made hedges to protect the farm animals and crops, and he introduced crop rotation into the small farms which made up the parish. But the standard of living of the people was very low, money was scarce, yet they were compelled to make a contribution to the Church. Small farmers who rented their farm from the landowners had to pay rent in kind, and often half the farm produce went to the owner of the land. In a poor year there could be near starvation and I was interested to learn that scurvy was not uncommon.

The ramblers club was almost ecumenical and on this occasion we were visiting some of the cairns erected in the hills to commemorate the Protestant martyrs who died during the thirty years of the 'killing times'. Old Andy, intelligent and well/read, a man with a keen sense of humour, had been smoking his pipe and listening intently to what Bob had been saying. Laying his pipe on the grass he looked at Bob and said, 'Bob, do you think it was all worthwhile?' They had been friends for many years and could debate and argue at times quite forcibly, yet always retained respect for each other.

'The years which preceded and followed the establishment of our parish were difficult ones,' said Bob, 'but in the end people like you and me were free to worship in whatever manner they chose; although to achieve this the people of Ayrshire in particular were subject to the tyranny of the clerical and military authority of King Charles II.'

Bob was asked to tell what happened and how the people of Muirkirk had been affected. The younger members of the club had been taught this during history lessons at school, but that could not compare with Bob's talk on the Muirkirk moor where some of the action actually took place.

'Prior to the Union of the Crown in 1603,' he said, 'King James VI had worked quite harmoniously with the Protestant reformers. However, when he went to London he became remote and on his death the Stewart reign continued under Charles I who, like his father, believed in the divine right of kings and was unhappy about the existence of an independent and powerful Church in Scotland. He was determined to have one Episcopalian religion for the whole of Britain and in 1633, the year the parish of Muirkirk was established, Charles was crowned in St Giles' Cathedral in Edinburgh, the service conducted with full Anglican rites. The General Assembly was not allowed to meet, but the Presbytery and the kirk session were retained. The King realised the English Book of Common Prayer would not be acceptable and produced a Revised Prayer Book for the Scots. When this was read from the pulpit in St Giles' in July 1637, there was an uproar, the new book was considered another mass; the following year a group of Scottish nobles met in Greyfriars Kirk in Edinburgh and signed the National Covenant. They expressed both national and religious opposition to the King and reaffirmed the Acts of Parliament which formulated the Calvinistic religion and the liberty of the Church. When the King surrendered to the Scottish army in May 1646, still he refused to accept the Covenant, and accordingly was handed over to the English who executed him in 1649.

The Church of Scotland was largely unaffected by the years of Cromwell's reign but when Charles II came to the British throne in 1660, he introduced into the Church bishops from whom the ministers would take their orders. The Episcopalians were very much the dominant rulers of the established Church in Scotland and bitterly opposed by the men of the Covenant. When the first minister of the parish of Muirkirk retired after thirty years, his successor, known to be a supporter of the Covenant, was removed from office by the Crown and replaced by an Episcopalian minister. 'When,' said Bob, 'the Royalists again imposed their policy to unify the Church in Britain more than three hundred ministers in Scotland refused to comply and were forced to abandon their churches and manses and hold illegal services or conventicles for their congregations. In the parish of Muirkirk, the wild open moorland where we are sitting at present was the scene of many of these conventicles, and the caves and farms in the parish became the refuge for the increasing number of ministers and adherents who opposed the government.'

Willie had been looking at some flowers he had collected but he was listening intently.

'Bob,' he said, 'this would be around 1677 when the government imposed martial law in Scotland to enforce Episcopacy.'

'That's true,' said Bob, 'and a large number of Highland troops were drafted into the south-west of Scotland to assist the government troops in searching out the covenanters and Ayrshire was the seat of greatest unrest.'

'What happened to the people of the Muirkirk parish?' asked one of the young men.

'I was coming to that,' said Bob. 'They were subjected to extreme cruelty by the Highland troops, who after only three months were sent back to their homes laden with plunder.'

Willie in the meantime had laid out the wild flowers he had collected, and turning round said, 'Bob, you told us that the Crown had replaced the minister because he had covenanter sympathies. How did his successors behave?'

'They were even more tyrannical than their predecessors,' said Bob. 'Troops were stationed at the door of the church on Sunday and the names taken of those who attended the service. Regular non-attenders were punished or forced to leave home, take to the hills and swell the ranks of the covenanters. Sentries had to be posted at open-air conventicles to protect the congregation from surprise attack by government forces under John Graham of Claverhouse, who was called the butcher. He was feared and hated by the parishioners of Muirkirk, and as many as eighty men of the parish were martyred for their beliefs during those thirty years of the killing times.' Bob stopped and for a full minute everyone was silent as if in an act of respect for those who had suffered in those moorland hills so many years ago; then he added, 'It has been said, and I would agree, that during his reign Charles II was motivated by a fanatical revenge on the people of Scotland who had handed his father to the English.'

'You'd better tell us how it all ended,' said Willie.

'Well,' said Bob, 'when Charles died he was succeeded by James II and although a Catholic, he agreed on a general religious tolerance whereby a person could worship the way he or she wished. When Mary and William of Orange were crowned in 1688, persecution ended and Protestantism and indeed religious tolerance were restored to Scotland.'

'Did things improve for the people?' asked one of the club members.

'Not really,' said Bob, 'the Church in the eighteenth century exercised dictatorial powers to suppress the abuses which often followed the rockings, penny weddings, and even funerals.' The rockings, I learned, were gatherings of people in one another's houses where musical instruments were played, songs sung and stories told. Ale made from barley was drunk and these popular evenings helped to brighten the lives of the people. The penny weddings were named because the guests had to contribute to the wedding expenses and there as with some funerals, drunken disorder resulted. In spite of the tyrannical approach of the kirk session the rockings and penny weddings persisted to the twentieth century.

It was Andy who pointed out that the purely rural existence of the villagers in the parish of Muirkirk and indeed in other parishes in Ayrshire was coming to an end. They were on the threshold of the industrial revolution in which Muirkirk would play a central role.

'There would,' he said, 'be an influx of new inhabitants from different parts of the country and indeed from different countries. The standard of living and housing would improve but at the same time there would be much misery and in the end the village would suffer the fate of many towns and villages throughout Britain who were caught up in the industrial revolution.'

Andy was standing next to a cairn which had been erected in memory of John Loudon McAdam, the world famous road builder. He took the pipe out of his mouth and pointed to a small piece of the road. 'This is where it all began, this is where McAdam made his first experimental road,' he said, and with a wide sweep of his arm, pointed to the remains of many coal heaps, large and small, that littered the countryside. Although there had been some haematite mining in Muirkirk in the early part of the eighteenth century, it was around 1786 when Lord Dundonald built the tar kilns here on the south side of the village and established the British Tar Company for the manufacture of tar, lampblack and varnish from the abundant deposits of coal which existed in the moors. Andy pointed to some old stone heaps which he said were houses built near the tar kilns for the workers and their families. As we walked towards the village past the long rows of miners' houses and the two-storey buildings for the railway workers, under the railway station bridge, he stopped in the Furnace Road and gazed sadly at the massive, now derelict, structure of the Muirkirk Ironworks where flames from the blast furnaces had lit the vicinity of the village for more than a century, and whose existence had raised the population from around 600 to nearly 5,000. 'Andy,' I said, 'I remember seeing the gates of the blast furnace close in 1923. How did it come about and what brought about its closure?'

'A group of Glasgow businessmen came to Muirkirk around 1787 and discovered a vast deposit of iron ore, coal and limestone, and the yield of iron from this deposit was valued at £140 million. A blast furnace was set up here, since water from the River Ayr was available, and the first iron was produced in 1789. Seven years later the ironworks was fully operational, with three large blast furnaces, an extensive forge to make bar iron and a foundry. Fifty thousand tons of coal were used yearly, more and more coal mines were sunk and the need for labour increased. The ironmasters built houses for the foundry workers and coal miners who were promised and given work for years to come. Indeed manpower shortage was so acute that it was decided to employ women and boys in the coal mines and in 1800 there were forty-two women and fifty-two boys working underground.'

'What kind of work did they do?' I asked.

'They transported coal to the pit bottom in the shallow mines and other women carried the coal in carrier bags or buckets on their backs, climbing up ladders to the surface,' Andy replied, 'and in the deeper mines which had primitive winding gear, the women worked on the pit surface.' Willie asked what women and boys were paid until Parliament prohibited their employ-ment around 1840, and what hours they worked.

'All miners,' said Andy, 'worked from 6.00 a.m. to 7.00 p.m., six days each week the men were paid twenty-five shillings (£1.25), boys up to ten years of age received six shillings (30p), those aged twelve to thirteen were considered half a man and got twelve shillings (60p) and women received slightly more than boys.' These wages appear miserable but at that time they were con-sidered quite substantial and the families were able to buy better food and fresh vegetables as a result of better farming, with new techniques of crop rotation. In spite of the long working hours the health of the community, which was now approaching 3,000, had improved.

The ironworks was in full production by 1810 and the only one in Ayrshire. Raw materials were abundant and deeper pits were sunk. By the middle of the century the Ironworks Company and coal mines were acquired by Bairds of Gartsherrie who in 1869 owned twenty-six of the forty-eight ironworks which had been developed in Ayrshire. Andy told us this company introduced more efficient hot blast processes which cut costs dramatically; and coal consumption fell for each ton of iron produced. The company extended the forge, built brickworks and a sawmill, constructed a large chemical works and used the waste gases from the furnaces to manufacture ammonia and pitch. In time a new deep coal mine, Kames Colliery, was sunk and this was the coal mine I had visited.

The first iron was transported by coach roads to the developing industrial cities of Scotland. By the middle of the nineteenth century with increased production there was a need for a more efficient means for dispatching the iron and coal, and the Glasgow and South West Railway extended its line from Auchinleck to Muirkirk and then to Lanark and Edinburgh. The station was built, and railway connections made to the coal mines and ironworks; now coal could be transported directly to the furnaces and the iron dispatched quickly to the industrial centres.

'How did the development affect the people in the village?' I asked.

'As you might expect,' said Andy, 'the population had increased to between 4,000 and 5,000, more new shops opened up and the train taking coal and iron from the village brought back goods of all varieties. In addition, people could now travel by train to towns like Ayr and Kilmarnock, and cities like Glasgow and Edinburgh came within easy reach.'

Most members of the ramblers club had gone home now and I was left with my three old friends at the closed gates of the ironworks. 'How did it all end?' I asked Andy.

'By the beginning of the twentieth century, the best of the iron ore had gone and for some time ore was imported from Spain, but by 1915 the writing was on the wall.'

I had been old enough to see the gates close on a venture which had lasted more than a hundred years, and had transformed this small, quiet, rural village into an active industrial centre. Coal mining continued well into the twentieth century until the closure of the Kames Colliery returned the village to its quiet, if severely scarred, rural beginnings.

Andy had passed his house as we walked to the gates of the ironworks. When I reminded him of this he said, 'I want to show you something,' and turning round he gazed over the banks of the river Ayr to the massive slag heap that towered above the village.

'It was slag from this heap that McAdam used to construct the hundred yards of road he built between the ironworks gate here and the gasworks which was constructed. His road was well tested by the heavy horse-drawn carriages which transported ore and coal to the furnaces and iron from it.'

I was surprised to learn that McAdam had not used tar as a binding agent on the stretch of road, and indeed that the use of tar for this purpose came much later. Andy stopped at the primary school in Furnace Road, and turning to me said, 'Now you will realise too that the school where you received your primary education stands on the historic site of the first road in this country.' He had come past his house to tell me the story of a hundred years of iron making, and remind me of how the macadamised roads of today originated in a hundred yards of roadway made of slag from the slag heaps which are still visible to motorists who today speed through this once-busy village.

As Andy retraced his steps, I continued up Furnace Road, past the gasworks to the main street of the village. Willie and Bob were coming with me to have supper at our home in the Glasgow Road, they were only slightly younger than Uncle Bob, yet both had been students at his evening classes and they were always welcome in our home. As we passed through the village, I remarked on the number of churches and church halls that were present in the village.

'Aye,' said Willie, 'that's true. During the period before the iron and coal magnates changed the living conditions of the people, an act of Parliament made the heritors and kirk sessions responsible for the housing and welfare of the people. They had to provide for the poor and maintain the parish churches. Many heritors were unwilling to use their own money and the kirk session decided the poor would be supported from church collections as well as the annual donations of the heritors. At the beginning of the nineteenth century when a new church was built to accommodate 1,000 people, the collections must have been quite substantial, and the needy received payment of two shillings and sixpence (12½p) per week. While the beneficial effects of industrialisation were experienced by most people in the village, and indeed in most villages in once-rural Ayrshire, the power of the heritors in the community was diminishing and the influence of the Church on the life of the people, though still considerable, was no longer as menacing as it had been in the past. In towns, where the social evils of industrialisation were more acute, the payment of a few shillings weekly to the increasing number of paupers merely led to an increase in drunkenness as a temporary relief from poverty and its inherent problems.' Willie stopped for a minute and looking at us remarked, 'It must have been terrible for those folk.'

Bob's comment was typical. 'Willie, what has this got to do with the number of churches in Muirkirk?' he asked as we stopped at the gate leading into our house. Willie eyed him up and down, as old miners were wont to do.

'This house was the original manse of the Chalmers United Free Church of Scotland,' he said, and pointing to the church next door, went on 'it and some other churches in the village were the result of the action of a group of reforming ministers, like Thomas Chalmers, who believed that social evils could only be dealt with by Christian charity and education and not by a weekly pittance.'

Willie had a great regard for men like Thomas Chalmers, who had been a lecturer in mathematics at St Andrews University before entering the Church.

'Was the system of patronage of clergy still in existence?' Bob asked.

'Yes, it was,' Willie said, 'but at the General Assembly in 1843, 470 ministers quit the kirk in the so-called "Disruption" along with many church elders, numerous schoolmasters and a large percentage of Church of Scotland communicants. So that was how the Church of Scotland has two Churches, the Reformed or Established Church and the Free Church. Because of the Disruption, Parliament deprived the Established Church of its power to administer poor relief and created parish boards to oversee the needs of the poor. Many ministers who joined the Free Church left well-paid ministries and faced the problem of establishing the new Church without funds to do so,' Willie told us. 'Some went to the colonies, founded the Free Church there and raised money which they sent to help finance the new venture in Scotland. The enthusiasm of the congregation for the Free Church,' Willie told us, 'was capitalised by Chalmers who initiated a scheme in which each member of the congregation would give one penny a week. By 1851 the Free Church had collected a large sum of money, ministers could be paid, new churches were founded, and 700 schools were built with the rapid expansion of education throughout the country. That is how there are so many churches in the village and all were well attended,' said Willie.

Uncle Bob had seen us standing at the gate and came out to meet us. He had been at a meeting and was interested to know how the ramble had gone.

'I think we all learned a lot today,' said Willie, as we entered the house where mother had supper waiting. It was late in the evening before our two friends went home; I had learned a great deal about the village and would have occasion later to thank Willie for his practical help in botany when I was preparing for the university examination in this subject.

CHAPTER 2

The Reformation and Scottish Education

I T IS CLAIMED THAT the Scots' obsession with education following the Reformation made it possible for young men and women from humble homes to study at a university and improve their status in life.

In the first *Book of Discipline* (1560), John Knox and the other zealous reformers declared it was the duty of the Church to educate the people and train their minds so that they could become familiar with the scriptures. Knox further proposed that the wealth of the old Catholic Church should be used equally to promote education of the people by creating a school in every parish, pay the minister's salary and deal with the relief of the poor. This enlightened policy could have made Scotland one of the best educated and socially advanced with the finance to fund education since this would create a powerful and vigorous Church and weaken the power of the nobles. Instead, the money to build and maintain schools, and to appoint and pay the salary of teachers became the responsibility of the heritors and kirk sessions. In Ayrshire some accepted this responsibility, but many didn't, and it was towards the end of the seventeenth century before a school in every parish became a possibility.

John Knox had further enlightened views on education. The parish schools would equip capable children, particularly sons of the clergy, to go directly to university assisted by bursaries, or to grammar schools in towns or burghs and then to university. Those capable young men would return and increase the number of clergy needed for spiritual and educational purposes. This, in fact, meant an extension of the grammar school system which existed in some towns and burghs as Church schools. In the Ayrshire burghs of Ayr and Irvine, the town councils had been involved with the Catholic Church in running their grammar schools and helped to make teaching appointments. Accordingly the transition to the new Presbyterian grammar school system was quite straightforward since the town council now accepted responsibility for the upkeep of the school and the salary of the schoolmaster.

Under the Catholic Church system the qualities expected of the teacher were scholarship and experience; now they were expected to instruct children in grammar, Latin and manners, by which the council meant teaching adherence to the Protestant faith. The schoolmaster was no longer an ecclesiastic who taught, but a full-time teacher, paid by and responsible to the magistrates and town council. The salary of teachers following the Reformation was £20 per year paid by the council plus school fees paid by the scholars. To protect the teacher from loss of income, the council prohibited the development of *adventure* or private schools. Only one grammar school was permitted in each town and, to ensure the schoolmaster's fees were paid by the parents of the scholars, the council appointed an 'honest man' as visitor to each quarter of the town. Those are the 'honest men' Robert Burns refers to in his poem 'Tam o'Shanter':

> Auld Ayr wham ne'er a town surpasses
> For honest men and bonie lassies.

The grammar school in Ayr was one of the first to supply its scholars with an English education on a footing with the classics. The schoolmaster taught classics and his assistant, called the doctor, taught English.

Under the Catholic school system there were song schools where boys were trained in church music, in manners and virtue. Those schools declined after the Reformation until King James VI, disturbed by the loss of the art of music and singing, requested the burghs to re-establish *song schools* to instruct the youth in the science of music. The council and honest men of Ayr responded and engaged a master to instruct pupils to sing and play the spinet as well as to read and write. The song school became part of the grammar school in some burghs in Scotland and remained separate in others; indeed they became the forerunners of the parish schools which the old reformists hoped to create in every village in Scotland. The town councils further decreed that, like grammar schools, there would be only one song school in each town and burgh. Since in time every man, woman and child was expected to be able to read the Bible, girls could go either to grammar or song schools but, unlike boys, they could choose to attend the private girls' schools which were created.

A number of parish schools did exist in Ayrshire at the time of the Reformation and the general assembly commissioned a 'scholarly' minister to visit the kirks and schools and remove or suspend incompetent ministers and their lay assistants or readers. While there is no information on the number or location of the schools, the existence of some parish schools indicates that

John Knox's contribution to Scottish education was to expand grammar and song schools in towns and create a school in every parish and village.

In Ayrshire the blueprint for parish schools already existed at the time of the Reformation; there were forty-two parishes, controlled by sixteen ministers, and a reader was present in every parish. Initially the reader was fully occupied with his clerical duties, and spent only a limited time in teaching the children. In time, as more ministers were trained, many readers became full-time schoolmasters and were selected for the post by the kirk session on their ability to teach reading and writing. Sadly the heritors in many parishes neglected their responsibilities, but in the Ayrshire village of Dundonald, a school was started in the church hall by the minister, a distinguished academic who had been schoolmaster of the grammar school in Irvine. In 1628 he drew up the Dundonald Articles which established the conditions of service for parish schoolmasters, the working day for children, and the subjects that would be taught. This document became an important landmark in the history of Scottish education and was adopted when a new school was built. The Articles declared that the schoolmaster should never leave the pupils unattended and if, for some reason he had to be absent, an assistant had to be there. During the months of October to February, school hours would be sunrise to sunset, and for the rest of the year they would be from seven in the morning to six at night with one hour off at nine for breakfast and lunch at twelve, the hour to be timed by an hourglass. There was a fixed time every day for writing. Latin students would present prepared work at fixed times, and pupils would attend church on Sundays and learn the catechism. Since teaching in universities was conducted in Latin, some capable young men went to university at the early age of thirteen years, and so the schoolmaster in some parish schools had to be able to teach Latin and grammar.

Limited progress was made in creating village schools in the seventeenth century, and this was attributed to the religious problems during the reign of the Stewart kings and the unwillingness of the heritors and kirk sessions of many parishes to meet their obligations. Only when Protestantism was firmly established, and the educational system for parish schools strengthened by three Acts of Parliament, was progress made. The schoolmaster had to subscribe to the confession of faith and his qualifications, efficiency and deportment as a teacher of youth were subject to inspections by the Presbytery. The 1696 Act repeated earlier Acts stating that heritors must provide schools in every parish and settle a salary for the schoolmaster of between 100 and 200 merks* in addition to what he received in private fees

---

* A merk is two-thirds of the pound of currency concerned, i.e. when Scots, depreciating along with the rest of the currency, finally reaching thirteen and one-third pence of English currency. It continued at this valuation after abolition of Scots currency in 1707.

from pupils. If heritors failed to act, twelve honest men were to act in their stead. Only half the forty-two parishes in Ayrshire appeared to have schools, and many children were taught at home by tutors, ministers or readers; and while both children and adults might learn reading at home, a considerable number could not write.

Once more success of the Acts depended on the willingness of the heritors to accept their obligations. In some parishes they were ready to co-operate, in others they objected or paid the schoolmaster's salary with such inconsistency that he was frequently left in a embarrassing financial position. Building and repair of schools was a problem for most parishes at the beginning of the eighteenth century. This was the case in the parish in Muirkirk, where the heritors and kirk session decided against building a school. They agreed the village children could be taught in the church session room by the wives of the local shopkeepers. Indeed it was almost 140 years from the creation of the parish until the heritors and kirk session accepted the need for a school. One of the heritors offered grounds for the purpose on condition that 'the schoolmaster would not be allowed to sell liquor'. The schoolhouse, built of wood, was occupied in 1772, and consisted of two classrooms downstairs and two rooms upstairs for the headmaster and his family. Records show that he was paid £7 15s. 4½d. per quarter, with a free house and glebe where he could keep a cow. In addition pupils who attended the school paid him two shillings per quarter for tuition in reading and writing, and two shillings and sixpence for arithmetic. He was paid sixpence for registering the baptism of a child, and he acted as session clerk and treasurer of the Church for which he received fifteen shillings a year. The first schoolmaster appointed to Muirkirk parish school was Mr Maule, and the school hours and duties followed the lines laid down by the Dundonald Articles. Children were examined four times yearly to assess the knowledge they had acquired and the power of the Church was very much in evidence; the parish minister, if the occasion arose, could and did chastise and rebuke the headmaster. The first schoolmaster remained in post for ten years and his successor, who could teach Latin, received an extra three shillings per quarter for this subject. When he retired thirty years later, industrialisation of the village was well advanced, the population was in the region of 3,000 and a much needed new parish school was built in the main street of the village in 1814. In addition the village had three private schools, each with seven or eight pupils, and in addition the people were reading books from the circulating library that came each week to the village.

Unfortunately it was not a time of learning for every child; a number worked in the coal mines until a Government Commission in 1843 prohibited the employment of women and children in the mines. Then followed the 'disruption' and creation of the Free Church of Scotland, which in the ensuing years built 700 schools and led to a rapid expansion of education throughout the country. Parochial boards were established to deal with schools, and care for the poor. The heritors and kirk session now had responsibility only for Church affairs. State aid was given to Free and Established Church Schools and the exclusive legal powers which the reformed Church exercised over parish schools and the schoolmaster were removed when the Education Act of 1872 placed Scottish schools under the Education Department. Education was not compulsory at that time and pupils still had to pay; poor children paid one penny a week and children from better homes paid three pence. If the child did not bring the money to school, the teacher sent them home to get it, and often they did not return. By 1889 education in Scotland was free for all children and attendance at school was made compulsory.

Counties lost their distinct local character when the educational policy, inspection and supervision of schools came under the Scottish Education Department. The main task of parish boards was to deal with elementary education. New schools including colliery schools, built by the coal masters, were needed to house the increase in numbers of pupils, and the boards appointed teachers and other officers, and administered the compulsory attendance of pupils at school. The first teacher training college in Britain was formed in the Glasgow Education Society Normal School by 1837, and most men and women teachers in Ayrshire were 'normal' trained, leaving the school with a Government certificate of competence. The Education Act heralded the end of the era when a clever boy could go directly to university from a village school; the emphasis now was on elementary education. There was less time for classics and indeed few of the new certified teachers were as familiar with higher education as some of their university trained predecessors.

There was much discussion on the architectural requirements of the new schools. In the past no limit was placed on the number of children to be accommodated in a school room and many schools were built with one long room with or without classrooms. A Government Inspector at that time took the view that every class of pupils should be taught in a separate room of adequate size. Hall schools, he felt, made it impossible to grade classes. This advice seems to have been followed in Muirkirk, when the Furnace Road elementary school I attended was built on the historic site of McAdam's first roadway. It consisted of a reception hall surrounded by eight self-contained classrooms in which children were taught from age five until the majority left school at fourteen; most teachers were women, the older one had taken the certificate of competence at the 'normal' while the younger ones had graduated from Jordanhill Teacher Training College in Glasgow. There were two men on the staff who taught students in the last two years of the elementary course. A number of pupils, after the qualifying examination at age eleven, proceeded to a three-year course in the Higher Grade which was sited in a territorial hall in the village. Here all pupils studied English, as well as history and geography, mathematics, science, and two languages (French and Latin). All teachers in the Higher Grade were university graduates with honours degrees in English, Science or Languages. The headmaster, Mr Gordon, taught Latin. As time passed students would drop out of class to take up posts in banks, shops and family businesses and at the end of the third year the number of students who wished to continue the three-year secondary education at Cumnock Academy had dropped to three. Approximately the same number would go to Cumnock from schools in the surroundings villages, and take the necessary subjects to enable them to enter for an ordinary or honours degree course at a Scottish university in arts or science, or embark on a degree in medicine. There was always a wastage of students during those three years and the number who went from Cumnock to the University in my time would be about ten per year.

Scottish education from the very beginning has been based on merit and it owes much to the Church's philosophy of 'hard work and social obedience.' It is true many Scots became obsessed with education but many who were capable of acquiring knowledge were prevented from doing so because of lack of parental encouragement or by virtue of family circumstances. About thirty boys and girls set out with me into the brave, new world of education in 1920, and stayed together until the qualifying examination at about the age of eleven, when the class split. One group, as I explained, continued to the higher grade and the rest languished in what was called the advanced division until they reached fourteen and could leave school. The boys would go into the mines, or become farm labourers or shopkeepers and the girls became domestic servants. Many of those pupils had poor or mediocre school records, yet some of the best students in the class ended in the advanced division and on many occasions the headmaster would send for the parents and try to persuade them to agree to their child moving to the higher grade. Sometimes the master was successful, more often he failed. The child had to start work as soon as possible to help feed and clothe the other children in the family. This was frequently the lot of the clever eldest boy or girl of a large family who left school so that clever younger brothers and sisters could have a university education. Fortunately many of those talented young men were rescued by the evening continuation classes. Many became pupils of my uncle and in time graduated as mining engineers. Others attended evening classes in marine, civil or mechanical engineering and took the Higher National Certificate in engineering. Indeed many of the great ships built on the Clyde or large civil or mechanical constructions here and abroad were built by men from Scotland who continued their education at evening classes.

The situation in Scotland was clear; every school child could go to university if they had the ability and the parents were willing to make the necessary sacrifice to allow them to do so. A few years after I qualified in medicine I had further opportunity to confirm this when I was on a visit to Muirkirk and met the wife of a miner who had died. In conversation I enquired for her family and learned her elder daughter was finishing school at Cumnock Academy.

'She will be going to university now,' I said.

'How can she?' was the reply. 'My husband has died and I'm left with three children to support.' If her daughter received a full bursary she would be willing to let her continue her education. I visited the parish minister who was chairman of the Ayrshire Education Committee, he arranged a bursary for the girl who went to the university and became a teacher. There is little doubt that the Scots appreciated the value of education but not every parent would or could make the required sacrifice for the family. Soon I would experience this as I prepared to go to Glasgow University in the autumn of 1932.

During that summer I enjoyed the rambles with my old friends, played golf on the local course, and took part in football matches when I played for one of the local teams. I returned home one evening from one of the matches and saw something was disturbing my mother. Always she was interested in the results of the match and enquired how I had played, but on this occasion she made no enquiries about either. Later in the evening she told me of her meeting with Mr Gordon, headmaster of Muirkirk Public School, who asked what I intended to do now my time at Cumnock Academy was finished. She had a great respect for the headmaster but on this occasion she was hurt and deeply upset.

'What did you say to him?' I asked.

'When I told him you were going to Glasgow University he looked astonished.'

'University,' he said, 'he'll never make it, it's a waste of his time and money. He should become a professional footballer, that's what he's good at.' I said nothing but she continued.

'I told him you might not make it but you were going to get the chance.'

This conversation had a profound effect, and brought home to me the influence some Ayrshire mothers had on their family and the respect and importance they attached to education. Boys, they would say, who don't work at school and take advantage of an education are destined to a life in the coal mines, while girls who scorned learning would end in domestic service.

I became more conscious of the maternal role in a family and understood more clearly their hope and desire that their sons and daughters would go to the university and become teachers. Mother was determined Mr Gordon was not going to destroy her hopes for me and my failure to cope with university was something she could neither conceive or accept.

Some teachers have the facility to impart knowledge by making the student interested to learn and Mr Willie Inglis, my first English teacher at Muirkirk, had this ability.

He was a stimulating person who was loved and respected by the whole class. It was a pleasure to work for him and, as I contemplated university, I remember him saying, 'There is nothing in this world you cannot do if you want it badly enough and are willing to work hard enough to get it.'

This advice helped me in the nine years I would spend at university, where I learned how to study, to enjoy knowing things and above all to stand on my own feet.

The first day at university is an event in the life of any seventeen-year-old. I found lodgings, which cost twenty-five shillings per week full-board, with a nice family who lived in a pleasant upstairs flat near Yorkhill Sick Children's Hospital and close to the University. The room was shared with an older schoolfriend who had taken a degree in English and was finishing a teacher training programme at Jordanhill College.

I did not know what to expect on that October morning in 1932 as I made my way to the university along Kelvin Way, past the bowling green and art gallery on the left. I stood for a minute on the bridge over the River Kelvin and looked at the statues perched on each corner of the bridge. Nine years later, on the morning after the German air raid on Glasgow in 1941, I would stand on the same spot on the bridge and hold the green remnants of a parachute which hung on the iron railing bordering the bowling green. The statues had disappeared from their place on the bridge and lay in the waters of the River Kelvin. The bridge had withstood a direct hit by a huge 1600-pound landmine which had floated down by that parachute.

It was just as well I did not know what lay ahead. Then I was able to appreciate the splendour of the university perched majestically on the hill above the tree-lined slopes which rose up from the river Kelvin. I was conscious of the early autumn tint of the trees in the park as I continued along Kelvin Way past the putting green and the statues to Lord Kelvin and Lord Lister. Kelvin Way joins University Avenue at the Students' Union, and this was the terminal for the white university tramcar which passed Central Station and was used by most students who lived at home and commuted by train to university.

I did not follow Kelvin Way to University Avenue but took the rather steep path upwards through the woods to the front of the university. This short-cut had been used by generations of thrifty students who came by train and to save a penny tram fare walked to the university by way of Charing Cross, through Kelvingrove Park, across Kelvin Way and up the steep path to the front of the university. The path joined a road which came from University Avenue, past the departments of Engineering and Chemistry, in front of the university tower and the main buildings of the university. The road continued down past the Principal's residence, the Natural Philosophy and Zoology departments on the right, Materia Medica, Physiology and Biochemistry on the left, and continued downwards to join Argyll Street. The buildings and wards of the Western Infirmary lay on the right.

I remember, on my first day, standing outside the front entrance to the university, and reflecting on the vision of those individuals who chose this Gilmourhill site, when the university moved from its original quarters at College Street in the east end of the city. The site is spectacular; the Gothic buildings of the university look down on the River Kelvin, the Art Gallery, Kelvin Hall, Yorkhill Sick Children's Hospital and beyond to the docks on the River Clyde. I turned and passed through the main door and under the tower which most students would climb once in their career. The tower housed the university clock whose chimes would become familiar to me as it had been to generations of students. The clock struck every fifteen minutes and the chimes were a constant reminder, during class and degree examinations that time was running short if answers to the questions were to be finished on time.

The stairs to the right of the entrance hall led to the Administrative Offices of the university and the Principal's office, and many years later I would climb those stairs on my visits to and discussions with the Principal, Sir Hector Hetherington. A door to the left of the landing led to the Randolph Hall where in years to come my wife and I, with fellow students, would take the Hippocratic oath before returning to the Bute Hall to graduate in medicine. The Randolph Hall was sited at the back of the Bute Hall and was opposite the rooms where meetings of the Senate and University Faculties were held. I never thought as I peered into these rooms that years later I would be involved in some university decisions made there, nor that in 1954 I would be interviewed and appointed to the University St Mungo Notman Chair of Pathology which was tenable at the Glasgow Royal Infirmary. I retraced my steps downstairs and into the cloisters which led from the clock tower to the Hunter Museum and the front entrance to the Bute Hall. The cloisters were dark, cold and windy, flanked on the right by the science and on the left by the arts quadrangles. Each quadrangle had a central grass sward in which trees had been planted. Lecture theatres, tutorial rooms and some examination halls were built around each quadrangle; and in the science quadrangle a temporary building had been constructed to house medical chemistry.

As I walked through the cloisters towards the entrance to the Bute Hall, I noticed a plaque on the wall. On closer inspection I saw it had been erected by the University of McGill, Montreal, in honour of James McGill, an arts graduate of Glasgow University who founded in Canada the university which bears his name. McGill is now one of the foremost centres of learning in North America. Little did I know as I examined the plaque that I would have close links with that university and fifty years later be awarded the honorary degree of Doctor of Science of McGill.

As I emerged from the cloisters. I could see, straight ahead, the examination hall and entrance to the Hunter Hall where I would sit many examinations, and where years later Margaret and I would attend the lunch which followed the award ceremony for the presentation of honorary degrees. I ascended the stairs to the Bute Hall and passed the robing room where Mr Main, the bedellus, would ensure the professors were properly attired to assemble in the Hunter Museum and join the procession on graduation day, into the Bute Hall.

On that first morning, as I opened the massive door I was impressed by the grandeur of the Bute Hall. Above the door was the large organ and down the length of each side of the hall were three rows of carved wooden benches which rose above the level of the floor. They were used by staff members of the university and their relatives during graduations and conversazions. At the top of the hall, which backed on to the Randolph Hall, was a raised platform on which stood a carved seat occupied by the Chancellor on graduation days. The graduands, wearing the gown of the faculty in which the degree was to be awarded, knelt on a stool in front of the Chancellor, were capped and, turning round, had the hood placed over their head and the appropriate scroll handed to them by the Registrar of the university.

To the right and left of the graduation platform were rows of individually carved bench seats where in later years I, along with fellow professors, would sit and watch the graduation ceremony. Down each side of the hall was the elevated public gallery from which relatives could watch the ceremony, and behind the gallery, down both sides of the hall, were beautiful stained glass windows commemorating great figures in art, science and literature.

By now a group of students had assembled at the office of Dr John Thomson, the Adviser of Studies, and I joined them. When I was leaving Cumnock Academy, Mr Martin, the Rector, told me to enrol in a course which would lead to an honours degree in mathematics and natural philosophy and thence to teaching. I had consulted the university calendar and decided my first year subjects would be mathematics, natural philosophy and chem٬ istry. Dr Thomson was in a bad mood that morning, and his bouts of temper had a disturbing effect not only on the emerging student but on those of us waiting at the open door. The student in front of me was having a bad time and I left my place at the top of the queue, went back to the end and consulted the university calendar once more to make sure I knew the subjects I needed for my four-year course and that my certificate of fitness was in order. One hour later I emerged with my course approved. Now I could register in each of the three subjects I would take and so begin my first year studies in the Faculty of Science. Years later I found myself in the company of Dr Thomson at one of the honorary graduation lunches and reminded him of the effect he had on the new students of my generation. He laughed loudly at my story; age must have mellowed him for I found him a delightful lunch companion at the many graduation luncheons we had together.

The lecture theatre in natural philosophy was large and accommodated between four and five hundred students. Each one was given a seat number, and a member of the technical staff of the department would be present at every lecture, and take attendance by noting the number of empty seats. Professor Taylor Jones, a rather small dapper Welshman, was extremely popular, his lectures were well attended and he established a great rapport with us early in the term. During his lecture on gyroscopes and spinning wheels he sat on a stool on which he revolved furiously to the great delight of the class. Once when he turned to write something on the board one student shouted in a loud voice, 'Peep, peep.' The professor turned round in apparent anger and glowered at the class; no one moved, all was quiet. Slowly he turned to write on the board, and once more we heard in a loud voice, 'Peep, peep.' This time as he turned, there was a smile on his face.

'What kind of car are you?' he asked.

'Rolls Royce, Sir,' to which the professor retorted to the great delight and a cheer from us all,

'To me you are more like a Rudge Woolworth.' It was a good lesson on how to deal with and gain the confidence of students.

I used to meet the professor frequently as I moved between classes and he would always wish me 'Good morning' and enquire, 'How are you today?'

I thought it wonderful that a man in his position knew me, until I realised he spoke to every student he met whether they were in his class or not. At the end of the first term, when the results of the class examinations had been posted, he announced that he would be willing to go over the examination paper with each student. Inevitably a long line of students waited outside the office to see the professor. I shall never forget my experience when my turn came to see him. He thanked me for coming and began reading the first of the three questions I had answered. His expression changed as he turned the pages of my book.

'My goodness,' he said, 'they have been very severe on you here. I am going to give you eight marks more.' This, I thought was wonderful. It was worth the time and trouble to come and see him. By now he was at the end of my second question and in a few minutes I heard him say, 'What have we here? I'm afraid they have been very lenient with you. I'm giving you eight marks less.' I was back where I started, as he looked at me with a smile on his face and said, 'Would you like me to go over the last question?'

This I felt was a decided risk and I said, 'No, Sir,' and left the room. There is no doubt Professor Taylor Jones left his mark on me. I learned from him how to win a student's confidence and respect and this would help me later when I was involved in student teaching.

There were daily lectures in each of the three first-year subjects and twice weekly practical classes in natural philosophy and chemistry, but it was the chemistry practical class in gravimetric analysis which had a lasting effect. During the first two terms of the course we had to carry out, in duplicate, estimations of ten different elements. Failure to achieve duplicate results meant repetition and after eight weeks I was still on the first element and at the end of the first ten-week term I had completed successfully only two different elements, but finished the rest without any repeats long before the end of the second term. I learned from this class, early on in my career, the importance of care, perseverance, and attention to detail in pursuit of a problem, an experience which proved valuable to me later in my research career. On reflection I am convinced this course was meant to be the hurdle that decided if a student would be able to cope with and be accepted for the honours course in chemistry.

I found the first year course a heavy one and was pleased when the degree examinations in June were over and I had been successful in all three subjects. There were no vacation jobs in the summer of 1933, and I spent most of my time golfing and reading the subjects I would take in the next university year.

As I said earlier Uncle Bob had organised the ramblers club so that the young miners who attended his evening continuation classes in winter could be kept together during the summer and be exposed to the broad educational programme. As the days shortened and the rambling season came to an end, he arranged evening lectures for them on a wide variety of subjects by teachers of varied talents. One of the lecturers I remember best was a young man whose parents came from Muirkirk: Dr John Stirling was a tall, handsome young man with fair hair. He had just returned from a period of study in Germany where he had gone after graduating in biochemistry at Glasgow University. No one had ever impressed me so much as this young man; I was captivated by his lecture. I did not know what biochemistry was until he explained it was the branch of chemistry concerning food and the way enzymes in the digestive tract deal with the different components in food. He talked about the chemical mechanisms which exist in the different organs of the body and their role in the economy of the body.

John spent the night at our home, and by bedtime I had decided to change course and embark on an honours degree in biochemistry; the chance meeting with this young man was to change my life.

That evening he confided to Uncle Bob that he was having trouble with his eyes and an examination later showed he had a brain tumour from which he died in a few months. He was, I was reliably informed, the most brilliant student to take the degree in biochemistry at Glasgow University; and on numerous occasions I have wondered what contribution to science this likeable young man would have made if his life had been spared.

He had impressed me and on my return to the University in the autumn of 1933 I embarked on an honours degree in chemistry, which I completed in 1936, taking biochemistry as my special final year subject.

There were no systematic lectures in the final year, only extensive prescribed reading on the subject and a small research project which I carried out under the guidance of Professor George M. Wishart. I learned how to work on my own, how to use a library to abstract and assess the value of scientific papers, and how to prepare and deliver a scientific paper before the assembled members of staff and other students. Above all I learned from Professor Wishart himself how to tackle a research project. At that time, bovine tuberculosis was common in cattle in the west of Scotland and pasteurisation was being introduced to render the milk safe to drink. Nutritionists were divided on the effect of pasteurisation and my research project was to determine if there was any difference in the gastric digestion of raw and boiled, not pasteurised milk. The professor visited me in the laboratory every morning, asked if I had any problem and regularly inspected the notebook in which I kept details of my experiments and results. At the end of each month, I spent an afternoon with him in his office, discussed my results, the conclusions we could draw and then planned the next month's experiments. I did not produce anything of significance but I did learn how to tackle a research problem and what I learned from Professor Wishart was to help with my research in later years.

In June 1936 I graduated Bachelor of Science (BSc) with honours in chemistry, but remember very little about graduation. At the time teaching posts were few in number and difficult to get and I did not know what to do until I received a letter from Professor Wishart asking me to come and see him.

'Squire,' he said, 'what have you decided to do?' I told him I had no plans.

'If you like,' he said, 'I can arrange for you to do three years' postgraduate study in Germany, but I would prefer you to return to the university and take a medical degree. 'This,' he said, 'would open many avenues for you to exploit your training in biochemistry. Since you will have a great deal of spare time in the first two years of the course, I will make you a demonstrator in biochemistry, this will help with expenses and you can carry on some research in the department.'

After giving some thought to the proposals, and with mother's enthusiastic support, since she said my father had always hoped I would be a doctor, I decided to take a medical degree and in October 1936 began the course which was to last until 1941.

I found the course in medicine long and laborious but it did not reach the standard I had experienced in chemistry; nor did I find any teacher who inspired me with a desire to specialise in any branch of medicine. During the second year of the course when I demonstrated in biochemistry, one of the students in my practical class was a very attractive young lady whom I later married. Margaret always maintains I gave her a lower grade than she merited in her practical class. Our relationship developed in the ensuing years, we studied together and it gave me great satisfaction when in 1940 she won the William Hunter Medal for surgery, a prize we both treasure to this day.

Before the war it was the custom for medical students from Glasgow to go in the summer to the Rotunda Hospital, Dublin, to deliver the fifteen babies required for the course in obstetrics. Students enjoyed their experience there and the fifteen deliveries at Rotunda were accepted by the University of Glasgow. The arrangement was cancelled during the war and instead, two students were sent to houses in the poorer areas of Glasgow to conduct the deliveries. I was due to go on district on 19 March 1941, and at that time shared lodgings in a basement tenement flat near Yorkhill Sick Children's Hospital with John Colquhoun, who was also a medical student. Our landlady, Miss McFarlane, was a friend of Margaret's family and quite unaccustomed to the task of looking after two young medical students. She was over sixty years of age, small in stature and with the most marked rickets I had seen. She always wore a black hat, even in the house. She was a fine singer and had been a member of the Glasgow Orpheus Choir.

On the night of the 18 March 1941 John and I were in our room preparing for next day's class examination in paediatrics at the university. The air raid sirens sounded at eight o'clock and a few minutes later there was a terrific explosion. Our bedroom door burst open. John and I complete with books, were blown off the chairs where we were sitting, onto the floor. We were unhurt and I went to the kitchen to find Miss McFarlane, complete with hat, lying spread-eagled on the floor, the kitchen window nearest the blast had been blown in, glass lay scattered over the floor, but mercifully she was unhurt. I went into the street and could hear the steady drone of planes overhead.

The window of the grocer's shop opposite our flat had been shattered and tins of fruit, meat and vegetables were being blown up and down the street by the wind which was growing stronger. When I returned to the bedroom, it had been invaded by a group of very frightened lady neighbours who were determined to remain there until the all-clear sirens had sounded. The room was in darkness apart from a glow from the remaining embers of the coal fire, and in spite of the air raid we knew we would have to sit the examination next morning. Accordingly we undressed, got into bed and were soon fast asleep. When we woke up it was light and the ladies had gone.

The 1600 pound landmine that nearly hit us, had come down by parachute and landed on the Kelvin bridge, only two hundred yards from our lodgings. The tenement building which lay between us and bomb had taken the full force of the blast and protected us from serious injury. Next morning as Margaret and I walked along Kelvin Way to the university we found a remnant of the green parachute hanging on the bowling green railing. The statues had disappeared from the bridge and lay in the River Kelvin, and a small sports car was lying in the large bomb crater. The owner of the car was an air raid warden, who had been told the docks were on fire and sped along Kelvin Way from the university to end up in the bomb crater. The university had sustained little damage apart from broken windows. Indeed Glasgow was lucky, it suffered little, in contrast to Clydebank which was severely damaged and where whole families were killed.

After the class examination Margaret and I went to the Royal Infirmary where she had a lecture, and I made my way to the students' residence at the Royal Maternity Hospital to begin my fifteen deliveries on district. On the way we met a number of people who told us that an area round the Royal Infirmary had been cordoned off because a landmine with an attached parachute was suspended between two coal houses, and some of the local population, thinking it was a German soldier on the parachute, had rushed forward to attack him with spades and sticks. They soon scattered when they saw the landmine swinging to and fro on the parachute between the two buildings.

There were about twenty students in residence when I arrived. Some like myself were beginning their deliveries, some had completed half the required number, the remainder had almost finished the course. We were arranged in pairs on an on-call rota posted in the residence. Most patients whom we delivered had no doctor and when they went into labour the husband, son, daughter or neighbour would come to the hospital and the two 'young' doctors, as we were called, would go with them to the patient's home and deliver the baby. The domiciliary service was an exciting experience and for the first time I felt like a real doctor. Sister McDonald, an experienced, understanding but strict disciplinarian was in charge of the student district maternity service and gave explicit instructions which we had to follow as she handed over the black bag and explained what it contained. There was a safety razor and spare blades, scalpel, pressure forceps, cotton wool and swabs, an enema syringe, eye lotion and a bottle of antiseptic. 'First,' she would say, 'wash your hands and prepare the patient.'

This meant shaving the patient's pubic hair, a procedure which from then on would be referred to as 'prep' the patient. Forceps and scalpel were boiled and a basin filled with boiling water, to which antiseptic drops were added, was left to cool and used to clean the mother and baby after delivery. If a tear occurred during delivery this would be notified to Sister McDonald who would repair it next day during her visit to the mother. After delivery, pressure forceps were placed on the umbilical cord and the portion of cord attached to the child was ligatured and cut. When the placenta was delivered it was examined carefully to ensure it was intact and none of it torn or retained in the uterus. The placenta was rolled up in a brown paper bag and taken back to the hospital where it was carefully inspected. One student was responsible for the delivery of baby and placenta, while the other attended to the baby, ensuring the airway was clear and free of mucus. It was always a great moment when the baby cried and a new life was created. When the baby had been washed and the eyes cleaned, it was examined for any defects such as hair lip, or cleft palate, and a finger was inserted into the rectum to ensure the anal passage was patent. Students would follow this routine religiously and I am sure most of them, like me, doubted how necessary it was. Later while doing a locum in England I delivered a child and, when I carried out the procedures we had been taught on district, discovered the child had an imperforate anus. The child was sent to hospital for immediate treatment.

My first night on district was memorable. After supper, as we talked, the phone began to ring in the residence and I was about to get my first experience of maternity work on district.

As my partner and I walked up the hill from the residence to the maternity hospital, the air raid sirens began their wailing noise. Sister McDonald handed over the black bag and introduced us to the messenger who would take us to the patient.

'I think you had better wear this,' she said, and handed each of us a steel helmet. Our patient lived about three miles from the hospital in Bridgeton and we walked in single file after the messenger keeping close to the buildings on the way. The night was very dark, and the street lights shaded in accordance with air raid precautions (ARP). I could see nothing as I looked upwards to the sky but heard the continuous monotonous drone of the aeroplanes. While hundreds of planes were flying overhead it appeared as if one plane was flying backwards and forwards above me. Searchlights flittered across the sky, anti-aircraft guns fired incessantly and in the direction of the west end of the city, the docks and in the Clydebank area, bombs were exploding and tongues of fire shooting upwards into the sky. The docks, the oil tanks on the Clyde and Clydebank itself were taking another pounding.

As we made our way along the streets the pubs were disgorging their clients and some drunk men lying motionless in the gutter completely oblivious to the devastation that was occurring. Eventually we reached the patient's home in a tenement flat near the River Clyde and I started to examine her when a landmine exploded about four miles away near the Co-operative building in Nelson Street. Fortunately it was too far away to cause us any trouble, but I was to hear more about the bomb when I returned to the residence.

Our patient was having good contractions, and as I felt them and listened to the foetal heart, everything, I said to her, was fine. This was her first child and she had been in labour for some hours.

'Are you afraid of the bombing?' I asked her as another contraction took place.

'No,' she said. 'I've more to worry about than Hitler at the moment.' The labour was progressing satisfactorily and my colleagues and I talked about our future prospects now we were nearing the end of the medical course.

'What's wrong with your leg?' he asked.

'Nothing,' I said, 'I've got another flea.' I rolled up my trouser leg and there entangled in the hairs of my leg and in the vicinity of a raised red bite was the offending flea which I held securely between my thumb and forefinger.

'What are you gong to do with it?' asked my colleague who happened to be English.

'Have you never hear the old Scots saying:

there is nothing sae [so] wae [wretched, quiet] as a weel washt [washed] flea, there is nothing sae crouse [spirited] as a weel washt lous [louse]?

I asked. He hadn't, so I gave him a demonstration, and held out my left hand which I cupped. I asked one of the women present to get a teaspoon and fill it with water, and told my colleague to pour the water into my left palm. When this had been done I proceeded to place the flea in the water where it rested quietly and without a struggle. 'You see,' I told my colleague, 'there's nothing sae wae as a weel washt flea.'

This demonstration impressed him, as I quickly despatched the offending flea between the nails of my thumbs. He would get plenty of opportunities to test this Scottish aphorism during his term on district.

Although the planes still flew overhead, no bombs dropped near us and the ladies present in the delivery room were amused at the antics of the two 'young' doctors. I was temporarily relieved of my itching and the patient's labour was progressing satisfactorily. In another three hours we delivered a healthy baby boy and Sister McDonald's procedures were carried out meticulously.

Dawn was breaking as we left the house just as the all-clear sirens sounded. We were fortunate to get a lift back to the residence in a Corporation dust-lorry. The driver spotted the black bag, our passport to immunity in the slums of Glasgow, hailed us and in a short time deposited us safely at the hospital. We handed over the black bag, and brown paper parcel, with placenta, which Sister McDonald would examine later in the morning. It was a night we would always remember, as we slumped into bed tired but curiously exhilarated. We had brought a new life into the world in the midst of death and destruction, but what the world would hold for him we would never know.

I slept well into the evening and rose in time to hear my colleagues relate their experience of the air raid. Eric had been in the process of making his first delivery when the bomb we heard landed in nearby Nelson Street. The bed collapsed in the house, the lights went out and he had to complete the delivery by candlelight. No further air raids occurred and I completed the required deliveries in time and with some amusing experiences.

Malcolm and I were called to a dilapidated tenement flat behind the old Cathedral Street bus station. The patient, whose name was Daisy, was lying in a small box bed. As I drew back the bedclothes to examine her I was met by a veritable circus of performing fleas. I replaced the clothes quickly and asked about her contractions; she hadn't had any yet. It looked as though we were on a false alarm. Sitting in the room was a lady who smoked, continuously, Wild Woodbine cigarettes; her claim to fame, we heard, was that her husband had been murdered. After three hours and with the patient showing no signs of contractions, I suggested to Daisy that maybe she had made a mistake with her dates. Suddenly the Wild Woodbine lady announced between drags on her cigarette, 'Daisy, are you sure it's a wean (baby) you've got there? Is it no' a rabbit?' To which Daisy replied with alacrity, 'If it's a rabbit I've got here, it's not a doctor you should have sent for, you should have sent for a ferret.'

It was certainly Glasgow humour at its best. Malcolm and I left without any delivery. It was a false alarm, but we took back to the residence a record number of fleas and an amusing experience.

It was inevitable that we would have a BBA, or born-before-arrival, which did not count for our required total of fifteen births. Ian and I were called to a patient in Maryhill. Two girls in their early twenties, daughters of the patient, came to the hospital to get us. It was early evening and we could get a tramcar to a stop near the patient's home. It was raining heavily and I ran with the girls to catch the tram which had arrived at the stop. We climbed the steep stairs of the car and waited for Ian, only to discover he had missed the tram. I was not too concerned. I had the black bag, he knew the patient's address and would come in the next tram. I sat with the girls in the front upstairs compartment above the driver and paid the penny ticket for each of us. We didn't talk much, although the girls kept looking anxiously at me and speaking in whispers so that I couldn't hear what they were saying. Eventually the older one said to me in a broad Glasgow accent, 'You look awful young to be a doctor. I hope ye ken your job.' This broke the silence and I asked her about her mother and how many weans (children) she had.

'Fifteen,' said the girl, and the awful thought crossed my mind that her mother would have been in labour before the girls left home to come to the hospital. We're in for a BBA, I thought, and sure enough when I entered the room where the mother was in bed, the baby was born, howling vigorously and like the mother, she was safe and well. I had finished the necessary chores, and mother was sitting up in bed with baby when Ian's rain-soaked head appeared round the bedroom door.

'Were you in time?' he asked. 'No,' I replied, 'I was too late. It was a BBA.'

After a number of BBAs and false alarms I completed the work on district, a lot wiser and more humble. I had seen abject poverty and the dreadful living conditions of these people, and their gratitude for the little service we had been able to provide. In fact we had done very little, we sat in a room with the patient and relatives, listened to their stories, some amusing, some tragic, and let nature take its course. A few colleagues did run into difficult labours, a retained placenta or a haemorrhage, when a call to hospital and an experienced obstetrician was soon on the spot.

I was now in the last ten weeks of my medical studies and with five other students was in the professorial medical unit at Stobhill Hospital which was run and financed by Glasgow Corporation. I worked with one of the medical residents and would receive new patients, examine them and write up the case notes which were then examined and checked by the resident doctor and the unit consultant. On one occasion a frail old lady was admitted and I examined her as if she was my clinical patient for the final practical examination in medicine, which was approaching. I went into great detail, questioned her about previous illnesses and her present complaint before carrying out a thorough physical examination. I was delighted with my effort, which surely would have been successful in the final examination. Suddenly I realised I had spent so much time with the examination that the old lady had missed afternoon tea. I apologised and her reply touched me.

'It was worth it,' she said. 'I have never had such a good examination in my life.' I saw the nurse in the duty room and explained what had happened. A cup of fresh tea and a cake was produced from the nurse's own supply and my old lady had her examination and afternoon tea.

The final examination took place in September 1941. It lasted three weeks and in the end I qualified Bachelor of Medicine, and Bachelor of Surgery (MB, ChB). Mother used to say she thought I could be a professional student, but I was tired after nine years of study at the university. It was time I started to make a living and Margaret and I now wished to become engaged.

CHAPTER 3

General Practice, Tuberculosis and the Sanatorium

AFTER GRADUATION it was customary to do a six-month residence as a house surgeon and then a house physician, for which the princely sum of 19*s. 2d.*, plus board, was paid. I wanted to have more contact with patients in their own environment and went into general practice as one of two assistants to Dr Jim Sweeney in Coatbridge, a busy industrial town in Lanarkshire. Here most men patients in the practice were employed in the steel works or coal mines and paid National Health Insurance for themselves and family. Money was deducted from their weekly pay packet by the employers and sent to the practice doctor. This weekly payment covered medical attention, prescriptions and a line from the doctor for absenteeism from work. Older people who were not covered by insurance joined a club and paid sixpence weekly to the doctor who employed a man as a collector. The club patient was entitled to medical attention and prescriptions which were dispensed by the doctor from the surgery. A few families were private patients who paid for each surgery and home visit and prescriptions. I was paid a salary of £300 per annum with free board and lodgings.

Dr Sweeney would be up at seven in the morning and had made a number of house calls before we met at breakfast. Any problems would be discussed and visiting lists prepared before proceeding to the nine o'clock morning surgery. This was always busy and lasted until eleven when a start could be made on a large list of house calls. In the afternoon Dr Jim would see a few private patients, then return to the surgery to spend more time with patients who had been seen in the morning and whose clinical condition required a more detailed examination. Initially I attended those sessions, especially when I had seen the patient at morning surgery and felt in need of his opinion. Whenever possible I would attend his weekly maternity clinic when the patient's blood group was noted, blood pressure determined and urine checked for albumen. If any abnormalities were detected the patient was referred to the local maternity hospital for treatment and subsequent delivery. As a result most deliveries carried out in the practice were straightforward and done usually by the midwife. Only on one occasion was I required to apply forceps and this was more to convince the midwife that I could do so. On another occasion the midwife phoned to say her patient had severe post-partum bleeding and she had sent for the hospital flying squad. The woman's blood group was known from the weekly clinic and the surgeon and nurse from the hospital were at the patient's home and had set up the blood transfusion by the time I arrived. Even in those early days I could appreciate the need to establish afternoon clinics and the importance of the flying squad.

Evening surgery was held primarily for men and women who would come on their way home from work. New urgent and often not so urgent calls had to be made before the day's work was over. Dr Jim usually finished work about eight o'clock and subsequent evening and night calls, road accidents, and the not infrequent accidents in the steel works were left to the assistants.

During my first month in practice I was with Dr Jim in the surgeries, listening to his discussions with patients and watching him examine them. I looked at the prescriptions he wrote and became familiar with the different health insurance forms that had to be filled up when a patient came for treatment and when they were ready to be signed off and return to work. I watched him make a diagnosis and treat a multitude of skin lesions and infectious conditions I had never seen in hospital; and noticed his concern on seeing a young woman with a skin condition which he said was typical of secondary syphilis and later proved to be so. On another occasion an attractive young girl with blond hair and wearing a soft knitted hat came into the room along with a very respectable lady who was well known to Dr Jim. The girl was in her early twenties and had been working in a large midland town in England. The old lady was very worried. The girl, she said, had been neglected and the reason was there to see when the girl removed her bonnet. Her blond hair was matted, she had been infected with head lice and with scratching she had developed impetigo. This, said Dr Jim, was a case for the poor law hospital where the head would be shaved clean and the skin infection treated. This, he said to the old lady, would never have happened if she had stayed at home with you.

After surgery he took me on house calls and introduced me to the patients in the practice. Most of them were Catholics and, knowing I was a Protestant, said, 'There are two things I am gong to ask you to do while you are here; if you feel a patient is gong to die I want you to tell the relatives and ask if they would like a priest. If,' he continued, 'you are at a confinement and think the baby might not survive, I want you to baptise the child,' and he proceeded to show me what to do. Those duties I carried out as conscientiously as I could and in doing so became on friendly terms with many priests.

Early one morning I was called to see an old lady who had severe chronic bronchitis and was dying of cardiac failure. I did what I could for her and asked the relatives if I would bring a priest. I waited until I knew he would have finished morning prayers, called at the church house and drove him to the patient's home where he attended to her. On the way home I remarked that I thought she was a little better and without thinking asked him what he had done to effect the slight improvement.

'Well,' he said, 'as part of the ceremony I sprinkle holy water on the patient's face and as I did so the cork come out of the bottle and she got the contents of the bottle over her face.' We said no more but on future occasions when I called him, I would say, 'Father, did you remember to bring the healing bottle?'

After a month's induction by Dr Sweeney, I was given my own surgery, house-call list and an old Morris Minor car. I was now on my own. Since I had never owned a car, and had only had three driving lessons I did not relish having to drive on the busy main street of the town. Inevitably the worst had to happen, and in a quiet area of the town near a school. I was driving carefully and stopped at the junction to a main road. Unfortunately a car was parked on the main road, which obliterated my view of any oncoming traffic. I moved forward gingerly, when a car appeared suddenly and instead of my foot landing on the brake, it hit the accelerator, the car was propelled forward and crashed into the side of the oncoming vehicle. At this moment the school bell rang and the street at the site of the accident filled with yelling children. It did not help that they thought I had got the better of the accident, nor did I get any joy when a policeman made me get back into the car to test the brakes, presumably to decide if I knew how to handle the vehicle. This episode landed me in the local newspaper which announced that a local doctor had appeared in court, was found guilty of a traffic offence and fined £2 or twenty-eight days' imprisonment, and had my licence endorsed. Dr Sweeney paid the fine and deducted the £2 from the first pay I ever earned. I was beginning to realise what a sheltered life I had led. Those days were over and more problems were in store for me.

During the surgical receiving night I attended in hospital as a student, abdominal emergencies seemed to present no great problems. How different they were when I saw them in the middle of the night at an early stage of the illness. It was two o'clock in the morning when the phone rang, and I dressed to go to the call. The car would not start and I had to cycle the two miles to the patient's home. The house was clean and tidy and I was ushered into the bedroom where a tall, muscular man was lying. He had severe abdominal pain which didn't appear to radiate down his left arm. His abdomen was extremely tender and rigid and he lay motionless in bed. Had he perforated or was he having a coronary? What would my former colleagues, who were resident in the Glasgow Royal Infirmary, say if I sent him in as a heart case when indeed he had perforated? I talked to the relatives and said I would like Dr Sweeney to see him; at this they were very relieved. I cycled home, knocked on the bedroom door and when Dr Jim appeared, described what I had found and he agreed to go back with me. He dressed quickly; we got into the car and in no time we were back at the house and he examined the patient. He called me over to the bed, made me feel the rigid abdomen and said, 'Look at him. He's in severe pain but is lying perfectly still in bed and not moving from side to side. He has perforated and must go immediately to hospital.' On the way home he said, 'As a general practitioner you can expect to see illness at an earlier and often at a more difficult stage to diagnose. It doesn't matter if your diagnosis is wrong or what your colleagues think about it. What is important in general practice is that you recognise when a condition is serious and when the patient is ill and needs to go to hospital.'

I would benefit from this lesson. Some months later I was called to see an old patient whom I had treated for severe chronic bronchitis and emphysema. I saw him within fifteen minutes of a sudden attack of severe abdominal pain, and benefiting from Dr Sweeney's lesson, I diagnosed a perforated peptic ulcer and acute generalised peritonitis, and sent him to hospital where, in spite of being a poor anaesthetic risk, he had immediate successful surgery. This was one of the many lessons I would learn from Dr Jim and use later when I went to a village practice in Cleland, Lanarkshire.

There was never a dull moment in Dr Jim's practice, whether on house calls or in the surgery. Life was always interesting, sometimes amusing but at times tragic. A large tenement building stood not far from the surgery, on the main street of the town and adjacent to the local football ground. An alleyway or close in the middle of the tenement led to a square in which there was a further collection of tenement buildings, which I looked on as my infectious disease and skin wards, and visited them every day. Very soon I could recognise the red-tip strawberry-colour tongue and skin rash of scarlet fever, the morbilliform rash and red eyes of measles, and the sickening cough and vomit of a child with distressing whooping cough. Above all there was a disturbingly high incidence of very severe gastro-enteritis in children. 'Boil the water and get rid of that dreadful dummy teat,' I would say.

Often the child was so dehydrated I had to send them to hospital for a saline infusion. Rheumatic fever was common and I saw a number of children with St Vitus' dance or chorea. Rheumatic heart disease was quite common in the adult population; and frequently I would encounter broncho-pneumonia

in children and lobar pneumonia in adults being treated by repeated application of mustard poultices to the chest and, in adults, waiting for the crisis
to occur on the tenth day of the illness when the temperature would drop
and the patient would recover. I was called one evening to my infectious
disease wards to find a baby with broncho-pneumonia. The young mother's
husband was in the army and she was in great distress. The baby's cot was
in a room lit by the flames from a coal fire which burned in the hearth. The
window was closed and the curtains drawn. The room was hot and stuffy and
this was not helped by the collection of relatives who gazed pathetically at
the child lying in the cot and smothered in blankets. After sponging the child,
dressing her in a loose nightgown and removing most of the burdensome
bedclothes, I opened the window and let fresh air into the room. All relatives
were moved out of the room and the mother told she could have one at a
time to sit with her. I had with me some of the then new drug, sulphapyridine
(M & B 693) which would be used instead of the dreadful mustard poultice
which the old ladies had already applied to the child's chest. They were not
impressed by my refusal to use this long-established treatment of pneumonia,
and were equally upset when I put them out of the room. I showed the young
mother how to crush the white tablet in a spoon, mix the white powder with
milk and give it to the baby. I left instructions when the next dose was to
be given and left the room. Later in the evening I returned to find the drug
had been administered as I directed, the room was airy, only one relative was
with the mother and the child was peaceful. The child continued to improve,
and the drug had been successful, to the surprise of the old ladies who now
saw the end of mustard poultices. During my last visit, the young mother
with tears in her eyes pressed a ten shilling note into my hand. I knew she
could ill afford this and said the baby's recovery was sufficient reward for
me. But I knew enough of the sterling qualities and kindness of the working
people to understand she wanted to show her gratitude and this was her way
of doing it. When I told Dr Sweeney, he looked at me, smiled and said,
'Wasn't that nice, doctor?'

There were many tragic moments but they were balanced by amusing ones,
like the mother whose child had impetigo. A starch poultice was used first
to remove the crust before the area was painted with gentian violet. I had to
instruct her how to make the poultice and said, 'Take the starch powder and
mix it with water to the same consistency you would use when starching your
husband's shirts.' She looked at me earnestly and said. 'I don't know how to
do this. I send my husband's shirts to the laundry.' This amused me, as very
few working people used the laundry in those days.

Back injuries and low back pain were always a good excuse for exemption
from work, and a weekly national insurance line was needed from the doctor.

It was difficult to prove a man was not in pain as he hobbled into the surgery to collect his weekly line. John, a steel worker, was one such patient. One Monday morning a lady came to the surgery to collect a prescription for a cough bottle. 'Doctor,' she said, 'I saw John walking out of the surgery with the aid of a stick. He doesn't need his stick on Saturday night in the Barrows at Glasgow Cross. I saw him jumping about, displaying and selling model aeroplanes. He was doing a roaring trade.'

'Was he?' I replied as I continued writing her prescription, but I looked forward to John's next visit to collect his sickness line. When he appeared next time in great discomfort, and managed with difficulty to sit down in the chair opposite me, I said, 'How did the sale go at the Barrows on Saturday, John?' and before he could answer I went on, 'I'm glad you are now able to return to work,' and handed him a line to say so. John, to his credit, never complained or argued. 'You win some, you lose some, doctor,' was his only comment as he walked out of my surgery and back to the steel works.

It was the patient with tuberculosis and the fear and hopelessness of patients with this illness that caused me great concern. As a student, during ward rounds in hospital, the word tuberculosis was never used in the presence of the patient. It was called Koch's infection, after the distinguished German bacteriologist who discovered the tubercle bacillus. In my undergraduate days I had seen patients with tuberculosis of bone and joints, kidney, bladder, lungs and other organs, but I was little affected by their illness. Now they were my patients and I was responsible for them. Most were adult men and women with chronic pulmonary tuberculosis who would receive treatment in the many sanatoria which were present in the country. Many older patients had open pulmonary tuberculosis, and during their frequent bouts of coughing would expectorate copious amounts of sputum which contained tubercle bacilli. If untreated they were a constant danger to children and young adolescents in their household. This young group were also at risk from old grandparents whose chronic bronchitis was indeed open pulmonary tuberculosis. In those days young children and adolescents were at risk if they consumed raw milk which came from a tuberculous cow.

Indeed life at that time was hazardous and I was disturbed and distressed at the number of young children of two or three years of age who had been infected by the tubercle bacillus and I knew would die of tuberculous meningitis. The illness pattern was very characteristic: the child had recovered from an attack of measles or whooping cough and became ill with a severe headache, fever and vomiting. It was an attack of vomiting which caused the parents to send for me; by this time the child was seriously ill and required hospitalisation where the diagnosis was made and verified by lumbar puncture. The illness was always fatal.

This illness could present in a most bizarre manner. One evening, an attractive teenage girl came to the surgery and said her hair was falling out. I found nothing on physical examination but when she returned two weeks later she had a headache and was tired. Her face was flushed and she had a fever which became worse in the next few days. The headache by now was very severe and she was sent to hospital where she was found to have tuberculous meningitis, and she died a few weeks later.

Tuberculosis could affect people of all ages in such a variety of ways and the outlook generally was bad. If I was to learn more about the disease and what was being done to treat it, I had to spend some time in a sanatorium. At the end of a tiring but valuable six months in general practice with Dr Sweeney, I was fortunate to be appointed assistant medical officer to Dr Charles Cameron at East Fortune Sanatorium, which moved in the early part of the war from Drem in East Lothian to Bangour Hospital near Bathgate.

Dr Cameron was a tall thin man in his early fifties. His hair was grey and thinning, his eyesight poor and he wore thick glasses. He walked with loping strides and on windswept rainy days, which occurred frequently in the exposed sanatorium, and wearing his doctor's white coat, he had the peculiar habit of holding his umbrella so that it protected his chest and trousers leaving his head and thin grey hair exposed to the rain. 'My hair will dry but my trousers won't,' he would say as I looked at him with surprise. As I remember there were eight wards, each with thirty beds, to deal with all forms of adult and childhood tuberculosis.

The unit had its own x-ray facility and operating theatre, while the laboratory services were shared with the emergency medical services created after the outbreak of war. I was the only assistant in the unit, and acted as resident for all eight wards. I saw all new patients and wrote up their clinical history along with my clinical findings in the case sheets which were checked meticulously by Dr Cameron. The patient was x-rayed by him, and he developed and reported the plates. I was with him in the x-ray room and he showed me what to look for and how to read an x-ray. Each film had the date stamped on it and was placed in a large brown envelope with the patient's name at the top. The x-ray films were kept in sister's duty room and produced by her when we were discussing the patient's progress during ward rounds. As time passed the number of x-ray films increased and the brown envelope became quite bulky. Dr Cameron would, with meticulous care, remove all films from the envelope, look at the original one and once examined, place it face down on the bed. This procedure was followed with each film in the sequence they had been taken. When he had assessed the progress or deterioration of the patient, he carefully replaced the films in the folder. He turned to me on the first day of my residence and said, 'That is how I expect you to deal with x-ray plates. In hospital they have no system, the plates get mixed up and so much time is lost getting them into chronological order.'

I came to the sanatorium to learn something about this complicated illness, how it presented and what treatment was available at that time. Sometimes young adult patients would be admitted with tuberculous pleurisy, when clear fluid would gather in the space between the surface of the lung and the lining of the chest wall, causing the lung to collapse. Dr Cameron would precuss the chest with his long bony fingers, map out the level of the fluid and with needle and syringe aspirate the clear fluid which was usually free from tubercle bacilli. This finding indicated that we were dealing with early tuberculosis which required a long period of rest, good food, and fresh air to build up the patient's resistance. The absence of detectable tubercle bacilli in a clear pleural effusion was, he said, an early warning and if heeded the patient would be cured. Later in my career I would understand the underlying pathology of this early form of tuberculosis.

More often the patients were admitted with well-established pulmonary tuberculosis. A few died very quickly of acute tuberculous broncho-pneumonia, called by the layman 'galloping consumption'. In the more common chronic tuberculosis of the lung, treatment depended on the extent to which the diseased lung was adherent or stuck to the chest wall. If there were no adhesions or they were minimal, the treatment was artificial pneumothorax or phrenic avulsion. If the adhesions were marked and the lung plastered onto the chest wall, major surgery in the form of thoracoplasty was carried out.

The whole idea in treatment was to collapse the lung, allow it to rest and give the tuberculous process a chance to recover by building up the patient's resistance with good food, fresh air and rest. Just as a broken leg was allowed to rest and heal by putting the leg in plaster, so the lung was encouraged to heal by methods I would now experience. In *artificial pneumothorax* air was injected carefully into the pleural cavity on the affected side and the lung collapsed. The procedure had to be repeated at regular intervals since the air would be slowly absorbed into the surrounding tissues and the lung would re-expand. It was not long before Dr Cameron decided I could be trusted to do a pneumothorax, but care had to be taken with those patients where there were adhesions. Induction of a pneumothorax could tear the adhesions from the surface of the lung and leave a hole through which air could rush into the pleural cavity and give rise to a tension pneumothorax. If this is severe it causes a shift of the heart and severe shock, and if untreated, could be fatal. This form of iatrogenic or doctor-induced pneumothorax occurred once when Dr Cameron was inducing air treatment on a patient with chronic lung disease. A large bore needle was inserted into the pleural cavity and the air drained through a rubber tube into a bottle of water which was kept on the floor at the patient's bedside. The air from the pleural cavity could be seen bubbling through the water. Unfortunately other adhesions kept the lung suspended, the hole on the surface of the lung remained patent and the air kept filling the pleural cavity quicker than it could be removed. Eventually the patient died but it was a salutary lesson and taught me how necessary it was to assess fully the extent of the underlying lesion before deciding on the form of treatment. As time passed and I gained in experience and confidence, Dr Cameron put me in charge of two wards for pulmonary tuberculosis and I had full responsibility for recommending to him what I thought treatment should be.

If the lesion was localised to the lower lobe of one lung, and I suspected that adhesions would preclude the use of artificial pneumothorax, I would suggest *phrenic avulsion* and would assist him in the operation theatre with this procedure. Through an incision in the neck he would expose the phrenic nerve which innervated the diaphragm. When Dr Cameron crushed the nerve with forceps the diaphragm would jerk upwards causing the base of the lung to collapse; and so, it was hoped, rest the tuberculous lung in the same manner as an artificial pneumothorax.

A different type of treatment had to be used for patients with chronic lung tuberculosis when the lung and chest wall were firmly fixed together. Artificial pneumothorax and phrenic avulsion had no place here. Often the tuberculous process had ulcerated into the air passage and left a lung cavity into which surrounding vessels could herniate, then rupture, causing a fatal haemorrhage. The patient at this stage with lung cavities, was a danger to himself and to the public, since the tubercle bacilli were widely disseminated during bouts of coughing in the vicinity of the patient. This was how the children and the young girl I had seen in general practice had become infected and died of tuberculous meningitis.

Dr Cameron was very insistent that patients with lung tuberculosis were taught the importance of and indeed practised personal hygiene and shown the danger of disseminating the disease. They had to cover the mouth with a disposable paper handkerchief when coughing and deposit the copious purulent spit into an antiseptic container which was covered immediately. Patients with open tuberculosis were warned of the danger of swallowing their sputum, which could result in tuberculosis of the throat with hoarseness, and give rise to multiple tuberculous ulcers in the small and large intestine.

The operation *thoracoplasty* was designed to collapse the lung in those patients, deal with the cavities which had formed, prevent a fatal haemorrhage, and protect the public from dissemination of tubercle bacilli. Dr Cameron and I would select the patients, and a distinguished thoracic surgeon from Edinburgh would come to our unit weekly and operate. The atmosphere in the operation theatre was always tense as the surgeon removed the ribs on the affected side to allow the lung to collapse. Cameron would watch over the operation with eagle eyes, 'One and half ribs only,' he would say to the surgeon. 'Stop now. Stop. That is enough.'

He insisted that the operation be done in three stages, with intervals of three weeks between the operations. Dr Cameron would personally change the patient's dressings on the morning after the operation and I would marvel at the careful and considerate manner he moved the patient in bed as he changed the bandages. On one occasion when he had finished the dressing he turned to me and said, 'If the operation is a success, the surgeon gets the credit. If it is a failure, I carry the can.'

He was a difficult man to work for and could be cruel both to patients and nursing staff, yet in spite of this the staff were devoted to him. They accepted that only the highest standard of performance was good enough and those were the standards he set himself. He would make the plaster casts for patients with spinal tuberculosis and when the time came for them to get up and walk he made their spinal braces.

He was ill at ease with children in the children's ward, although one attractive little five year old girl with dark eyes and brown curly hair completely captivated him. She was recovering from tuberculous glands in the neck and was ambulant. When Cameron entered the children's ward she would run to him, take his hand and together with Sister Barr and myself do a ward round. In one of the beds was a dear little blond girl of four, she was quite thin and suffered from abdominal tuberculosis caused by drinking infected milk. Her illness was like the tuberculous pleurisy, an early lesion which had been discovered in time, and she would recover. From time to time fluid would collect in her abdomen which became tense and painful. That morning I took fluid off the abdomen to relieve the pain. As Dr Cameron examined her and in an attempt to get his sympathy, she kept saying, 'My belly's away in the pail,' but her remark evoked no response. He was only making sure I had done my job properly.

About the end of the summer, while he was on holiday, there was an outbreak of jaundice in the children's ward and on careful study I found an interval of twenty-eight days between one outbreak of infective hepatitis and the next. In addition I noticed some patients had sub-clinical attacks with loose stools but no jaundice. Dr Cameron showed great interest in my case notes and I was beginning to feel I had been accepted, but I was in for a shock. On returning from weekend leave, I was called to a patient in the female surgical ward who had surgery for a tuberculous kidney. Her blood pressure was markedly raised, she had bouts of sickness, intense headache and became drowsy and semi-comatose. I decided she was having an attack of hypertensive encephalopathy and to ensure the remaining kidney was not the cause of the trouble, took off blood and when I had completed my other duties would go to the laboratory and carry out an estimation of the blood urea, which I expected to be normal. I was quite sure of the diagnosis and, after consulting my textbook, began the recommended treatment expecting the crisis to be brief and the patient to soon recover. Meantime Dr Cameron had arrived in the ward, got hold of the heat cage I had placed over the patient's legs and hurled it up the ward, then took the syringe with morphine and needle I was about to use and threw them out of the open window. Sister was in near panic as I was ordered into the duty room where he locked the door and put the key in his pocket. He took the patient's case sheet and started writing. Suddenly he stopped and rounded on me.

'Surely,' he said, 'you should not start treatment until you have made a diagnosis.'

'I have made a diagnosis. The patient is suffering from a sudden rise in blood pressure. She has hypertensive encephalopathy.'

He looked at me with utter contempt.

'Hypertensive encephalopathy. If you see a bird sitting on a roof top in London it might be a cockatoo, but it's more likely to be a sparrow. Did the professors in Glasgow not teach you that common things are commonest?' I stood my ground.

'My diagnosis is correct. I want to eliminate uraemia and have taken blood from the patient. If you will open the door I'll get on with the rest of the work and get this estimation done.'

He ignored my request and turned to write further notes on the case sheet. I had had enough, so I opened the window of the duty room, climbed out and finished the rest of my rounds.

As he came into a ward, I walked out, but eventually he stopped me and said, 'I've started the treatment you prescribed. Will you let me know the blood urea result when you have done it?'

I found as I expected, the level of urea in the blood was only slightly elevated; the patient had suffered a sudden rise of blood pressure and fortunately the crisis was short-lived and she recovered. When I phoned Dr Cameron with the result, he said, 'I'm doing a phrenic evulsion this afternoon. Would you like to assist me?'

During the operation he could not find the nerve which appeared to lie at a lower position than normal. I waited for some time before saying, 'Dr Cameron, it looks as if it's lower down today,' and pointed to the nerve. As he crushed it with forceps the diaphragm jerked upwards and he looked at me.

'Symington, this has been the most humiliating day in my life.' That day I discovered the real Dr Cameron, one who could admit to being wrong. I was nearing the end of my six months' appointment when he asked me if I would stay and make my career with him. 'I can't,' I replied, 'I've just passed my medical for the Army and am being called up.'

When I left he gave me a testimonial with details of my experience and ending 'some testimonials are given with reservation. This one is given with pleasure.'

I went to work with Cameron to try to learn about and understand the varied clinical appearance of tuberculosis in patients. I learned a great deal about pulmonary tuberculosis, that the different treatment schedules were designed to rest the diseased lung, while rest, good food and fresh air would raise the patient's resistance to the offending bacillus. He taught me that tuberculosis of bone, joint, kidney and other organs was part of the generalised condition and not an isolated disease. While surgery might deal with the local lesion, this must be supplemented by a search for other sites of the disease and the application of the customary sanatorium measures to raise the patient's resistance. This was the first time I had been taught the importance of holistic or whole body treatment of disease. Nevertheless it would be another two years, when I came under the influence of Professor John Blacklock, that I would understand how the varied patterns of tuberculosis I had seen were brought about.

When in October 1942 I left East Fortune for good I was depressed by the enormity of the problem and convinced that a cure for tuberculosis was nowhere in sight. I certainly never suspected that in the space of little more than three years tuberculosis would be cured by chemotherapy and in future years patients would heave a sigh of relief when told they suffered from tuberculosis and not cancer.

Dr Cameron was appointed Professor of Tuberculosis in Edinburgh University, and years later I visited him and his wife in their retirement home in Lesmahagow in Lanarkshire. He was certainly a fine clinician and I was privileged to have worked with him.

Three weeks after I left East Fortune I had not received my Army call-up papers, and in December 1942, began as a locum with Dr Sanderson in the mining village of Cleland in Lanarkshire. He had been a medical officer in the Colonial Medical Services in Tanganyika and returned to this country because of illness.

The most important day in my life was 19 March 1943, when Margaret and I were married and set up house in the village. After a honeymoon of three days we were back at work. She was a medical officer in the local general hospital under Dr John Reid who was a contemporary and great friend of Dr Cameron and an equally fine clinician. Dr Reid was superintendent in charge of Motherwell Fever Hospital and visited Cleland twice weekly. The hospital had 200 beds and was run by Lanarkshire County Council. During the early stage of the blitz on London, patients were evacuated to Cleland and a senior resident surgeon was appointed. Margaret, in addition to general medical duties, was anaesthetist to the hospital and performed minor surgery. Visiting consultant surgeons and physicians came weekly from the Glasgow teaching hospitals.

I was given a great deal of freedom to run the general practice, and learned very soon how valuable it was to have access to the laboratory and radiological facilities of the hospital on the doorstep. Although I had three surgeries daily, home calls and all the night work, I found the patients less demanding of the doctor and more understanding of our difficulties than in the previous practice in Coatbridge. In fact, they had been well trained by the old doctor who had the practice and this was an important aspect of general practice I had to learn.

In the early 1920s many people looked on hospitals as places where you went to die, but now most patients in the practice had a respect for hospitals and had no hesitation about going there for consultation or treatment. Some older patients in the practice still considered it an admission of failure if the doctor had to send them to hospital. On one occasion I was called to see an old lady who complained of vague abdominal pain and discomfort. She was surprised when I asked her daughter to get her undressed and into bed so that I could examine her. On palpating the abdomen I found she had a large tumour of stomach. Sensing my concern, and before I could say anything, she looked at me and said, 'Young man, I hope you are not going to send me to hospital. When I broke my leg the old doctor looked after me at home and he would do the same here.' It was the excuse I needed.

'Let me see your leg,' I said, and on examining her I found she had three inches of shortening in her leg. This was before the days of litigation so I decided to act like the old doctor, the tumour being too advanced for surgery.

One year later I still had no notice of my call-up and on making enquiries was informed I would be notified in due course. In fact, they had lost my papers. I felt I was not making any use of my training in biochemistry, but was unsure what could be done. One evening at dinner, Margaret told me she had been speaking to Dr McCallum Lang, the medical officer of health for Lanarkshire, who enquired what I was doing. 'There is,' he said, 'a great future in pathology for someone with his training in science and medicine.'

It is interesting to think that a chance meeting with a young biochemist in 1933 had been responsible for me studying this subject at university, and ten years later a chance remark made to my wife would guide me into a career in pathology.

I got time off from my general practice duties to take the honours science course in pathology at the Glasgow Royal Infirmary under Professor John Blacklock. This involved afternoon classes and was done in addition to the usual surgeries, house calls, evening and night duties of the practice. Professor Blacklock was an authority on tuberculosis, and on completing the course he offered me the post of assistant lecturer in his department. I told him about the army call-up and a few weeks later he informed me the army authorities had agreed to his request that I should be trained in pathology then go as a pathologist to the army. In June 1944 I became an assistant to Professor Blacklock.

CHAPTER 4

The Beginning of Adrenal Research

The pathology department at Glasgow Royal Infirmary was built at the turn of the century, when Professor John Teacher was head of the department. It was a replica of Professor Aschoff's department in Freiburg, Germany, where Teacher had studied, and it was opened by Sir William Osler, the distinguished Canadian pathologist and clinician, when he occupied the Regius Chair of medicine at Oxford. The vertical limb of the T-shaped building housed the laboratories of morbid anatomy or pathology on the ground floor and those for bacteriology and clinical chemistry or chemical pathology on the first floor. The horizontal arm of the building was equally spacious and designed as a teaching museum. For many years the ground floor of the museum was used as a lecture theatre, tutorial and demonstration room for pathology and bacteriology.

'If you are to command the respect of the technical staff here, and be able to criticise their work and train technical staff when you are in the Army, you must become a first-class technician,' the professor would say to me. Accordingly I was apprenticed to Davie Johnstone, one of the senior technicians whom I helped to prepare slides for the students' practical class. Professor Blacklock was very particular about the quality of the class slides and reviewed them frequently. A list of new material required was prepared and posted in the doctors' room and suitable specimens found at post mortem or at operation were handed to me as possible replacements for the students' collection.

During the academic year the students had daily lectures in pathology or bacteriology, and had practical classes and tutorials in both. Each morning after clinics, instruction was available to them in the autopsy room. After each lecture Davie and I would set out a demonstration in the museum to complement the lecture. Relevant specimens from the museum cases with details of the patient's clinical history and a description of the naked-eye

61

changes in the organ were set out on long tables in the museum along with microscopic slides of the disease process. As the lectures progressed the demonstration was extended until the macroscopic (naked-eye) and micro-scopic appearances of the diseased organs of the whole system were on display. If in certain systems, like alimentary, respiratory and genito-urinary, bacteri-ology was involved, the appearance of different micro-organisms on culture plates and what they looked like under the microscope was added to the demonstration. Students would spend hours on the demonstration, which Professor Blacklock would visit daily and check that everything was in order. I found the demonstrations an excellent way to learn the subject since I had to go over them with students in the tutorial group allocated to me and deal with any questions they would ask.

Blacklock was an outstanding lecturer, a great showman, extremely kind to students, and never making them feel uncomfortable when they were questioned in front of fellow students. His lectures were always stimulating and unique in method of presentation, which was designed to make the student remember. In his lectures on tumours he would place a number of stools on the lecture bench, and pushing them aside with both arms would say, 'I am a simple tumour and cause my effects by pushing tissue aside, but only do harm when I press on vital organs. I am now a malignant tumour,' and he would push his arms through the legs of the stool to show how the cancer can invade and destroy tissues and spread to distant parts. Almost from the beginning he would allocate some lectures to me and it was quite common for him to slip into the back of the class to find out how I was performing. There was never harsh criticism, only sound and helpful advice. As time passed, the number of lectures I gave was increased until I was allocated one or two systems each of ten lectures.

The professional examination in pathology and bacteriology was held in June, at the end of the academic year, and those who failed could resit in September. The examination consisted of a written paper and a practical in pathology and bacteriology, and the results of those tests were known to the examiners when the student appeared for a viva or oral examination before two examiners. I sat in at the viva with Blacklock and the external examiner from Dublin and it was a valuable learning experience. The students would meet in one of the practical classes and be called in turn to the museum for the viva.

The examiners sat together at a table on which they had placed a number of jars of pathology specimens and bacteriology culture plates. The candidate sat on a chair facing them and I took my place at the side of the professors. Before the student came in, Blacklock turned to me and said, 'The function of the viva is to give the student the opportunity to tell us what he or she knows about the subject, and for us to decide if they can be allowed to progress to the next stages of their studies; and to get the best out of the student it is important for the examiner to make them feel at ease.' Then with a smile and a wink to the external examiner he said, 'And of course, we want to find out how well Tom has listened to me and taught the student how to deal with the viva.' In the tutorials he would say to me, 'There are three things you should teach the student when they examine a specimen. Look at the specimen carefully from the front, turn it round and see the back and what additional information is present. Once this is done, name the organ if possible, describe the changes you see and give your diagnosis or differential diagnosis.'

Some students took the oral examination in their stride, others would appear pale, their hands sweaty and trembling. Blacklock would spot the student who needed reassurance, talk to them for a few minutes, ask them if they enjoyed the course or what they had arranged for the summer. When they appeared calm, he would say, 'I just want to ask you a few questions,' and hand them one of the specimen jars. If the student had a reasonable performance in the rest of the examination or had failed miserably, the viva would be quite short; if they were on the borderline he would try to put them at ease and discuss the specimens with them. It was masterly to watch how the student responded to the questioning, and I remember thinking how easy it would be to confuse and terrify them. At the end of the viva he would say to the student, 'That wasn't so bad, you have shown me you should have done better in the written and practical papers.' If, after the viva, he felt the student's knowledge of the subject was lacking, he would say, 'Well, Miss or Mr X, I think you'll need to spend another three months in the department and come back to see me in September.'

It was always a pleasure to listen to him dealing with a bright student, such as Miss M. She was in my tutorial group and when she appeared at the museum door he said, 'This is the student you mentioned, Tom. We'll see how good she is,' and winked at the external examiner.

'Good morning Miss M.,' he said as the young girl sat down at the table. She was pale and her hands were shaking as he handed her the first specimen. She looked at it carefully, examined it back and front and said, 'It's the lung of a young child and on the pleural surface is a small necrotic tuberculous lesion called the Ghon focus,' Then she pointed to a large necrotic tuberculous gland lying under the bifurcation of the bronchus (windpipe). It had, she said, ulcerated into a blood vessel and this was the cause of the small pin-point nodules of miliary tuberculosis which could be seen throughout the child's lungs. She pointed out all the lesions as she described them and continued, 'I would say this child had miliary tuberculosis and died with tuberculous meningitis.' This, I thought, was exactly what had happened to the children and the young girl I had seen in general practice.

The Professor continued, 'How do you think she got this infection and how did it develop?' Miss M. continued, 'In all probability the child lived in a family where there was a patient with open tuberculosis, or with a grand-parent who had undiagnosed pulmonary tuberculosis.' In answer to his second question she continued, 'When the bacillus is inhaled and passes into the air passages, it is ingested by the white blood cells – leukocytes – which try to kill it. However, the bacillus is protected by its thick fatty coat, survives and uses the white blood cell as a carriage to transfer it to the pleural surface of the lung, where it grows to form the Ghon focus,' and once more she pointed to it. 'The tubercle bacillus is now carried in the lung lymphatics back to the hilar glands which become enlarged. The combination of Ghon focus and enlarged hilar glands,' she said, 'is called the primary complex.'

The Professor interrupted her, 'You said, correctly in this case, the hilar glands have ulcerated into the blood vessel and the tubercle bacilli spread throughout the body to produce a type of blood poisoning.' Then, looking at her, he said, 'Does this happen with every child or young adult infected with tuberculosis?'

'No,' said the girl, 'the outcome depends on a number of factors such as the virulence and dose of the tubercle bacilli, and the sensitivity and resistance of the patient.'

'Tell me,' said Blacklock, 'what happens when a child or young adult meets a small dose of tubercle bacillus or one of low virulence.'

'In that case,' said the girl, 'the primary complex will form, but will heal and be calcified or even ossified.'

'Are the bacilli dead in those calcified or ossified glands?' she was asked.

'No. It has been shown that tubercle bacilli can live even in ossified glands. If at a later date the patient's resistance falls, reinfection by the tubercle bacillus, either from them or a new outside source, can occur and this is how adult pulmonary tuberculosis arises.'

'Look round the table and choose a specimen showing adult pulmonary tuberculosis,' said the Professor. The tremor had gone from her hand. She sensed her viva was going well as she selected the new specimen and began describing it.

'It was,' she said, 'an advanced case, with obvious surface adhesions and much destruction of lung tissue.' She pointed to a large ulcerated cavity in the lung and a ruptured blood vessel projecting into it.

'What,' said the Professor, 'happened to this patient?' and, pointing to the ruptured vessel, she said, 'I suspect the patient had a fatal haemorrhage.' Indeed, I thought this was the type of lung tuberculosis Dr Cameron would recommend for rib resection (thoracoplasty) to close the cavity and prevent the fatal haemoptysis which had occurred.

The Professor was enjoying this viva and, since Miss M. was the last candidate before lunch, said he would like to carry on. It was clear from his next question he wanted to see if she understood how tuberculosis of brain, kidney, bone and adrenal glands was brought about.

'What is meant by chronic dissemination of the tubercle bacillus?' he asked her.

'This,' she said, 'occurs when the blood is invaded by a small dose of tubercle bacilli or by organisms of low virulence in a patient whose resist⸱ance is high. The organisms settle out in different organs in the body and produce circumscribed tuberculous nodules.' The Professor continued with his questions.

'Look at the specimens on the table and pick the ones which show evidence of chronic tuberculous dissemination.' She selected a brain, and described an area of localised tuberculosis (tuberculoma) which she said might have been considered as a brain tumour. She picked up a specimen of adrenal glands showing cortical nodules which were being replaced by tuberculosis. Since both adrenal glands had been extensively replaced, she thought the patient would have had Addison's disease. Now I realised what Dr Cameron meant when he said bone, joint and kidney tuberculosis were not isolated diseases; they had risen from another tuberculous site and treatment had to be directed to this site as well by the general measures of good food, fresh air and rest.

'I think, Miss M., you've had enough from me,' said the Professor, and passed her to the external examiner. After some searching questions in bacteriology which she answered, she was told she could go.

'She's good, Blacklock,' said the external.

'Very good,' said my Professor. She had done well in both written and practical exams. Her performance in the viva was impressive and she was given distinction.

The professional viva could be entertaining as well as instructive, and Professor Blacklock would tell many amusing stories. On one occasion he was examining with Sir Robert Muir, his old chief, the doyen of British pathology, and a confirmed bachelor. A young lady was having her oral and Sir Robert handed her a specimen of a cartilaginous tumour of finger. The swelling, about three inches in diameter, had been cut across, so that the finger, two inches long could be seen projecting from the tumour. Sir Robert was using the specimen to encourage a discussion on the different types of simple tumours, how they produced their effect and the difference between them and malignant tumours. The lady took the specimen, her hand was shaking and she kept looking at it.

'Well,' said Sir Robert, 'what is it?' and when she didn't reply he pointed to the finger and said, 'What is that?' She hesitated, blushed, and in a hushed voice said, 'Penis, Sir,' to which Sir Robert replied, 'What! Not with a nail on it!' The young lady, said Blacklock, had not been taught to look at both sides of a specimen.

On another occasion Blacklock was examining in Ireland when a young male student was brought into the room.

'This man is brilliant. You can ask him anything,' he had been told. Blacklock found him quite outstanding and decided to question him on his own speciality – tuberculosis. He answered all the questions with great confidence.

'How many types of tubercle bacilli are there?' asked the Professor.

'Three, Sir,' said the young man.

'No,' said Blacklock, 'there are four.'

'No, Sir. Only three.'

'Well, what are they?'

'Human, bovine and avian,' said the boy.

'But,' said Blacklock, 'there are four – human, bovine, avian and reptilian.'

'No, Sir. There's only three in Ireland since St Patrick slew all the reptiles.'

Yes, vivas could be funny.

A few months after joining the department, in addition to teaching I was placed on a rota for post-mortem and routine surgical duties, one month on each, and one month free. John Rodger had been the post-mortem room attendant for many years and in that time had acquired a considerable knowledge of pathology. It was he who taught me to carry out a dissection and prepare the organs for the eleven o'clock class demonstration. The chief of wards, staff and students in this clinic would enter the autopsy room, troop down the steps to the front of the theatre and occupy the seats behind and above the dissecting bench where the dissection organs were displayed ready for demonstration. Professor Blacklock, in wellington boots, would enter the dissecting room and don a white surgical gown, thick rubber apron and rubber gloves.

After a welcome to the clinical chief, his staff and students, he would ask one of the clinicians to give the patient's history, their findings and diagnosis. Although I would have this information from the post-mortem request form, the Professor encouraged us to carry out the autopsy and refer to it only when the dissection had been completed.

'You will be more careful and thorough with the dissection if you start from scratch,' he would say. After the clinical history I would hand him the organs in turn, when he would examine them carefully and describe the pathological changes to the students. If the post-mortem showed some prin- ciple he had dealt with in the lecture course, he would choose a student whom he would mention by name and ask him or her to describe the changes he or she saw but he never made a student feel ill at ease.

He would conclude the autopsy by reviewing the pathological findings and the cause of death, then instruct the houseman what to put on the death certificate. After the clinicians had gone he, on occasions, would re-examine an organ and say, 'This we will preserve as a specimen,' and he took infinite care in its preparation.

He was equally particular about the post-mortem report I would send to the clinicians, and after most post-mortems I would take material for histo-logical examination and any significant microscopic appearance would be added to the report. When this was complete it was reviewed by the Professor and, when he approved, we both initialled the report and it was sent to the ward.

Always instructive, the autopsy room class could have its amusing moments. On this occasion the Professor of Medicine, who was partial to a good malt whisky, was present with the staff and students. The patient had died of a haemorrhage from ruptured oesophageal varices, caused by a cirrhotic liver. I passed the knobbly yellow liver to Blacklock who held it up for the students to see, and with a glint in his eye said, 'Well, Professor, you see what whisky does to your liver?' To which his colleague replied, 'That, Blacklock, is what happens to the liver when you can't digest whisky. I can digest it.' The students looked forward to and enjoyed those exchanges.

When the Professor was away or unable for some reason to take the autopsy room demonstration, my medical colleagues and I had to conduct the class on our own. Most chiefs and their senior staff were understanding of our junior status. Many of them had spent a few years in pathology as part of their surgical or medical training and were only too keen to help us when problems arose. Donald Hay, the chief technician, like John Rodger, was always helpful. It was not uncommon in those days, for patients with polio-myelitis to end up undiagnosed in the autopsy room. On one such occasion when I had completed the dissection and had not found the cause of death, Rodger whispered, 'Look at the pink colouration of the brain. Cut into the mid-brain,' and sure enough, there was the necrotic dead tissue found in poliomyelitis. 'Now,' he said, 'you'll have to take out the spinal cord.'

It was my experience that the clinicians were rarely wrong in their diagnosis, but in this case they had never suspected polio, and on this occasion the chief was not amused. Most chiefs would regard such an occasion as a salutary lesson, as I found years later during an autopsy on an old man who had pyrexia of unknown origin. He was in one of the wards of Dr Joe Wright, a very talented physician, and had been treated with a variety of antibiotics without effect. On dissecting the neck I found a tuberculous gland which had ulcerated into the jugular vein to produce the small pin-point nodules of miliary tuberculosis I found in the lungs. This was the same type of tuber-culous lesion I had seen in young children and young women and now it was appearing in an old man. When I pointed to lesions in the neck glands and lungs, Dr Wright looked at me and said, 'The only antibiotics we didn't give him were those against tuberculosis.' Then turning to the student he said, 'We can always learn from the autopsy room, and we should never forget that tuberculosis is still around.'

Blacklock continually emphasised the need for care in the autopsy room when dealing with patients who for various reasons had died of peritonitis. He laid down strict rules that had to be followed if the pathologist punctured a glove on a bony spicule or sustained a cut finger, which happens not infrequently during dissection.

'You will stop immediately, whip off the gloves, wash the hand thoroughly and pour antiseptic solution on the cut,' he insisted. A first-aid box with antiseptic solution, cotton wool and plasters, as well as eye drops, was kept in the post-mortem room. When the cut had been treated and protected by a plaster dressing and a fresh pair of gloves worn, the dissection or autopsy demonstration would be continued. The clinicians accepted these interrup-tions, for in the pre-antibiotic days it was not uncommon for pathologists to die from blood poisoning following infection in the autopsy room.

The post-mortem room discussion with clinicians was an early form of medical audit, where their clinical judgement, diagnosis and treatment were there to be seen and discussed. Likewise it was a test of the ability and efficiency of the pathologists who had to perform before Professor Blacklock and the chief and staff of the surgical and medical units of the hospital. In addition, it was my introduction to the surgeons with whom I would deal during my month on surgical routine.

The month on post-mortem duty was followed by one on surgical, when specimens from surgical theatres came to the department, along with a form with the patient's name, age, sex and a short clinical history. I would receive the specimen, record it and its number in the day book, then examine and describe the macroscopic appearance of the specimen, which I recorded on the back of the request form. Small specimens were placed directly into a jar containing fixative, while representative blocks were taken from different areas of larger specimens and fixed. A number similar to that on the form and in the day book was placed with the specimen in the jar with fixative and Blacklock would impress on me how important it was that the number and specimen were never parted, particularly when the specimen was small. After fixation the specimen was passed through a series of dehydrating jars before being cleared in chloroform and embedded in paraffin wax, when it would be passed to a technician who would prepare a slide for microscopic examination. I would write my histological report with the diagnosis on the back of the requisition form, hand it to the typist who would return to me a report form detailing the macroscopic (naked-eye) and microscopic appearance of the lesion and my diagnosis. This I would check, sign and send to the wards.

The Professor impressed on us how important it was to accept full responsibility for the specimens and the damage that could result if specimens were lost or the numbers mixed up.

Diagnostic histopathology is, in a way, recognition of patterns and is analogous to the way we recognise individual human beings or animals. No one who has seen a dog would fail to distinguish it from a cat, but only if they are familiar with the different species of dogs would they be able to identify each species. In the same manner each pathological lesion has its identifying features and these are learned slowly from experience, help from senior colleagues and reference to books and published articles.

In my early days, Blacklock would look at every slide with me and read my reports. Gradually, as I gained in experience, he would say, 'You are now capable of reporting on your own. You must now accept responsibility for the diagnosis, but if you are not sure, I'm always here.' I was now in at the deep end.

I became familiar with senior and junior clinicians during the autopsy demonstrations and became even closer to them when on surgical routine. They would come to the department and together we would look at the slides from their patients. On other occasions they would invite me to come to the wards to see a patient whose diagnosis might be presenting some difficulty.

During my frequent visits to the wards, I would meet Dr Tom Bryson, the hospital superintendent, who took a great interest in my activities. In time I became familiar with his role in the hospital, his wisdom and the tactful manner with which he dealt with the surgical chiefs and their problems.

There were five surgical units in the hospital and each was run by a chief of wards who had three consultants under him. Each unit had one receiving day per week and double receiving every six weeks. On receiving day, which would last twenty-four hours, the junior consultant would be in casualty and dealt with all injuries, including fractures. He would see acute surgical emergencies and send them to the wards for treatment by the chief and his two consultant colleagues. The chief went home in the late evening and the two consultants would complete the work which often took them to the early hours of the morning. Next day and for the rest of the week, in addition to elective surgery, the chief and unit consultants had undergraduate teaching duties. All consultants were part-time, the chief received no remuneration and the others were paid £50 per year. Consultants who did not have private means had a part-time appointment in general practice or an attachment to anatomy or pathology. Consultants in medicine and other clinical specialties were also part-time and poorly remunerated. Attachment to a large teaching hospital was prestigious and helped them make contact with general practitioners in the region. It was generally accepted that clinical consultants were approaching the age of forty before they were established in private practice with rooms where they saw private patients and with facilities in private nursing homes. However, in hospital only the chief of wards had control of beds and the waiting list. Consultants were dependent on the goodwill of the chief before they could admit into a hospital bed any non-emergency patient seen on private consultation. The patient for elective surgery could be placed on the waiting list, but it was the chief who decided what patient should be admitted from the waiting list. It was this dictatorial power of the chief that caused such discontent among many younger consultants. Many chiefs in the past had suffered themselves under the system and once in control, saw no reason why things should be changed. The patients they were called to see on private consultations by general practitioners, would be taken to private nursing homes if they could pay, and to beds in their hospital wards if they could not pay. Some chiefs who were excellent surgeons, or physicians, did not fear competition from their consultant colleagues, and allocated beds to them in the hospital. Those were the best and most successful units, attracted the best staff and were most popular with undergraduate students.

Dr Bryson, the medical superintendent, exercised considerable influence in the hospital and took an active interest in the control of the waiting list. He would check up on the list every Monday morning and, armed with this information, pay a visit to each chief of the surgical units.

'Your waiting list for hernias is too long, John,' he would say to the old surgeon. 'I'm distributing some to other units,' and he mentioned the names of the patients and the units who would be told to take them. Dr Bryson and Miss Manners, the matron, ran the hospital with great efficiency, pride and in some units with a rod of iron. Indeed, the Royal Infirmary was a great family and I was pleased to be a part of it.

I was to learn that an academic department of pathology has three functions: it provides teaching for the undergraduate and postgraduate students, it provides a post-mortem and routine diagnostic surgical service for patients in hospital and its staff must be involved in research. I was progressing favourably in the first two and became involved in the third in a surprising way.

One day I was called to the Professor's office. Lying on the table in the middle of the room were two specimen jars and in each one was mounted a black tumour, the size of a lemon. 'Do you know what they are?' he asked me and when I replied in the negative he continued. 'those black tumours are phaeochromocytomas and arise from cells (phaeochromocytes) in the centre of the medulla of the human adrenal gland. The tumours produce large quantities of adrenaline – like substances called catecholamines, and the black colour you see is produced when the tumours are placed in a fixative of formalin and potassium dichromate.' He continued, 'The surgeons and physicians involved with the two patients from whom the tumours came are pestering me to get a report since they wish to publish. See what you can make of them,' and he handed me the two specimen jars, dozens of paraffin blocks from the tumours, both post-mortem reports and paraffin blocks taken from different organs at autopsy. This assignment by the Professor was the beginning of my twenty-five years' research on the human adrenal gland. It was to take me to different countries in the world and enable me to meet many distinguished scientists.

But first I had to learn something about the two normal adrenal glands, where they lie in the body, the different names used to describe them, the nature of the chemical substances produced by them and their function in the body.

The adrenal glands, I would learn, are part of the endocrine system, and produce chemical substances called hormones which are passed directly into the blood, not through ducts. Accordingly, all endocrine glands are referred to as ductless glands. The adrenals, two in number, are frequently called the suprarenal glands since they lie, like a cocked hat, immediately above the upper pole of each kidney; each gland weighs about four grams.

If a cut is made through an adrenal gland it will be seen to consist of two parts, an outer yellow fatty shell called the *adrenal cortex* and an inner centre, the *adrenal medulla*. The cortex produces a series of hormones called *corticosteroids* and, at the time of my study, all that was known of their function was that some had a role in carbohydrate or sugar metabolism and were called *sugar-active corticosteroids*, while others had an influence in salt metabolism and were referred to as *salt-active corticosteroids*.

Later I would learn that the adrenal cortex stores only minute quantities of corticosteroid hormones, and when they are required by the body, another endocrine gland, the pituitary, releases one of its hormones, appropriately named adrenocorticotropic hormone (ACTH), which passes in the blood to the adrenal producing corticosteroids from the yellow lipid precursors (cholesterol) stored in the cells of the adrenal cortex. Whereas cells of the adrenal cortex store only minute quantities of hormones, the phaeochromocytes or cells of the adrenal medulla, as Professor Blacklock had told me, store larger ammounts of their hormones, adrenaline and noradrenaline, which are called catecholamines. The tumour I was to study, phaeochromocytoma, arose from the phaeochromocyte cells in the adrenal medulla. I was now ready to tackle the problem I had been set.

I went to the wards, saw the chief physician for the first patient, told him I had been asked to deal with the pathology and said I would like to discuss the clinical history with him. He was delighted and proceeded to tell me he had been called, on private consultation, to see a young married soldier of twenty-one years who suffered attacks of excruciating headaches which were increasingly in frequency and severity. During an attack he would sweat profusely and become violently sick. The consultant found his blood pressure was extremely high and decided to admit him to his wards in the Royal Infirmary. On his evening visit he asked the resident about the patient and was surprised to learn his blood pressure was normal and he was quite well. This, he realised, was the typical history of a patient with phaeochromocytoma and, after further tests during which his blood pressure rose alarmingly, the tumour was located in the right adrenal gland and he was sent to surgery. The blood pressure was carefully monitored during operation. At first it was normal, then rose suddenly when the surgeon handled the tumour, and remained high until a clamp was placed on the adrenal vein and the tumour removed. The blood pressure fell precipitously and continued downwards in spite of intravenous infusions of adrenaline, until the patient died. The second patient, a female of thirty-seven years had a similar clinical history. However, in her case the blood pressure between paroxysmal attacks fell, but never to normal levels, and remained elevated. She too went into post-operative shock and died after surgery. These two patients presented me with some interesting problems and the Professor had unwittingly started me on some intriguing research.

I cut and stained the blocks he gave me, became familiar with the characteristic cellular pattern of those tumours and noted prominent vascular spaces packed with tumour cells in the sections I made. When I used special stains to show the framework of the tumour I was fascinated to note that large vascular spaces were lined only by tumour cells. I prepared sections from the chrome-fixed blocks the Professor had taken, stained them with a Giemsa solution and produced a beautiful olive-green colouration of the catecholamine granules in the cells of the tumour and in the tumour cells lying in the vascular spaces. The olive-green staining of the granules is called the chrome reaction. I reported my findings to Professor Blacklock, and together we prepared photomicrographs of the lesions, carried out a literature search and with the clinicians wrote a clinico-pathological paper on 'Phaeochromocytoma', which was published in the British Journal of Surgery. I was invited later by the Royal College of Surgeons in London to give a lecture on my work.

This exercise stimulated me to ask a number of questions. How were the catecholamines held in the tumour granules? What released them and why, in some of the reported tumours I reviewed, was the patient's blood pressure permanently elevated following a paroxysm? Above all how could the fatal post-operative collapse be prevented and the patient survive?

All those interesting problems were dwarfed by an event which was to change our lives. On 21 March 1945 our first son, Robin, was born after Margaret had a difficult labour. She had worked as a medical officer in Cleland until a few days before the birth. Now she would look after him in our own home in Uddingstone, Lanarkshire, and I would travel by bus to the Royal Infirmary. It was customary in those days to prevent herniation of the umbilicus in babies by applying a six-inch wide flannel binder tightly over the umbilicus. One evening I asked Margaret for a piece of the binder, which was made of protein material. I cut it into a number of one-inch squares which I immersed overnight in a 1% solution of adrenaline, then suspended them in a 5% solution of potassium dichromate. After washing in water I stained the binder cloth with Giesma and produced the same positive olive-green chrome reaction I had found in granules in the tumour cells. When I repeated the experiment with a piece of cotton cloth, a negative result was obtained. I did not pursue this study and years later it was shown that the catecholamines in normal adrenal medulla cells are attached to a chemical called adenosine triphosphate (ATP) in a ratio of 3:1 whilst in the tumours it is 10:1. In this form the granules are very unstable and if for any reason the patient is stressed or the tumour is handled at operation, the granules break down and the catecholamines are poured into the blood spaces I had demonstrated, producing a severe attack of high blood pressure.

My experience with the two patients made me conscious of the existence of this intriguing illness and over a period of two years I collected tumours from departmental records. To my surprise I could never show a positive chrome reaction in material taken from any of them. Indeed, when I reviewed the literature, the tumour was often reported as being chrome negative. What had Professor Blacklock done and how had I achieved a positive chrome reaction with my binder experiments? Indeed, I had not used 10% formalin in them. When I repeated these experiments by treating the flannel with 1% adrenaline then immersing it in an equal volume of 10% formalin and 5% potassium dichromate, I could not get the olive-green colour of a positive chrome reaction when the binder was stained with Giemsa solution. I found the acidity of the formalin solution was eluting or removing the adrenaline from the flannel and it was also eluting the catecholamines from the granules in the tumour. Further binder experiments showed the pH of the formalin dichromate solution had to be rigidly controlled to between pH 4 and 6 and, as so often happens, a paper by Swedish workers confirmed my observations. When I told the professor about my results he was interested and said he must have been lucky to use the correct pH for his dichromate solution.

My results were interesting, but the main problem for the patient was to try and prevent paroxysmal attacks of hypertension which followed attempts to localise the tumour, and the fatal post-operative collapse which followed its surgical removal. I conducted experiments with rats which I injected over a period of weeks with increasing daily doses of 1/1000 solution of adrenaline in an attempt to reproduce the conditions found in the patients during paroxysmal attacks of hypertension. Along with Archie Goodall, a young consultant surgeon in the Royal Infirmary, we anaesthetised the animals and monitored the blood pressure at intervals after an infusion of catecholamines was given to simulate what would happen when the tumour in a patient was handled. As expected, our tracings showed marked elevations of blood press-ure, but as time passed the blood pressure kept falling and no amount of catecholamines could restore it.

Our experiments confirmed that treatment with adrenaline and noradre-naline had no role to play in the post-operative collapse of patients following surgery, and the answer to the problem came in a most unexpected manner. It was customary for me to look at the adrenal glands of all animals used in the experiments, and on this occasion I decided to examine the lipid or fatty material in the cells of the adrenal cortex which, in the rat, completely surrounds the medulla where the catecholamines are produced. I found lipid was very depleted in the cortical cell while lipid material could be seen passing into the vascular spaces of the adrenal medulla. I had not seen this before and it intrigued me. But how could I determine the nature of this material? All we knew of the adrenal cortex in the 1940s was that it was essential to life, and by the time I was looking at my problem, some progress had been made. It was known by this time that the two sets of steroid hormones were synthesised from the lipid material (cholesterol) in the adrenal cortex, but their chemical nature had not been determined. As I mentioned earlier, one group was involved with carbohydrate or sugar metabolism and was suitably named 'sugar-active' or 'glucocorticosteroids' and would be represented today by the steroid hormone, cortisol. The other group controlled salt and water metabolism and was referred to as 'salt-active' corticosteroids, of which aldosterone would be the modern example. At the time of my experiments only deoxycorticosteroid acetate (DOCA), a salt-active corticosteroid, was available for experimental study.

Today a battery of sophisticated techniques is available and would have helped me detect minute quantities of both sets of steroid hormones. It is salutary to look back more than forty years and examine the methods I had available for my study. Indeed, there was no available assay to help me decide if salt-active corticosteroids were present in the lipid secretions in the rat experiments, but Professor Dwight Ingle of Chicago University had developed a bio-assay based on the regeneration of liver glycogen I could use to determine if sugar-active glucocorticosteroids were present.

I set up two series of animal experiments. In one the animals had both adrenal glands removed, in the other the animals remained intact. Both sets of animals received a single injection of 1/1000 adrenaline to simulate a hypertensive crisis in a patient with phaeochromocytoma and estimations of liver glycogen and blood sugar were carried out at half hour intervals in both series. In the group with intact adrenals the glycogen content of liver fell for the first half hour, then began to recover and was back to normal in three hours. During the same period the blood sugar level rose and remained high to the end of the experiment. When the test was repeated with animals whose adrenals had been removed, the liver glycogen quickly depleted and never regenerated, whereas the blood sugar rose initially, fell to low levels and never recovered. The Ingle assay, as it was called, had shown the lipid material did at least contain sugar-active steroid hormone.

At this stage, I was called to the army and it would be another two years before I could resume my research. In that time chemists had been able to synthesis cortisone and cortisol and when I resumed the studies, on my return from the army, I had a supply of those steroids to work with. I found that pre-treatment of animals with cortisol protected them and the adrenal from the stress of adrenaline injections and this pointed to a method for dealing with patients with phaeochromocytoma.

Pneumography, or the passage of air around the adrenal gland, was a technique used by the surgeon to visualise a tumour in the adrenal gland and with a phaeochromocytoma this procedure can precipitate a paroxysmal attack. I discussed my result with the surgeon, showed him how cortisol had protected the animal and he agreed that he would try steroid pre-treatment before he attempted pneumography to visualise the tumour. This proved successful, the patient received 100 mgs cortisol intravenously, and he carried out the visualising procedure with no ill effects. Likewise steroid cover was given to new patients with phaeochromocytoma that came our way. 250 mgs of cortisol was given intramuscularly on the evening before the operation and 100 mgs intravenously before the anaesthetic. There was no further post-operative collapse and every patient survived; the best way to treat shock was to prevent it.

The last year of my pre-army research was done when I was undergoing training in bacteriology, where I learned media preparation, sterilisation of surgical instruments, gowns and culture media. I learned how to deal with and report a variety of swabs, sputum and other materials from surgical and medical units. Soon my experience in bacteriology and biochemistry would prove of value in the army.

I completed a few remaining animal experiments, and had made a summary on cards of all relevant literature, completed all necessary photomicrographs and on the first week in November 1947 I reported to the RAMC Depot at Crookham. A month before this Professor Blacklock had appointed me to a post as Lecturer in Pathology and I received one payment of my salary of £650 before being called to the army.

CHAPTER 5

Military Service in Malaya

After three weeks' physical training at Crookham, I went to the Army Public Health unit nearby for a series of inoculations and a course of lectures on tropical medicine. I remember very little about the course apart from a lecture on typhoid fever by Colonel Lynch, when he remarked that the best treatment for typhoid was hot, sweet tea. I would think about his remark in the next few months. Postings were announced at the end of the course, and I was sent to the Far East to take charge of pathology at the British military hospital (BMH) at Kuala Lumpur. I was given the rank of Major and as the Deputy Assistant Director of Pathology (DADP) was responsible for all pathology in Malaya.

I had never been out of the country, except for a short holiday in Belgium in 1939, and did not relish the separation from Margaret and Robin since there was no way of knowing how long I would be in the Far East. On 28 January 1948, I flew in a York aircraft from RAF Lyneham, Wiltshire, and as I boarded the aircraft snow was falling. It was bitterly cold and I was wearing an army greatcoat. Sitting behind me on the plane was a Wing Commander who was taking up a posting in Singapore. He was a marvellous companion and during the five-day flight to Singapore, pointed to many places of interest below. The first stage of our flight was to Malta, the George Cross island, where we landed on a beautiful spring evening in time to go to Valetta, see some of the damage caused during the war and have dinner before returning to RAF headquarters where we spent the night.

Next morning our departure was delayed by aircraft engine trouble. Eventually we were on our way and flew along the Mediterranean over Tel Aviv and the Dead Sea to arrive at the RAF Habbaniyah Airport fifty miles to the west of Baghdad in Iraq. As the aircraft came in to land it was getting dark and the River Euphrates, which arched round the airport, was coming nearer and nearer as the aircraft hit the ground and ran along the runway. Suddenly the engines roared into action, the aircraft took off and circled the airfield before the young pilot landed safely. I did not think there was anything

Author in RAMC (Malaya) with the rank of Major.

unusual about this until the pilot came up to the Wing Commander and apologised. 'Never mind,' he told the pilot, 'you took off when you needed to and you will learn from this experience.'

We were off next morning at 8 o'clock, along the Euphrates and heading for Karachi. My friendly Wing Commander touched my shoulder. We were over Babylon, he said, and later, pointed to the River Tigris away in the distance. As we flew over the sea, the water was so clear I could see the rocky bottom and the shadow of the aircraft reflected on the water, then it was over the Arabian Sea and along the coast of Iran to Karachi where we spent the night. After dinner in the RAF Mess, I met the Medical Officer who invited me to visit his small hospital to see a patient with poliomyelitis. As I entered his office I saw on a desk a copy of the British Journal of Surgery and in it was the article I had written with Professor Blacklock. He was amused when I showed him the article and said he would read it now with more interest.

The flight from Karachi along the coast of India was over sea and I saw very little until we crossed the coast of Ceylon and landed at the airport at Negombo where we spent the night. Next morning on the last stage of the flight, at the Wing Commander's request, I saw Sumatra, or Indonesia, from the pilot's cabin. We flew up the Strait of Malacca, with Malaya and the thick jungle of trees on the left and landed at Changi airport in Singapore. The temperature was in the 90s, and the humidity high and I felt very uncomfortable in my officer's serving dress.

An army truck took me to the British Military Hospital in Singapore where I spent four days getting a proper tropical kit. Meantime in the space of twenty-four hours a local tailor made me two pairs of light flannel trousers and two white short-sleeved shirts. Next evening I boarded the night sleeper at Singapore for Kuala Lumpur and reported next morning for duty at the British Military Hospital. This was part of the City General Hospital located on the outskirts of the town in Batu Road and close to the world-famous Institute of Medical Research. Here I was to remain for almost two years.

I found that BMH Kuala Lumpur had well-qualified medical, surgical and anaesthetic staff, most of them like myself being conscripts. The laboratory I was to run was a large barn-like building and reasonably well equipped to deal with problems in clinical pathology and parasitology. Staff Sergeant McDonald and Corporal Byers were regular soldiers who were well trained in laboratory technology, and there was an extremely good conscript techni-cian, Eddie Coxall, who had been trained in bacteriology and haematology at St Bartholomew's Hospital in London. The rest of the technicians were conscripts and I had to train them how to use a microscope and carry out simple techniques in bacteriology and parasitology.

I found that tropical medicine is essentially laboratory medicine and most of the illnesses I encountered were caused by organisms of some sort. Diagnosis and treatment of the patient depended to a large extent on identifying the causal organism. I encountered different forms of dysentery, numerous parasitic worm infections and saw many patients with syphilis, malaria and scrub typhus. Soon after my arrival I was fortunate to make the acquaintance of Dr Richard Greene, chief of Bacteriology at the Institute of Medical Research, who helped me a great deal with the more difficult problems I would encounter. He was an Australian and had been many years at the Institute. As I entered his office he rose, shook my hand and offered me a seat at the table in front of him. After telling him why I had come he said, 'Your problem is this,' and proceeded to summarise what I had said, then, turning to a large collection of books of Institute records, he selected a volume, opened it at the relevant page and read from it the answer to my question. There was not time for small talk. He asked if that answered my question and I left, but I knew I had someone I could always turn to when in difficulty.

Malaria was common among soldiers who would forget to take their anti-malaria drug. The condition was diagnosed by identifying the parasite in blood which was taken from the patient, a slide prepared and stained appropriately to show the parasite. This brought me into contact with Dr John Field, another senior member of the Institute and an acknowledged world authority on malaria. He had been a prisoner of war in Changi jail in Singapore during the Japanese occupation, and during that period he wrote and illustrated his book on the thick-film techniques for the diagnosis of malaria. He gave me a signed copy which I treasured.

However, it was the disease scrub typhus which fascinated me, and brought me into contact with the Director of the Institute, Dr Raymond Lewthwaite. He had been in Malaya since the 1920s and at that time, he told me, if four of his colonial colleagues went into the jungle on a survey, three could develop the illness and one would die. He worked on the problem until the Japanese invasion, escaped to Burma where he teamed up with a British entomologist, made contact there with the American scrub typhus research team, and at the end of the war brought this American group to Malaya to test their new antibiotic, chloromycetin, on patients with the disease. I was in Kuala Lumpur when the Americans arrived.

The story of Lewthwaite and scrub typhus is a success story achieved by few individuals in their life. He talked to me about the illness, the organism that caused it, how it was carried and how patients were infected. When a native village in Malaya was evacuated, rats moved into the area. The rats carried in their ears a species of mite, the trombiculite mite, which in turn harboured a small organism slightly larger than a virus, called Rickettsia Orientalis which was the cause of the disease. When soldiers or civilians passed through a rat-infested scrub area, the mites from the rats' ears got onto the soldiers' bare legs or bodies, bit them and introduced the rickettsia. A small, black scab called the eschar formed at the site of the bite, its presence being an important diagnostic feature of the illness. Dr Lewthwaite showed me how to detect the rickettsia by injecting a patient's blood into the peritoneal cavity of young immature mice; after a few days the organisms could be stained and identified microscopically in peritoneal scrapings of cells from the undersurface of the diaphragm.

James Williams, my room-mate in the Officers' Mess, was the physician in charge of scrub typhus patients in the military hospital and he supplied many of the early patients who were treated successfully by chloromycetin. During the two years I spent in Malaya I saw about one hundred patients in hospital with scrub typhus and there were no deaths.

There was an interesting and indeed important sequel to the chloromycetin story. The family doctor had in his wards in the hospital, the wife of a senior army officer. She was admitted with headache and abdominal discomfort, her temperature was elevated and she was toxic. A blood culture was taken and sent to my laboratory. Next morning I found the family's doctor, a Colonel, waiting for me at the door of the laboratory. He was very agitated. The patient was now seriously ill and he wanted to know what the blood culture would show. When I examined the culture plate I was surprised to find a pure culture of typhoid bacillus: we had a patient with typhoid fever on our hands. James Williams was looking after the patient now, he came down to the lab and after some discussion we decided to approach the American scrub typhus team, explain we had a seriously ill typhoid patient and request they let us have some chloromycetin for trial. They agreed. Williams administered the drug and a repeat blood culture was negative twenty-four hours after treatment was started. The patient made a complete recovery. My thoughts went back to Colonel Lynch's lecture on typhoid at the army hygiene unit and the treatment with hot, sweet tea. Now we had a drug to deal with this dangerous illness and I often regret I did not write to the Colonel and tell him the story.

I traced the source of the patient's illness to a houseboy who was a typhoid carrier and he was hospitalised and treated in the civilian hospital. A few weeks later when our patient had recovered and was receiving a final clearance test, she informed me that the houseboy had left hospital of his own accord and was employed as a houseboy with the NAAFI manager. When I told the manager he was employing a typhoid carrier as a houseboy and he would have to go, he remarked, 'He's the best boy I've ever had.'

The diagnosis of tropical illness required good laboratory cover and I was constantly in the wards, discussing problems with James Williams and the other consultant, Henry Giles. I was finding the laboratory side of tropical medicine fascinating and rewarding. In the evening James would study the case notes of the patients with scrub typhus he was treating with the American physicians, and from time to time would draw my attention to some point. The case report and temperature chart of our typhoid patient were of particular interest and I can still picture him as he turned round, looked over his glasses and said, 'My, my, this chloromycetin works. It's great, Tom.'

While James was busy with the chloromycetin study, I was writing my MD thesis. I had brought a complete history of all the patients I had collected with phaeochromocytoma, along with the summaries I had made on the cards of any relevant literature on those tumours. I had notes of my animal experiments and the cards I had prepared of the results, conclusions and relevant literature.

I had brought my copy of Sir Clifford Albutt's *Composition of Scientific Papers*, a necessity for any young person about to write a thesis or scientific paper. I decided the thesis would consist of five parts and placed the relevant information and cards for each section in five large envelopes which I opened only when I was ready to write the section. When I reviewed the literature I learned to note carefully the name and initials of all authors in the article, the proper contraction for each scientific or medical journal, followed by the year of publication, the volume underlined, and the first and last page of the article. This attention to detail always pays dividends. It prevents frustration and obviates an unnecessary visit to the library. I completed the thesis in six months, had it typed in duplicate and mounted the photomicrographs I had brought with descriptive titles in a separate volume. The thesis was submitted to the University of Glasgow and I was awarded the degree of Doctor of Medicine (MD) with Honours.

The Officers' Mess at the BMH was small and apart from the registrar and company officer, the rest of us were doctors. When I arrived, James Williams' bedroom was in the Mess and he was the wines member. Each officer purchased a five shilling bar book with which to buy drinks and the Malay barman, Chiniah, who was also our houseboy, would keep the used bar chits in a shoebox. Each night when the bar closed, James and I would go downstairs, check the level of alcohol in the bottles, calculate the theoretical sales and check them against the bar chits which we kept in our room and burned at the end of each month. On the Monday morning, empty bottles complete with wrappers were returned to the NAAFI and new stock bought. I took over as wines member from James, adopted the same procedure he had devised and, like him, made a very good profit. Subsequent wines members were not so successful. Some did not carry out a nightly check and destroy the chits at the end of the month. Chiniah was quick to spot this and it was only during his tenure as wines member that an astute company officer discovered Chiniah had kept the chits and used them at night for his own enjoyment.

The execution of Japanese war criminals by hanging was in force when I arrived in Malaya and it was the duty of the most junior medical officer in the unit to attend the executions. Dr S. had joined us recently and was sitting rather disconsolately, in a corner of the Mess when I entered.

'You look ill,' I said. 'Anything wrong?'

'I've been told I've to report for a hanging tomorrow, and I'm not looking forward to it,' he replied. Meantime Norman, another medical officer, had entered and heard our conversation.

'I've never seen a hanging and would love to go. I'll take your place,' he said.

Next day we all waited for Norman's return and the chance to hear his report. He came into the Mess visibly shaken and muttered, 'It was horrible, horrible. They just strangulated him,' and disappeared to his room for the rest of the day.

A few weeks after I arrived at the unit, James and I, with two other colleagues, motored to the sea at Port Dickson and on the way stopped for curry tiffin at the government guesthouse in Seremban. Port Dickson lay on the coast that I had seen when flying up the Strait of Malacca en route to Singapore. When we arrived at our destination the sea was calm and beautiful and I was attracted by the rows of coconut trees which lined the beach and the large expanse of golden sand which seemed to stretch for miles. It would be another thirty years before I saw this beautiful beach again.

The week after our visit to Port Dickson the army held one of its traditional tattoos which I attended and enjoyed. That evening, on returning to the Mess, I listened to a broadcast from London and in it the Foreign Secretary, Ernest Bevin, was saying, 'Malaya is the jewel in the British Empire. The dollar earnings from the export of tin and rubber are greater than the dollar earnings of the whole of the United Kingdom.'

Next day the Chinese communist uprising began in Malaya. We were told by the Commanding Officer of the hospital that the communists were massing for attack on Kuala Lumpur and we were expected to draw up plans for the defence of our departments. This we did with a gun emplacement here and there, but the exercise was meaningless as no weapons were available and most of us had no firearms training. Sometime later I was issued with a revolver and six round of ammunition, but I never learned how to fire it and indeed, never had any need to do so. Since loss of one's weapon was a court-martial offence, I kept the revolver and ammunition safely locked in a teak chest lined with camphor wood, a lovely piece of furniture still in our present home.

The insurgents were mainly Chinese communists who had been trained by the British as jungle resistance fighters during the war with Japan. When war ended they retained their weapons which were hidden in camps they established deep in the dense jungle. In China at this time the victorious communist army under Mao Tse-tung was sweeping menacingly south and the days of the Chinese government under Chiang Kai-shek were numbered. In the light of events in China the communist uprising in Malaya must have been disturbing to the equanimity of the British authorities. Their concern was not lessened by the poor relationship which existed between the Malay and Chinese communities. The Chinese were active, dynamic businessmen, whereas the Malay were quiet and easy-going, who nevertheless were unwilling to give up the reins of power which British control had entrusted to them. The thought of civil war between the two communities was a possibility which fortunately never occurred. While the Chinese community in both towns and villages may have been blackmailed and threatened to provide support for the insurgents, the latter were largely isolated from both Chinese and Malay communities and carried out their war from camps deep in the jungle. The war developed into a series of ambushes in the country of military patrol units, personnel and families travelling on leave to the rest centre in the Cameron Highlands, but most often attacks were directed at rubber planters, their families and workers. No doubt the uprising was destined to take place, but I have little doubt that Ernest Bevin's comments convinced the communist leaders that persistent attacks on rubber estates would affect the morale of the planters and the dollar earnings of rubber for Britain. I had great admiration for this group of men and women who had built up the rubber estates and employed generations of loyal Malay and Chinese workers. Their loyalty had been sorely tested during the Japanese occupation and would be once more by their insurgent fellow countrymen. The widely dispersed nature of the rubber plantations meant the planters had to take responsibility for the protection of their families and estates, with back-up support, when required, from the civil police and British army.

In the months following the emergency, the British army grew in strength and, at the request of the army hygiene unit, I had to test the suitability of the water in the small lakes around Kuala Lumpur where army camps were being sited. On those occasions I was given, as my bodyguard, a young soldier complete with sten gun who sat behind me in the jeep and preceded me through the dense jungle to the lakes I had to test.

As more and more troops came to Malaya the ambushes became stereotyped and altered only in frequency and severity. Casualties from the rubber estates were the responsibility of the local hospitals. Our casualties occurred when troops were ambushed on their way to deal with attacks on rubber estates, or in their search for insurgent camps. Soldiers and their families going on leave to the Cameron Highlands were prime targets and occasionally the ambulance train from Singapore to Kuala Lumpur and on to Penang would be attacked. To deal with this, Ghurkas with machine guns were positioned on the roof of the train.

The uprising and increase in army casualties meant changes for me in the laboratory. When I arrived in Kuala Lumpur all transfusion fluids and culture media were shipped to us from Britain. Now I was given the necessary equipment and told to make the transfusion fluids and culture media we required. Eddie Coxall, our St Bart's-trained technician, successfully undertook this work. I organised a blood bank to deal with emergencies and prepared blood transfusion packs which were dropped by parachute into the jungle so that the unit medical officers could tranfuse severe casualties on the spot. As the strength of the army increased, I arranged for every soldier entering Malaya to have his blood group determined and a list sent to the commanding officers. When an ambush occurred, the medical officer of the unit involved would phone the laboratory with the number of casualties we might expect and the blood group of each man. I would contact the commander of the army units stationed around Kuala Lumpur, tell him the number of casualties we were expecting and the blood groups required. He would announce that there had been an ambush and ask for volunteers of men with the required blood groups. The young soldiers would come to my laboratory and I would remind them of the danger of passing on venereal disease to the casualty by a blood transfusion. I asked each one in confidence if he had been in contact in the last four weeks with any ladies of the night. If they had, I would tell them to return to their unit, see their medical officer and get him to refer them to the special treatment centre. I took off blood from the remainder, confirmed their blood group and sent the donor into a room adjacent to the operation theatre where my assistant Ian McLean took off a pint of blood and passed it to the surgeon in the theatre ready for transfusion. On one occasion a casualty with blood group B required ten pints. There was never any problem getting volunteers. The soldiers realised it might be their turn next. I always rechecked the donated blood with a positive Wasserman test for syphilis, but in every case the blood was negative. The men were on their guard and they behaved honourably.

The state of emergency and the need for transfusion services meant that in my capacity as Deputy Assistant Director of Pathology (DADP Malaya) I became more involved with other medical centres in Malaya. My office as DADP was at district headquarters, a few miles from Kuala Lumpur and adjacent to that of the ADMS, Colonel Douglas Bluett. We met frequently and I kept him informed about the blood transfusion service, the scrub typhus research project, the progress of the patient with typhoid fever and, as well as the results of my water testing, we would discuss any other points that might arise.

One day, following one of our discussions he said, 'I hear you play golf. I would like to take you for a game at the Selangor Golf Club.' This was a typical country club with tennis courts, swimming pool, two championship golf courses and dining facilities. Although it was a private club, members of Forces could apply for membership. After a few games with the Colonel he suggested I apply for membership and after a game with some members of the committee, I was accepted for membership of the Selangor Golf Club. During the Japanese occupation, the eighteenth fairway of the golf course was used as an aircraft runway. Now it was restored to its original condition, although machine-gun posts manned by civil police were present around the perimeter of the course.

The Colonel's game improved with a little advice here and there and I suggested he enter for one of the club tournaments which he won and was presented with a magnificent rose bowl. He was obviously thrilled and in a moment of weakness asked if there was anything he could do for me.

'Yes,' I said, 'I've applied to the army to get my wife and son to Malaya,' and without any hesitation he replied, 'You have no chance. If you had a short service commission I might have been able to do something.' and there the matter closed. A month after our discussion I received a cable from Margaret telling me the army had arranged a passage for them on the SS *Devonshire* sailing from Liverpool at the end of August 1948. During our next golf match I told Colonel Bluett and all he said was, 'I'm glad. That's good news for you.' It was then I realised the value of golf and the interesting people I would meet through this game. I had been fortunate to win the April monthly medal over the Selangor course and was asked to play for the army against the senior golfers in a four ball match. My army partner was an excellent low handicap player and one of our opponents was the governor, Sir Henry Gurney, who had been a single handicap player. I enjoyed the game with him and the discussion which followed, and was distressed to learn that the next day on his way to the Cameron Highlands his party had been ambushed and he was killed.

The laboratory was well-established now and coping well with the added problems caused by the emergency. Only a few surgical specimens were processed and reported, and the post-mortems I performed were invariably the result of suicide or some tragic preventable accident. Russian roulette was a game practised by young soldiers with little to do when they were off-duty. A single bullet was loaded into the revolver, the chamber spun, the muzzle held against the side of the head and the gun fired. When the chamber was spun, the weight of the bullet should carry it to the bottom of the chamber, but sometimes this did not happen, with fatal results. I found it very distressing when I had to perform an autopsy on those young men.

I was not keen to be involved in identifying any snakes brought into the laboratory, but soon realised I was expected to pass judgement on them and decided if they were poisonous. The natives treated snakes with great respect and snake bites usually occurred when natives trod on them inadvertently while working in the fields. The snake bite I was involved with occurred late one Friday evening when a Sergeant-Major from one of the Guards regiments was walking from the mess where he had been drinking, to his sleeping quarters. He was wearing sandals when, he said, he felt a bite on the top of his foot and was brought immediately to the casualty department of the hospital and examined by the casualty doctor. The Sergeant-Major had been through the whole of the Second World War and was resting quietly on a bed, smoking a cigarette as the doctor administered the snake anti-venom he had sent for and received from the Institute of Medical Research. Suddenly the Sergeant-Major announced, 'I feel funny,' and next minute he was dead. I knew nothing about this until the following morning when I carried out an autopsy and found the tell-tale petechial haemorrhages on the surface of the lungs and on the lining of the heart. He had died of anaphylactic shock. As a result of a series of wartime inoculations, he was sensitive to and reacted to the anti-venom that had been administered. He had not been bitten by a snake. In the darkness I suspect a twig had pierced the top of his open sandal and had given him the sensation of a snake bite. Later I learned that during the funeral, when the coffin had been lowered into the grave, the Guards fired the salute with blank ammunition. Suddenly the funeral party found themselves under fire from, they thought, the communists. The soldiers took up defensive positions and fired blank ammunition while waiting for the arrival of reinforcements. Suddenly there was a lull in the firing and the soldiers discovered the shooting was coming from the civil police who, in turn, hearing the salute, thought they were facing the communists. When order was restored there was a sense of relief that maybe the Sergeant-Major had had a good send-off and the type of funeral he would have appreciated.

Margaret and Robin were receiving their final inoculations in preparation for the sea voyage to Malaya, when I received a letter from Professor Blacklock telling me that the Chair of Pathology in Hong Kong was vacant and he had recommended me for the post. I was surprised and replied expressing my gratitude for his confidence but saying that I felt I should return to Britain and learn more pathology before aspiring to this. It was clear something was wrong in Glasgow when, in his next letter, he told me the Senior Lecturer in the department had left and he had recommended me for the post. The Committee of Management of the Royal Infirmary had rejected his suggestion and consequently he had resigned and was leaving to take the Chair of Pathology at St Bart's in London. This was all very sudden and I wrote to Dr Bryson, the Superintendent of Glasgow Royal Infirmary, asking for some clarification.

The Board, he wrote back, had appointed Dr George Montgomery to the Chair of Pathology as successor to Professor Blacklock. The Senior Lecturer post would be advertised and I would be given the opportunity to apply. Some months later he cabled to inform me the post was advertised. I applied with Dr Lewthwaite as one of my referees, and was appointed to the post while still in the army in Malaya.

The SS *Devonshire* took four weeks to sail from Liverpool to Singapore and there was great excitement as I watched Margaret and our little fair-haired three-year-old disembark from the ship. In her letters she told me, when staying at her parents' farm, how he would take the dog and say they were going to daddy Tom in Malaya. She recalled how he had been to a children's party and seen the cake decorated with candles.

'When I go to Malaya,' he asked, 'will I get a birthday cake with candles to kindle?' In preparation I had bought such a cake to celebrate his late third birthday and would collect it from the baker's on our return to Kuala Lumpur.

Eventually when they disembarked, I embraced them both at the same time and holding Margaret said, 'Let me look at this young man.' He wasn't impressed, showed no excitement and, as we walked towards a waiting taxi, looked at his mother and said, 'Is he coming with us, Mum?' It shows how soon a three-year-old forgets and how little he remembers.

We spent a few days sight-seeing in Singapore and buying dresses for Margaret, before taking the night sleeper to Kuala Lumpur and the furnished accommodation I had fixed in Auntie Legge's large house in Kia Peng Road. The table legs in the dining room stood in old cigarette tins which were partially filled with a chemical solution in an attempt to prevent ants from invading the clean white cloths covering the table. I produced the large birthday cake, lit the three candles and Robin roared with delight as he blew them out, had them relit and blew them out again. Eventually the remainder of the cake was put in a tin box which was placed on top of the wardrobe in our room. I had bought a small second-hand Standard car and took Margaret and Robin to see the town. We visited the hospital, drove down Batu Road to see the shops and stop at the Coliseum restaurant for a refreshment. On our way home I took them to the Selangor Club where they saw the swimming pool they would both enjoy so much. Robin was anxious to see his cake and light the candles once more but on entering the bedroom he was amazed to see an army of ants marching up the front of the wardrobe, through a small slit in the tin containing the cake. Indeed the cake was a mass of ants and the three candles projected only marginally above this sea of ants. Auntie Legge was called, took the tin away and that was the end of the cake with candles to kindle.

Because of the heat and humidity, Auntie Legge announced that Robin would need an Amah to look after him and she would arrange it. Next day An Young, a young Chinese woman, arrived at the house; she was a second wife who lived with her family in a compound of native huts near our house. Margaret was very satisfied with her and Robin took to her from the beginning. She became attached to the little blond boy and I can still see her carrying 'Lobin', as she called him, on her hip with one leg in front and one behind. Once Robin was settled, Margaret was able to return to medicine and took an appointment as a medical officer in the outpatient department of the civil hospital which was adjacent to the British Military Hospital.

In addition to the tropical diseases I was seeing, Margaret came across patients with leprosy and many Indian women with severe anaemia who required a blood transfusion. The husband on a number of occasions would give blood for blood group testing, but no more, and on occasions I was able to help with blood from our bank during a lull between ambushes.

As time passed we moved house to Golf View Road to share with two army families the top floor of the beautiful home of a Ceylonese planter. We employed an old Chinese cook and his wife who were excellent, and each family took a month when they were responsible for the catering. Margaret and I found it cheaper to allow the cook to buy the food, and each evening we dined as a family. It was a happy and interesting phase in our life.

Soon it became clear that the emergency would last a long time and plans were drawn up to build a new military hospital in the country between Kuala Lumpur and Seremban. I saw the hospital completed and the new laboratory in working order. A short time after its occupation, Margaret came to see it and during our tour of the wards, the medical officer took us to see two young soldiers with rabies. They had been with their regiment in Greece and six months previously had been bitten by a dog. We never knew what happened to the dog, whether it was kept or observed, or shot as is more usual. In the circumstances the dog should have been kept in quarantine and if it had rabies it would die and the diagnostic evidence, the nigri bodies, found in the brain. The dog in question must have been rabid, for the two young soldiers had the disease and began foaming at the mouth when they saw and heard water running in the basin at their bedsides. This was the one and only time I experienced hydrophobia and never wished to see it again. The soldiers died two days later and I confirmed the diagnosis. Unfortunately during the autopsy I pierced my finger on a splinter of bone and, although unsure whether I could be infected in this way, the vision of hydrophobia and the worry of a long incubation period made me decide to take the anti-rabies vaccine. After administering myself sixteen doses of the vaccine subcutaneously into the abdomen, I was sore, depressed and ill, and gave up. Fortunately nothing happened, but my last three weeks of army service were spent recovering from the effects of the anti-rabies vaccine.

At the beginning of November 1949 we left Malaya, sailed home on the SS *Devonshire* to Liverpool and went on to Crookham to complete my army service and receive my discharge papers.

CHAPTER 6

Adrenal Research in the new National Health Service

OUR PARENTS were growing old and whilst we were in Malaya I saw Margaret was worried about her father's failing health. We were home only a few months when he had a shock from which he recovered partially but with mental deterioration. He had been an active, successful farmer who, in addition to his dairy farm, had grown mushrooms commercially and during the war had a thriving business in forced rhubarb for the market. He had settled his two elder sons in farms adjacent to his own, and the three farms were run as a single unit. Shortly after his shock he lost interest in the farm and fortunately was unaffected when his land was taken over by the Council for building purposes. He died, mercifully, before the first house was built, A few weeks later our second son, Alan John Forsyth, was born and named after him.

My family too, was growing old. Uncle Bob had retired from his position as Chief Mining Lecturer in Ayrshire, but could not settle and took on new teaching duties in the mining department of the Royal Technical College in Glasgow. I saw him every day at lunch, but in the long run the constant travel to Glasgow took its toll and he developed pneumonia. Although he recovered from the acute illness, his mind deteriorated and in the terminal phase of the illness, when I would sit alone with him during the night, he was no longer the mentally active person I had known and loved. He was back in his childhood, and it was a relief when the end came in 1951. He had never been ambitious for himself, yet he left a legacy of hope and achievement for the large group of young miners who studied under him, and who rose to positions of importance in the mining industry both in this country and in many countries of the world where mining flourished. His life had not been in vain.

Author's mother with Uncle Bob and Uncle George Steven (1949).

I returned to the pathology department at Glasgow Royal Infirmary in January 1950, to the beginning of a new and exciting era in medicine. The National Health Service had been introduced and Professor George L. Montgomery had been in post in the department for a year. I was able to resume my adrenal research on a wider scale and at the end of four years, would be appointed to the Chair of Pathology at the Royal Infirmary. I would spend three months in the United States and Canada in 1955 and develop links with basic scientists with whom many of my younger colleagues would work and learn new technology which they would later introduce into the department.

In contrast to pre-NHS days, salaried appointments of consultants and junior doctors had been made to all surgical and medical divisions and to special clinical units, like dermatology, gynaecology, ear, nose and throat, radiology and radiotherapy. The consultants were given the option of an eleven session full-time appointment or a part-time contract of seven, or later, nine sessions. The chief and the more established consultants were part-time and could engage in private practice. As time passed and young clinicians attained consultant status they would opt for full-time appointments, often for five years, until they became known and had established a reputation for themselves with the general practitioners. Then they would change and become part-time, rent consulting rooms in the west end of the city and treat patient in nursing homes or in private beds in Canniesburn Hospital.

All professors and senior lecturers in university clinical departments were full-time and not allowed to undertake private work; they had honorary consultant appointments from the Regional Health Board, which allowed them to treat patients. The university paid the salary of professors, senior lecturers and lecturers, while the regional health board paid for the hospital consultants and all junior clinical and nursing staff, even if their staff worked in a university clinical department. The senior technical staff in university departments were paid by the university while the juniors were all regional board employees. Some secretarial staff in academic departments were on the university staff, others were regional board. The salary arrangement was the result of an agreement between Sir Hector Hetherington, Principal of the University, and Dr Alexander Bowman, head of the Scottish Western Regional Hospital Board. It was a satisfactory arrangement for both parties and it worked to the advantage of both.

In Glasgow there were now five large teaching hospitals under the control of the Western Regional Hospital Board. They were the Royal, Western, Victoria, Stobhill and Southern General; each hospital was allocated a region and given the responsibility to develop the health services of that region and train staff, who in time would take over the regional hospitals. The Royal Infirmary supervised the health care of the population in hospitals in Lanarkshire and clinicians and pathologists were seconded to work there until suitable consultant staff had been trained. Due to the efforts of Professor D. F. Cappell, who occupied the Chair of pathology at the Western Infirmary, the salary of pathologists of all grades was kept in line with colleagues in the clinical specialities. This ensured a constant supply of first-class young graduates for training in laboratory medicine. In addition Cappell insisted that consultant pathologists, like their clinical colleagues, would qualify for merit awards. In later years I was to learn how those awards were allocated by a small group of very senior consultants who travelled throughout Britain and discussed the merits of every consultant in a region with senior consultants from the medical schools in that region. There were three grades of merit award and well-established criteria used to allocate the awards in each one. A 'C' grade candidate was a consultant who was highly regarded by colleagues in the medical community in which he or she practised. They were the consultants a doctor would choose to treat themselves or their families. They were the doctor's doctor. A 'B' grade consultant was one whose work was recognised nationally, and an 'A' award was reserved for someone who had an established international reputation.

In Scotland the Health Service was a great success: the regional boards and universities worked closely together for patients' care and teaching. Part-time and full-time NHS consultants in teaching hospitals were made honorary lecturers in the university and played an active role in undergraduate and post-graduate teaching. The Health Service was welcomed in academic departments. Salaries were good and money would become available for research, which flourished to a remarkable degree. A committee chaired by Sir Sydney Smith, Professor of Forensic Medicine in Edinburgh University, recommended that £250,000 be taken from the endowments of each large teaching hospital in Scotland to set up the Scottish Hospital Endowments Research Trust (SHERT). This was agreed, and the Trust established with Sir John, later Lord Erskine, as chairman and Dr J. M. Johnstone as secretary. The Trust was advised by an Advisory Committee for Medical Research (ACMR) whose chairman was a distinguished scientist, and the committee members were senior scientists and clinicians appointed from the Scottish universities and medical schools. Grant applications were reviewed by them and recommendations sent to the Trust for approval. My grant from the university for the purchase of animals for my original research was fifty pounds; the first grant I received from the Trust for my new adrenal research was five thousand pounds.

The department of pathology flourished under Professor Montgomery in the next four years. The spacious hall in the centre of the building was floored to create new laboratory space, the autopsy room was completely renovated and modernised with stainless steel dissecting tables. In time an additional laboratory block of three floors was built on land adjacent to and linked to the old building. The new building was equipped with modern scientific equipment and the staff responded to the new research facilities. I would look back with nostalgia to this period of medicine and to the dynamic group of young academic pathologists who were in the department when I returned from the army.

Teaching, routine post-mortems and surgical biopsies were dealt with as in the days of Professor Blacklock. I completed some of the animal studies still outstanding, but from now on all my research would be conducted with human adrenals, initially from post-mortem material but later from adrenals removed at operation as part of the treatment for breast cancer, and from patients with some form of adrenal disease. Alistair Currie joined the department when I did and like myself, was a protégé of Professor Blacklock. After he returned from army service we joined forces to carry out a combined study of the effect of stress on the pituitary and adrenal glands. In the patients selected for the study the degree of stress or trauma had to be severe, so that its onset could be timed accurately and the histological changes found in the adrenal could be correlated with the duration and severity of the stress. The patients studied had died of burns, peritonitis, pneumonia and fatal accidents and we carried out all autopsies within two hours of death, to obviate autolytic changes in the pituitary and adrenals. The study was spread over a period of three years and the autopsies were carried out at all hours, day and night. Our research was supported by a grant from the Scottish Hospitals Endowment Research Trust (SHERT). Currie's pituitary studies allowed him to establish his own pituitary group and to employ an experienced biologist who would use new technology to complement the conventional, but valuable techniques he used to identify the different cell types and hormones present in the pituitary.

Whereas I had been able to stain and identify the catecholamines in phaeochromocytoma and could visualise those substances in the cells of the normal adrenal medulla, steroid hormones are present in the cells of the adrenal cortex in such small quantities that they could not be identified by a staining technique, even if one had been available. When steroids are required in times of stress, pituitary ACTH, which Currie was studying, passes by way of the blood to the adrenal cortex and initiates changes in cholesterol, the fatty precursor stored in cortical cells, to produce the steroid hormones.

Nevertheless staining techniques could and did produce useful information. When I used the simple haematoxylin and eosin stain employed by pathologists to look at slides of the adrenal cortex I was able to identify the cells which contained the fatty precursor (cholesterol) as clear cells; those with no stainable fat I called compact cells (Figure 1A). In severe stress, when cholesterol is utilised to make steroid hormones, my studies showed the clear cells now became compact. When the stress continues, as in a severe fatal burn (Figure 1B), intermittent contraction of muscle bundles in the wall of the central veins dams back blood carrying ACTH, long enough for this hormone to diffuse into the clear cell and start the process. Eventually all cells in the adrenal cortex become compact and it was a common belief that such cells were dead and the adrenal cortex exhausted; my subsequent histochemical studies refuted this. I was able to use well-established techniques to identify, within the compact cell, enzymes of the Krebs cycle which create the energy a cell requires to perform its many chemical reactions, and to demonstrate the presence of ribonucleic acid (RNA) used to build and maintain the protein framework of a living cell. The presence in abundance of those energy-producing enzymes and of RNA indicated that the compact cell, far from being dead, was very active. Some years later when fresh adrenal glands from operations and new chemical techniques for measuring steroid hormones became available, our adrenal research group showed both clear and compact cells were equally capable of forming steroid hormones. The discovery of how they did this would have to wait, but it confirmed my earlier observation that there was no such thing as an exhausted adrenal cortex and this would become an interesting discussion point when Professor Hans Selye visited the department in the autumn of 1953 to talk about his work on 'Adaptation Syndrome'.

My collaboration with Currie led to invitations to present our work at a Ciba Foundation Symposium in London, and at various meetings of the British Pathological Society, where I met and discussed the progress of my adrenal research with Sir Roy Cameron, who became the first President of the Royal College of Pathology. The College established a lecture in his memory and in May 1969 I was invited to give the Cameron Lecture and relive his excitement when exploring new pathways in cellular pathology. The biochemical techniques he and his colleagues used were similar to those which my research group would use in future studies on the adrenal gland.

It was through my adrenal research that I met and collaborated with Norman Davidson who was Professor of Biochemistry at the University of Glasgow. His new department was sited near the old one where I had been trained. Davidson was an authority on DNA and his findings helped Crick and Watson create their model of DNA which won for them the Nobel Prize. Davidson and I carried out some work on RNA in the adrenal cortex and published a paper on the subject in the first edition of the Scottish Medical Journal.

I presented my research finding at meetings of the Scottish Society of Experimental Medicine and in 1953 became its secretary. The meetings were held three times each year and rotated round the four Scottish universities medical schools. At those meetings I met everyone in Scotland whose research involved the adrenal, and it was there I met Professor Guy Marrian and Dr Jim Grant who would later join me in Glasgow as head of steroid biochemistry in our adrenal research group.

The chance introduction to the adrenal gland by Professor Blacklock would now open more scientific contacts for me in the United States and Canada. The Board of Governors of the Glasgow Royal Infirmary consisted of lawyers, businessmen, senior clinicians and professors, in addition to the medical superintendent Dr Bryson, and Mr McIver, the hospital secretary. A considerable sum of endowment money still remained in the Board's control and it decided to establish travel grants for senior staff to go abroad and learn what was happening in medical centres elsewhere. This was an enlightened policy from which the hospital would benefit in the future. I was awarded a travel grant which allowed me to visit many medical centres in the United States and Canada where clinical and basic adrenal research was in progress. I was preparing my itinerary and had written to Professor Hans Selye in Montreal when he wrote to say he would be in Europe in the autumn of 1953 and would like to visit Glasgow and discuss the work Currie and I were doing.

Selye spent two days with us and spoke in the lecture theatre which was built on the site of the wards where in 1865 Lister first introduced his concept of antiseptic surgery. Selye talked of his work on the Adaptation Syndrome which he had published as a massive tome in 1946. This book caught the imagination of the medical world and a very large audience came to his lecture in Glasgow. Selye was a dynamic little man, a graduate of Prague University who emigrated to Canada where he carried out the experimental work on which his concept of the effect of stress was built. Briefly he postulated that an individual or, in his case, an experimental animal, when subjected to a stress to which they are not adapted, responds with an alarm reaction in which their adrenal glands produce excess adrenaline. This is what would happen when a cat encounters an aggressive dog: the back arches, hair stands on end, claws project and the animal prepares for fight or flight. During the alarm reaction Selye describes changes in the pancreas of the animals, which were identical to those I had found in my experimental animals when they were exposed to an initial adrenaline shock.

If the stress continues, Selye says, the animal adapts and is now in the stage of resistance when the adrenal cortex starts producing increased amounts of corticosteroid hormones, which bring about changes in the metabolism of body tissue. This was of particular interest to surgeons and biochemists in Glasgow, since in 1932 Sir David Cuthbertson, when on the staff of the pathology department at Glasgow Royal Infirmary, showed a significant loss of body nitrogen in patients in the first ten days following elective surgery or fractures. Later, when adreno-cortical hormones such as cortisone or cortisol became available, clinicians found that the administration of those hormones to non-stressed patients produced similar metabolic patterns to those observed after elective surgery or fractures. It appeared that Cuthbertson's metabolic response to injury would be the result of increased production by his patients of adreno-cortical hormones, as Selye had postulated. Selye went further: during this adaptation or resistance phase, diseases such as hypertension, rheumatic fever and rheumatoid arthritis developed, and those he believed were the direct result of increased production of adreno-cortical hormones. We must remember that when Selye published his work, we knew only, as I reported earlier, that adreno-cortical hormones were either sugar-active or salt-active steroids. While I was able to show, using the Ingle liver glycogen regeneration assay, that sugar-active or gluco-corticosteroids were secreted by the cells of the adrenal cortex in response to adrenaline stress, there was no assay available to determine if there was a similar increase in production of salt-active and mineralo-corticosteroids during stress. Nevertheless, at that time chemists had synthesised a steroid hormone which had a marked effect on salt metabolism. It was called deoxycorticosterone acetate or DOCA, and it was this substance that Selye used to produce the lesions which he believed to be rheumatic fever, hypertension and rheumatoid arthritis, and which he called diseases of adaptation. Selye's unitarian theory of adaptation diseases was challenged in a series of publications between 1950 and 1952 by George Sayers of the Western Reserve University, Cleveland, Dwight Ingle of Chicago and Lew Engel of Harvard Medical School, Boston. I was interested in their work since I had arranged to see each one during my visit to North America. Naturally I was interested in their objections to Selye's quite revolutionary ideas of disease. They produced evidence to show that the metabolic response to injury can occur in animals in the absence of the adrenal gland, when a fixed or normalising dose of the corticosteroid hormones is supplied. They put forward an alternative theory that the cortical hormone has a *permissive* or *supportive* role and is not the cause of the metabolic responses as Selye had postulated. A few years later Willie Crane, one of my assistants, spent a sabbatical year in Ingle's laboratory and became actively involved with Ingle in the permissive role of steroids in hypertensive vascular disease. Selye had produced the disease with DOCA implants into animals who received high salt intake from their drinking water. He described the salt loading of experimental animals as a conditioning factor, whereas Crane produced the full-blown disease in animals who had no adrenal, provided the salt loading was maintained long enough.

It was the third part of his adaptation syndrome, the *phase of exhaustion*, I would discuss with Selye. According to him, if the stress continues, the animal becomes exhausted and the adrenal glands no longer produce hormones. They are exhausted adrenals. When he came to Glasgow to discuss our work he agreed that the exclusively compact enzyme-rich adrenal cells I had found in patients who had died of a very severe burning accident were not exhausted adrenal cells. But he remarked, 'I never said the adrenals were exhausted. I said the body was exhausted. People misquoted me and it was they who said the adrenal was exhausted.' Some years later I had cause to remember his comment, when technical methods became available to determine the level of cortisol in blood. David Murray, one of my research group, discovered high levels of this hormone in the blood of patients who had died of severe trauma and whose adrenals had the histological appearance of the so-called exhausted adrenal. Selye was right. The body was not able to respond to the hormone in the last phase of fatal stress. Indeed, Murray showed that the process of dying was a stressor and the adrenals of dying patients responded by producing steroid hormones which the target cells of the body could not use.

Later during my visit to Canada I was able to see Hans Selye at work when I visited his Institute in Montreal. He was a superb experimental pathologist whose experiments were planned meticulously and the results carefully tabulated during the daily 'ward rounds' he made to his experimental animal units. The dissected organs and tissues from his experiments were prepared and stained in the usual manner using only haematoxylin and eosin stains. He used no complicated histochemistry or biochemistry and it was on the basis of those results he built his concept of the adaptation syndrome. He was first and foremost a theorist and would never think of challenging his theory as Sayers, Ingle or Engel had done to establish a permissive role for adrenal hormones. Indeed, Selye's reaction was, 'George Sayers is a fine experimentalist, but a poor theorist.' Charles Darwin could have had the Selyes of this world in mind when in his classic book *The Descent of Man*, published in 1871, he wrote, 'False facts are highly injurious to the progress of science for they often long endure; but false theories if supported by some evidence, do little harm as everyone takes a salutary pleasure in proving their falseness.' The scientific community certainly took a salutary interest, if not pleasure, in disproving Selye's adaptation syndrome, which had stimulated so much interest in adrenal research. This can only be to Selye's credit as his work benefited both endocrinology in general and the adrenal gland in particular.

In 1954 Professor Montgomery accepted an invitation to the Chair of Pathology in the University of Edinburgh and the Chair at Glasgow Royal became vacant once more. I was sorry he was leaving. The department was a happy one, my work was exciting and expanding rapidly and I had established close contact with Dr Jim Grant of Professor Guy Marrian's biochemistry department in Edinburgh. Grant was one of the best steroid biochemists in this country and his work and that of his research fellows was helping us to learn something of the important enzymes (hydroxylating enzymes) involved in the synthesis of the steroid hormones formed by the cells of the adrenal cortex (Figure 2). When I met him his research was conducted on animal adrenals but soon, in a successful co-operative study with my research group, we were able to provide him with human adrenals removed at operation from patients with breast cancer. Although the forty mile separation between Glasgow and Edinburgh did not detract from our co-operation, it would have been more satisfying if we had been in the same medical school. If Montgomery had invited me to join him in Edinburgh, I would have accepted because of the importance I attached to Grant's research. The invitation never came and like the other staff in the department I waited with not a little apprehension for the appointment of his successor. Professor Montgomery had created a good environment and provided the tools and the freedom to get on with the work, but would his successor be as liberal?

One afternoon after discussing the results of our study, Professor Davidson talked to me about Montgomery's move to Edinburgh. 'You will be applying for the post,' he said. 'You must, you must,' he repeated. I said I would think about it. Later that day I met one of the senior consultant physicians at the Royal Infirmary who informed me I would have the support of his colleagues who hoped I would be an applicant. That evening Margaret and I discussed the matter fully. I was now thirty-nine, and in the end decided I should apply. Next day I wrote to Dr Lewthwaite in Malaya and he agreed to be one of my referees, while Sir Roy Cameron agreed to assess my research work and publications.

I was in the process of confirming the time of my visit to the United States and Canada when I received a letter from the university inviting me to attend an interview for the Chair. At four o'clock in the morning Alistair Currie and I carried out an autopsy on one of the patients in our study, by ten o'clock I was on surgical duty and in the afternoon I had my interview, which was held in the university senate room. Six pathologists were interviewed in alphabetical order, and I was last. The committee consisted of the professors of medicine and surgery, a senior surgeon and physician from the Royal Infirmary and Professor D. F. Cappell who held the Chair of Pathology at the Western Infirmary. Sir Hector Hetherington, Principal of the University, was in the chair and my interview lasted thirty minutes. At the invitation of the Principal, Cappell began questioning and took up most of the interview time. He had read my thesis and most of my published papers, and commended me on my research.

'Do you feel the responsibility of running a large academic department would interrupt your research?' he asked, and when I said I didn't think it would, he said, 'Then surely you couldn't do justice to the routine surgical, post-mortem and teaching responsibilities of an academic department.' By now I could sense his antagonism which came to a head when he asked, 'In view of all the research you have been doing, are you really telling the committee you have been taking your share of routine duties?'

'This very morning, at four o'clock to be precise,' I replied, 'Alistair Currie and I carried out an autopsy and before I came to this interview, I had dealt with the usual number of surgical specimens.'

'All I can say is he doesn't work banker's hours,' was his comment, and turning to the Principal said he had no further questions. The rest of the interview was more cordial but I left the room glad that it was over and not hopeful for my chances.

Later in the evening a member of the committee came to see me. I had been strongly supported by the Royal representatives. The Principal had read a letter of support from Professor Davidson, but Cappell would not accept my appointment, and none of the other applicants were acceptable to the Royal members of the committee. Names of individuals who might be invited to the Chair were suggested and discussed, and in the end it was agreed the Principal should contact Professor Theo Crawford of St George's Hospital, London and offer him the Chair in Glasgow Royal Infirmary. Surprisingly I was pleased with this development. Crawford had been a senior lecturer at the Royal with Blacklock. I thought highly of his work and that of his wife, Margaret. They were actively engaged in research into coronary artery disease and I knew I would be encouraged to continue my research work.

The week following the interview I was in the animal operating theatre assisting Willie Crane with one of his experiments when the phone rang and I was told Professor Montgomery wanted to see me. I went downstairs, knocked on the door of his office and entered. He rose from his chair and said, 'Sit in this chair. It's yours. The Principal's been on the phone. You have been appointed to the St Mungo Notman Chair of Pathology at the Royal Infirmary and the Principal will see you tomorrow.' I remember going back to the animal house to continue with the experiments, but I could not concentrate on what I was supposed to do. Eventually Crane shook me by the arm. 'Are you all right? Is there something wrong?' he asked.

'No. I've got the Chair and have to see the Principal tomorrow,' was all I said. I phoned Margaret with the news and she was naturally delighted but surprised. It had been a long, trying time for her and she was only coming to terms with my unsuccessful news of the previous week.

Next day I reported to the Principal's office and found him seated behind a large desk. He pointed to the seat in front of him and said, 'You have taken on a big responsibility and I am sure you will be able to carry it. Is there anything you would like to ask me?' This surprised me as I had been told he was against my appointment, mainly because he was not in favour of inter-departmental promotion. I raised this point with him, talked about the Royal Infirmary travel grants and said I had been awarded one. It was my intention to spend three months in the United States and Canada, where I would make contact with scientists in basic science departments of the universities and make arrangements for my young pathologists to spend a year there and learn about rapidly developing fields of science, technology and biochemistry. They would return with new knowledge and new ideas which would benefit them and enhance the standing of our department. Those young men, I said, must feel they have prospects of promotion and be given the confidence to gain it in open competition. Sir Hector gave the scheme his unqualified approval. He kept in touch with our activity and progress and found financial support for the international conference I would run.

On one occasion I wished to appoint a senior biochemist to our research group and use a vacancy in the department for this new appointment. I went to see Sir Hector. 'Is your routine covered? What about teaching?' he would ask and when I said they were taken care of, he said, 'I think this would be a good appointment, but what did Davidson say?'

Professor Davidson was a tower of strength and a great support. When I wanted to make a biochemical appointment to our adrenal research group I would take the candidate's curriculum vitae to him and say, 'Is he good enough for your department and if so, will you give him an attachment to biochemistry?' This he did and it is advice that clinical departments in universities would do well to follow. Many university departments of medicine, surgery, obstetrics and pathology have senior biochemists or physicists on the staff. They have a vital role to play but I am convinced from experience with Davidson, that much more would be achieved if those appointments were made to a basic science unit and staff seconded to the appropriate clinical department. Such an arrangement would benefit basic science departments which in the past have been reluctant to become involved in applied research. This is changing, and older scientists who have lost their creativity for basic research can find the challenge of clinical problems very stimulating. In the same way, young scientists engaged in clinical research need spend only a limited period of secondment before returning to the basic science department in which they hope to make a career. My experience with Professor Davidson proved valuable when I became Director of the Institute of Cancer Research in London, and was able to direct, encourage and interest basic scientists in the clinical problems of cancer research.

During the many visits I paid to the Principal's office I would meet and talk to Dr Robert Hutchinson who was the university Registrar. He was a man whose advice I would seek on many administrative matters, and would learn from and enjoy the discussions we had as I waited to see Sir Hector. Robert was very devoted to the Principal and equally protective of him. Apparently Sir Hector had been receiving abusive letters from one of the professors and, as I waited in his office, Dr Hutchinson remarked, 'The Principal had another abusive letter this morning and when I sympathised with him and said I wished he wouldn't write such letters.' Sir Hector replied, 'Yes, he should write them. He shouldn't send them.' I think Dr Hutchinson was advising me what I should do if, in the ensuing years, I became irritated or angry with someone. I took his advice to heart. When the occasion arose and my very efficient secretary, Miss Nan Allen, would take shorthand notes of my angry, even scurrilous dictation, she would make no comments, type the letter, which was always a great improvement on my dictation, pass it to me and wait for me to sign it. I would read it carefully, sign and return it to her.

'Will I send it, or tear it up?' she would say and, looking at me remark, 'Now you'll feel better, I'll tear it up,' and she did.

The clinical and technical staff of the pathology department were very helpful to me in the first year of my appointment. The department ran well and we had very satisfactory results in the professional examinations in June. At the beginning of the second year I made arrangements to visit selected medical centres in the United States and Canada. Our daughter Esther Elizabeth Margaret was ten months old when I left Margaret to take care of the children. She was very supportive and encouraged me saying it would be for our ultimate good and for the good of the department. It was a long time to be separated from the family, but I would meet scientists and their wives who would become our lifelong friends. Mother came to visit us before I left.

'Mr Gordon, the headmaster at Muirkirk school came to see me yesterday and said how pleased he was to hear about your appointment. He had worried over the advice he gave me in 1932 and was pleased I had not accepted it.'

'Maybe,' I said, 'he realised I would not have made it as a footballer and felt it was easier for me to become a professor.' She laughed and said, 'Maybe, but I don't think that was what he thought.'

CHAPTER 7

Adrenal Trail
in the United States and Canada

TOWARDS THE END of August 1955 I sailed on the Queen Mary from Southampton and landed five days later in New York, where I spent a few days with Margaret's relatives before flying to Denver, Colorado en route to the Laurentian Hormone Conference at Estes Park. This is one of the top endocrine meetings in the United States and is by invitation. As the name implies, the meeting was held annually, at Mont Tremblant in the Laurentian Mountains near Montreal, and Hans Selye was largely responsible for the name and the customary siting of the conference. This was the first occasion it had been held elsewhere. Unfortunately Selye would not be at this meeting but he had arranged for me to visit him when I was in Montreal.

Whilst the National Health Service was having a beneficial effect on medical care and research in Britain, the National Institute of Health in the United States was, in the 1950s and 1960s, financing research in endocrinology and providing training scholarships in this speciality. At the conference I would meet most of the clinicians and scientists engaged in adrenal research. The meeting lasted five days. There were morning and evening sessions which covered all branches of endocrine work and the lectures were given by specially invited speakers. The morning three-hour session began at 9.00 a.m. and after lunch the delegates and their families were free to tour the beautiful Rocky Mountains or walk in the small town itself. The evening three-hour session began after dinner and private discussions would continue well into the night or early hours of the morning. I shared a room with Arnold Lazarow who was Professor of Anatomy in the University of Minneapolis. He was a stimulating, indeed brilliant, scientist whose only interests in life were his family and his research in diabetes. During the summer vacation he would take his family to the marine research station at Woods Hole in Cape Cod. They would enjoy the seaside holiday while Arnold would be free to pursue his experimental study on insulin production by isolated islet cells of the fish pancreas. At Estes Park Arnold and I discussed my itinerary and when he discovered I was due to lecture at the Mayo Clinic at Rochester, Minnesota, he invited me to visit his department in Minneapolis.

During the first session of the meeting I met Gordon Wolstenholme, Director of the Ciba Foundation, London, who asked me to review the conference for *The Lancet*. This was good, since I had to attend all the sessions, listen carefully to papers and discussions and prepare notes which I used in subsequent train and plane journeys to produce my report for *The Lancet*. Arnold Lazarow and I had regular discussions on the submissions and he helped to clarify some points in the non-adrenal papers with which I was not familiar.

After the conference I flew to Chicago and spent a few days with Dwight Ingle, with whom I discussed Selye's adaptation syndrome and his views on the permissive role of corticosteroid hormones. One evening I was having dinner at his home when he produced two letters Margaret had sent to his address.

'You will want peace to read them,' he said, and left the room. Apparently my two small sons had on their bedroom wall a map of America which they found in their *Buffalo Bill Annual*. This, Margaret said, they used to follow my journey and when my letters arrived they would refer to the map and say, 'He's in Sioux country now, Mum, I hope he'll be all right.' I told them about the covered wagon I had seen at Estes Park but had to wait till I got to Montreal before I was able to visit the Indian Reservation which I recorded for them on cine film.

Dr Ingle was highly amused by all this and later when he came back into the room I was smiling at what Margaret had written in the second letter. Bob Curran, one of my colleagues in the department in Glasgow had visited Chicago and when he came to see her said, 'Tell him not to go out at night as the streets around the University of Chicago can be dangerous.' Dr Ingle looked at me and said, 'This is correct. You must be careful,' and proceeded to tell the story of the English professor on sabbatical to the University of Chicago, who was warned of the danger of mugging. One cold, windy evening, when returning from the laboratory to his home, a man collided with him on the street and proceeded on his way. Remembering about the danger of mugging, the athletic, well-built professor instinctively put his hand into his waistcoat pocket only to find his watch had gone. Without a moment's hesitation he ran after the man, caught him by the upturned lapels of his coat, slapped his face and demanded that he hand over the watch. The man submitted meekly, handed over the watch, and on being released from the professor's grip, disappeared quickly and quietly into the night. The professor returned home to relate the sad experience to his wife.

'I never though this would happen to me,' he said, 'and although upset and disappointed, I made sure I got my watch back.' His wife looked on in disbelief as he showed her the watch. 'But,' she said, 'your watch is in the drawer,' and proceeded to retrieve it and show it to him. The professor gazed at his own watch in disbelief. He had been the mugger who had assaulted the man in the street. Next morning he went with his wife to the nearest police station to tell his story and return the watch. He took a box of cigars as a peace offering for his victim. The policeman could not conceal his amusement. 'He won't come here,' was all he said. At the time I felt Dr Ingle was relating with sincerity an incident that had really happened.

A few years later, on reading his Presidential Address to the American Endocrine Society I was fascinated by his brilliant satire on the aspirations and ambitions of American academics and, on reflection, felt the story he told me could be a satire too on British professors. My contact with Ingle's department would be valuable in the future when Willie Crane went there to work with him on the permissive role of steroid hormones.

I travelled by night sleeper from Chicago to Madison, Wisconsin where I had been invited to lecture to staff and students of the zoology department. Madison is a small mid-west university town which I liked and would revisit on many occasions. I went from Madison to the Mayo clinic in Rochester where I spent a week, staying in a hotel which was used by patients attending the clinic for observation or treatment. An underground passage linked the hotel with the clinic. My hosts had organised a busy schedule of visits which culminated in a lecture I gave to the endocrine group at the clinic. A dinner had been organised prior to the lecture and at the end of the dinner the chairman rose and said, 'It is customary for us to ask our British guests to say something about the British Health Service.' Here at the heart of conservative American medicine, I recounted the problems of British voluntary hospitals trying to meet the growing costs of patient treatment from public subscription and the miserable salaries paid to senior doctors. Now, I could say doctors were well-remunerated and the Board of Governors of hospitals had government support to meet the cost of patient care. I explained how each large teaching hospital in Scotland had to give up £250,000 of their endowment to set up the Scottish Hospital Endowment Research Trust (SHERT) which would help finance medical research in Scotland.

'Before nationalisation,' I told them, 'I had £50 from Glasgow University for my research. Now I have £5,000. I think you will agree this is an improvement.' The chairman in his reply, said, 'We have had many British doctors visit the clinic and not one of them made uncomplimentary comments about the Health Service.'

I travelled by bus from Rochester to Minneapolis and at intervals along the route kept seeing notices to visit the tallest Indian in America. This turned out to be a massive statue, the 'Peace Movement', located in the city hall of St Paul. The monument, in Mexican onyx, is thirty-six feet high and depicts an Indian chief rising from the flames, embodying the concept of the 'Great Spirit'. The figure is mounted on an invisible turntable which rotates in alternative directions in a ninety degree arc. This imposing monument is the work of Carl Milles whose creation 'The Hand of God' is a masterpiece in balance. In later years on a visit to the Milles Garden in Stockholm. I would see this work of art.

Arnold Lazarow's department and his research on diabetes was as impressive as I had expected, but I had come to Minneapolis on Lazarow's recommendation to meet David Glick who was Professor of physiological chemistry (biochemistry) in the University of Minneapolis and head of the unit of histo- and cytochemistry. David was a slightly-made, balding man in his mid-forties and in a quietly spoken voice asked if he could see the lantern plates I had brought of my work. As I handed him the plate showing the distribution throughout the adrenal cortex of some enzymes or chemical substances, he would show me a photograph of a rat adrenal to illustrate both localisation and concentration of the same substances in the different zones of the adrenal cortex. To appreciate Glick's study, it was necessary to understand what he meant by the zones in the adrenal cortex. When sections of the adrenal gland were first stained and examined under the microscope, the old histologists described three zones in the cortex (Figure 1A).

On the surface of the adrenal is the capsule and under this the *Zona Glomerulosa*. We know now that the cells in this zona form the salt-active corticosteroids, such as aldosterone. This zone is very prominent in rat and bovine adrenals but is variable in width in the human gland. Passing inwards the cells are arranged in perpendicular columns which are separated by thin wall blood capillaries. The old histologists called this the *Zona Fasciculata* and the cells here are distended by lipid and cholesterol: those are the cells I have called *clear cells*. The zona fasciculata in the normal gland occupies more than three quarters of the adrenal cortex and as I said elsewhere, the cells in this zona contain the precursors from which the corticosteroids are formed in times of stress. The third zone is the *Zona Reticularis* and the cells here are the *compact cells* I have described already. They are arranged in islands which are separated by dilated capillaries, the blood from which passes through the adrenal medulla into the central vein (Figure 1A). Very simply, Glick used a miniature cork borer which he inserted through the capsule of the adrenal and through each zone to obtain a core of tissue. He cut 6μ sections from the medulla outward, the first section was stained to identify the site in the adrenal and the next five sections were placed in small tubes for chemical analysis. This procedure of one section for histology and five for chemical analysis was continued throughout the gland and in this way he was able to localise and quantitate throughout the cortex the enzyme or chemical sub- stance he wished to study.

The histochemical stains I had used to localise enzyme to different zones of the adrenal gland were, he said, qualitative and it was highly desirable to obtain a considerable degree of simultaneous quantitation and localisation.

'The factor limiting this achievement is a technical one,' he said, 'and it may be necessary to sacrifice a degree of localisation to get reliable quantitation.' The discussion was very stimulating and, since his research was done exclusively on small rat adrenals, I pointed out that a major problem for him was to obtain, for chemical analysis, clean morphologically defined samples of cells from the zona fasciculata and zona reticularis of the small rat adrenal cortex. Until he could achieve this, the intracellular particulate fractions which are prepared for chemical analysis may contain varying amounts of both cell types.

I told him the human gland was much larger and separate samples of the two zones easier to prepare and identify. 'Why,' I asked him, 'don't you use human adrenals?'

'The answer is quite easy. Post-mortem human adrenals are no use for quantitative enzyme studies and I have no access to fresh, surgically-removed human adrenals.' This interested me. In the past year in Glasgow, adrenal glands were removed from female patients as part of the treatment for breast cancer and I showed him some photomicrographs of studies I had made on them. Once more he pointed out they were qualitative studies of enzymes which were part of the activities of all cells and not related specifically to the production of steroid hormones. I told him, prior to leaving Glasgow, that Sir Hector had resuscitated a vacant senior lecture appointment in chemical pathology and I had been able to induce Jim Grant to move from Edinburgh as head of steroid biochemistry into our adrenal research group, and bring his associate Keith Griffiths with him. Glick and I talked about the specific enzymes in adrenal cells which would convert the cholesterol in the clear cells to steroid hormones (Figure 2). The enzymes are called hydroxylating enzymes, since they add (OH) or hydroxyl groups to specific positions on the cholesterol molecule. When Glick learned that Keith Griffiths was working on a method for estimation of one of those important enzymes, he suggested that Griffiths might like to spend a year with him in Minneapolis when they could develop a micro-chemical method and determine the distribution of this hydroxylating enzyme in the zones of the adrenal cortex. Griffiths, who became Director of the Tenovus Cancer Institute in Cardiff, did spend a year with Glick and developed a micro-chemical technique for estimating the 11-hydroxylating enzyme (Figure 2).

It was clear that Glick's quantitative cytochemical techniques, when applied to human adrenals, could increase the scope of our study and I asked him to take me round his laboratory and describe in detail the procedures he used. The fresh adrenal, he was careful to emphasise, must be obtained with the minimum of delay, frozen at minus 20°C and the subsequent steps carried out in a cryostat. This is a refrigerator cabinet with two circular holes, about six inches in diameter, which allows the operator, wearing protective gloves and sitting outside the machine, to carry out work within the cryostat. A series of mechanical borers 0.5mm to 4mm in diameter had been constructed and a suitable one, attached to an electric drill, was used to bore a cylinder of tissue through the frozen adrenal gland. If the procedure was satisfactory, the cylindrical core obtained should contain cells from all zones of the adrenal gland from the capsule inwards. The cylinder of fresh tissue was mounted on a microtome within the cryostat and ribbons of frozen sections cut. The first section was placed on a glass slide and stained to identify the zone of the adrenal. The next few ribbons were placed in individual small reaction tubes and used for chemical analysis. This procedure of using one section for staining and the next few for analysis was followed until the whole gland had been covered.

'Quantitative analysis of fresh microtome sections,' said Glick, 'can be carried out using relatively simple techniques in which common, well-established macrochemical methods are scaled down, usually 500 to 1,000 times.'

Later the great sensitivity of fluorimetry induced him to develop techniques which would allow the chemical determination in samples considerably smaller than for the titrometric or colorometric analysis he had been using. In all newly-developed technical advances he would emphasise the need to obtain, simultaneously, a considerable degree of quantitation and localisation. In the ensuing years, in addition to Keith Griffiths, a number of my young assistants would have the opportunity to work with Glick. David and his wife Irena, a talented artist, became our close friends and he always visited us in Glasgow on his frequent visits to Europe. When he moved to Stanford University, California, he invited me and my family to spend a year with him at Stanford. His contribution to the work of our department was recognised by the University of Glasgow when, in 1970, they invited him to become the MacFarlane Visiting Professor and in 1982 awarded him an honorary LLD.

In retrospect it seems incredible how a chance meeting with Arnold Lazarow at the Laurentian Hormone Conference should lead to a meeting with David Glick whose cytochemical studies would have a profound effect on my adrenal research and whose friendship would extend over a period of thirty years. Sadly Irena developed cancer, which she bore with great fortitude, and she died a few days before I had arranged to see her.

I left Minneapolis after the first meeting with Glick and travelled by train to Chicago and thence to Cleveland, Ohio. My cousin John Murdoch and his wife Nan met me at the station and drove me to their home in Akron, Ohio, where I would spend the weekend. The last six weeks had been very tiring. I had been meeting new people, discussing their work and recounting mine. Everyone I met had been very hospitable and as we drove to Akron I said I was tired and looking forward to a good rest and a quiet weekend with them. They looked at each other but said nothing. John, like so many young miners from Ayrshire, came to the United States at the time of the 1926 miners' strike and found employment with Firestone Tyres in Akron. I was in for a surprise as I entered their lovely home. A feast had been prepared in my honour and I was introduced to the large number of men and women who had gathered there.

'I hope you don't mind,' said John. 'We would have been ostracised if we had kept you to ourselves. When Professor Hibberd, (who was one of Uncle Bob's students) came two years ago, old John X kept him to himself and the rest of the relatives haven't spoken to him since.' John and Nan took me round the assembled guests and introduced me to relatives of my father and mother I never knew existed. All had left the depressed mining villages of Ayrshire during the 1926 strike and all had made a success of life in their adopted country.

They talked with affection of my father and mother, what a good-looking couple they were and how sad it was that he should be taken away at such an early age. Their families too had suffered the ravages of the 1918 flu epidemic. They reminisced a great deal about life in the mining villages, the working conditions in the pits and the accidents that befell so many members of the family. Most of the men had left school at twelve to work in the Kames Colliery and one of them recalled how a young miner struck a large piece of coal with a pick and a flying splinter lodged in Uncle George's eye with the loss of that organ, and he was only fourteen years old. This started them on a depressing tale of accidents when I learned how Uncle Jimmy lost an arm, and Uncle Tom a foot. The family had suffered under the coal owners but I never heard any expression of bitterness. They talked nostalgically about the Belgian refugees who came to Muirkirk during the 1914–18 war. How the Belgian boys, called Ingelbinck, went to school with them and became their friends. They laughed at the stories of the Belgians who worked in the Kames colliery, of their families learning English which they spoke with a Scottish vernacular accent. I was able to tell them I had visited the Ingelbincks at their home in Wetteren in 1939 and after the 1939–45 war they had been regular visitors of Muirkirk.

The older members remembered with affection Mr Cunningham who was their headmaster at Muirkirk Public School and like my mother, referred to him as the 'maister'. My namesake they said, was exceptionally bright and very conceited.

'The things that I excel in are problems and deductions,' he would say to his fellow students. He always sat in the front row of the class watching the headmaster struggle on the blackboards with a difficult problem in mathe-matics, and would smirk when he saw the master was not going to solve it. The class always looked forward to this. They knew the boy was desperate to get to the board, but before this would happen the maister would administer the belt, then hand him the chalk and sit back while the problem was solved to the delight of his classmates. Unfortunately he did nothing in life for he died a young man, probably of tuberculosis.

Copies of the local newspaper and letters from relatives and friends kept them well-informed of local events back home. All spoke with pride when they told me about a recent article in the Muirkirk Advertiser about the six university professors who at that period had come from the village and had received their early education there.

Most of my relatives had at one time or another gone back 'home' on holiday. They had enjoyed the visit. None would go back to live there. America was their home. It had been good to them, their families had been born there and they were Americans. It was in the early hours of Sunday morning when the party broke up. My tiredness had gone. It had been an enjoyable evening and an interesting experience.

On the Monday morning I took a bus from Akron to Cleveland where I would spend the week with George Sayers who was Professor of Physiology at Western Reserve University. During the journey I reflected with amuse-ment on the Easter holiday I had spent that year with Margaret and the children at a small hotel in Crail near St Andrews in Scotland. The hotel stood on high ground on Roome Bay and had an uninterrupted view over the North Sea. The children loved it there. One evening after dinner, the children had gone to bed and Margaret was talking to a lady guest, telling her about my visit to America in the autumn.

'My nephew,' said the lady, 'is a professor in America. He was educated at Allen Glen's School in Glasgow and went with his family to Detroit when he was fourteen. He was for some time in the pharmacology department in the university at Salt Lake City, but is now Professor of Physiology in Western Reserve University, Cleveland, Ohio. Maybe your husband knows him,' Indeed, I had been listening to the conversation, and on hearing her nephew was in physiology, I asked, 'Is his name George Sayers?' and when she replied 'Yes,' I told her I had arranged to spend a week with him. It was quite a coincidence that I should meet George's aunt in a small hotel in Scotland, but again I was to find 'there is a divinity that shapes our end'.

Sayers, his wife Martha and their colleague Woodbury had developed an assay or method for detecting the level of ACTH in blood. This, as we have said, was the hormone produced by the pituitary gland and passed into the blood to reach the adrenal gland which it stimulates to produce steroid hormones. The assay developed by the Sayers group was to improve our understanding of certain diseases of the adrenal glands. Their study was an indication of the devotion, zeal and enthusiasm of research scientists. When I visited their home and met the family, I could only marvel at their dedication to research. Their assay required the presence in the laboratory of one of the team throughout the 24-hour period. Martha's shift began at midnight when the family chores had been done and the children were safely in bed. When she returned home at 8.00 a.m. George would take over and Woodbury would complete the 24-hour period. 'It was,' they said, 'very confining and we didn't have much of a social life during that period.'

The search for knowledge and truth may be difficult to understand by men and women who are motivated only by financial rewards, but for scientists like George and Martha Sayers and many like them, unravelling even the smallest secret of nature is sufficient recompense, especially if their research meets with the acclaim of fellow scientists, even if in later years, theories based on their results may be and usually need to be modified. Sayers had a group of young scientists who were working on problems related to the release of ACTH from the pituitary gland, and apart from the last night I spent at his home, after dinner I went with him every evening to see the progress of their experimental studies.

Sayers was very interested in and involved with the new undergraduate teaching programme for medical students being run in Western Reserve. In most universities in the United States and Europe, medical training is run on conventional lines. Systematic lectures and practical classes are conducted on each subject on a yearly basis, starting with anatomy, physiology and bio-chemistry, then pathology, bacteriology and pharmacology, and eventually medicine, surgery and obstetrics. The duration of the course might vary in medical schools in the two countries. The Western Reserve experiment is quite unique. Students were attached to a family from the poor area of the city from the day they started medical school until graduation. The medical course was organ-orientated and each system in turn was dealt with by a multidisciplinary team of lecturers. When the cardiovascular system was studied, students would learn about the structure and function of the heart and blood vessels from anatomists, physiologists and biochemists. Pathologists would then deal with the diseases which affect those organs and clinicians discuss the signs and symptoms produced and treatment given.

The next system was taught in the same manner until the whole body was covered. This multi-discipline approach to the study of medicine has much to commend it and demands a great deal of time and effort on the part of the staff.

When the course was initiated, most doctors were enthusiastic. Later many discovered the new curriculum was time-consuming and interfered with the time they could devote to research.

During my visit to Western Reserve I had the opportunity to meet Dr Goldblatt, Professor of Pathology, who had an international reputation for his research on experimental hypertension. I took the opportunity to discuss the medical course with him and get his thoughts.

'It's too early for me to decide. My elder son graduated under the old system and my younger son is doing the course at present. Maybe in years to come I'll be able to assess the present experiment.' I never got his final assessment of this imaginative course, but it did attract the attention of students who would normally have applied for admission to the well-established medical schools in the United States. I was glad I had made contact with Sayers and was able to discuss the Western Reserve teaching experiment. Afterwards he came to an International Adrenal Conference I held in Glasgow and visited his old school, Allen Glen's. Later, one of my new young assistants, Willie Duguid would spend a year with Sayers in Cleveland learning new techniques in biochemistry and experimental pathology which would help him in the research he conducted on pancreatic tumours when he became Professor of Pathology in the Montreal General Hospital in Canada.

I travelled from Cleveland by train, along the shores of Lake Erie to Buffalo and thence to Niagara Falls and Toronto. I took a cine film for the family, of the American and Canadian falls and of Hill's barrel in which the intrepid stuntman had gone over the falls and survived. I crossed the whirlpool on the aerial railway, from which I filmed the small boat, the *Maid of the Mist* as it was sailing up to the falls. On the aerial railway I met a young couple who invited me to drive with them to Toronto where they deposited me safely in the King Edward Hotel. I slept well that night, rose late and took a stroll to the shopping centre where I bought a present for Margaret. This made me feel better, though I was not sure I had made the correct purchase in the ladies' shop where I saw an attractive nightdress and housecoat.

'What size is your wife?' asked the assistant. I looked round the shop at some of the lady assistants and pointing to one of them said, 'Her size.' The present was parcelled and duly despatched to my home in Scotland. On returning home I enquired whether the parcel had arrived safely.

'It was a lovely surprise, a beautiful housecoat, and just my colour, but unfortunately the sales assistant you chose was two sizes bigger than me,' said Margaret. 'Well,' I said, 'the thought was good.'

I took the afternoon train to Montreal and was met at the station by Margaret's cousin, Jim Finnie, his wife, Catherine and their two small daughters, Jean and Betty. Jim had emigrated from Lanarkshire, Scotland to Canada in the late twenties, and had suffered many hardships when he developed frostbite and lost part of his foot. Undeterred, he studied accountancy and in time became professor of that subject at the George Williams college and which later gained university status. Jim introduced British-style football into the College and was coach to the team. Each week after a match, Catherine washed and ironed the muddy strips for the whole team and folded them into neat bundles ready for the next match. I continued to receive letters from my two sons and they always ended, 'Have you seen the Indians yet?' Well, in Montreal, Jim, Catherine and the two girls took me to the Indian Reservation of Caughnawaga where the chief allowed me to take a cine film of the village and I bought the children mementoes bearing the name of the Reservation. I am glad to say the Indian Reservation looked better on my film than it really was.

As I discovered on my first day at the University of Glasgow, McGill University in Montreal was founded by James McGill who was a graduate of Glasgow University. The McGill medical school has clinical academic departments in the Royal Victoria and Montreal General Hospitals and I found that Montreal had an active and broadly-based endocrine school. I spent the next ten days in the basic science and clinical departments of the school with an active interest in endocrinology.

I had made the acquaintance at the Laurentian Hormone Conference of Dr Don Heard, a respected steroid chemist and a confirmed anglophile who had studied in England. As a consequence of this meeting, two of his young colleagues in biochemistry, Vincent O'Donnell and Jim Webb, would come to Glasgow and work in my research group at the time we were studying two adrenal tumours from patients with the adreno-genital syndrome. In this form of the disease, some tumours produce large amounts of the female sex hormone oestrogen, and men with this rare illness develop large breasts, hence the term feminisation. When women are afflicted with this oestrogen-producing tumour their femininity is maintained and prolonged with age, but most of these tumours produce male sex hormones: the woman becomes virilised, her hair falls out and she becomes bald and muscular. Our young Canadian colleagues used radiochemical techniques to identify the different steroid hormones produced by those tumours and throw light on the enzyme defects which occurred within the tumour to cause a switch in the metabolic pathway.

I was looking forward to visiting Hans Selye's Institute where I was to lecture. He took me on a ward round of his animal hospital and laboratories and I was sorry to discover he had forsaken his work on the adaptation syndrome and was involved in a completely different problem. Many years later, on a return visit to Montreal, I took my wife to see him and this pleased him very much. As we entered his office he was seated behind a large desk which was severely dented by the heel of his shoe while he lay back in his chair. The sun, shining through the window at his back, cast a shadow across the room and as he stood up his shadow lengthened. On one occasion, he told us, a Japanese scientist entered the room and bowed to him saying, 'Now I have realised my ambition. I have stood in your shadow.'

I took the train from Montreal to Boston and enjoyed the beautiful countryside with its expanse of autumn colour on the trees in Vermont. Train journeys gave me time to think and reflect on what I had seen and learned. I had been delighted with the kindness and hospitality I had received and impressed with the work going on in the departments I had visited. I felt an affinity with McGill, its Glasgow connection and fine endocrine school, but in Boston I was conscious of the medical and scientific heritage of the Harvard Medical School and was to learn about the influence that Glasgow Royal Infirmary, through Joseph Lister, had had on surgery in Boston.

I visited many departments of medicine, surgery and pathology in Boston, but I had come especially to meet Lewis Engel, who was Professor of Biochemistry in Harvard Medical School, and to hear about his research on the production by the adrenal gland, of oestrogens and their role in breast cancer. I had met Lew and his wife, Peggy, at the Laurentian Hormone Conference and I wanted to explore the possibility of a secondment to his department for one of my assistants. Peggy was English and had been secretary to Kennaway when he was Director of the Institute of Cancer Research in London; it was in the Institute she met Lew when he was a research fellow there. Margaret and I visited the Engels in Boston on many occasions. One of my young colleagues, Munro Neville, worked with him in the Collins Warren Laboratories, and Lew spent a year with me in Glasgow as the MacFarlane Visiting Professor. He and Peggy became very attached to the Scottish island of Colonsay and went there every year until Peggy died. Lew was a regular visitor to our home when we were in London and came to our daughter's wedding in El Paso in 1975. Not long afterwards, while lecturing to his beloved Harvard students, he had a heart attack and died.

During his sabbatical year in Glasgow he was extremely interested in the Joseph Lister exhibits I had in the museum of the pathology department. He looked at the Lister portrait, his surgical instruments and examination couch, the students' testimonial to Lister, the conical flask with a specimen of Lister's urine, the carbolic spray and some catgut and carbolic dressings that Lister applied to patients' wounds after surgery. Engel's interest in Lister arose because the laboratory where he worked in Boston was named after John

Professor Lewis Engel, Harvard Medical School.

Collins Warren, who had visited Lister in Glasgow, and was one of the young surgeons who introduced the Lister antiseptic technique into American surgery. Lew told me about Warren's grandfather, John C. Warren, who in 1846 removed a large tumour from the neck of a young man under ether

Lord Lister when Professor of Surgery at Glasgow Royal Infirmary, 1860.

anaesthesia. This was administered by Morton, a dentist who used it for the first time in the building in the Massachusetts General Hospital that is now called the ether dome. Lew presented me with a picture of the ether dome

Specimen of Lister's urine used by him to teach his students his germ theory of infection. Specimen is in the Pathology Department at Glasgow Royal Infirmary.

which has a special place in my study and is a constant reminder of Lewis Engel and our many discussions.

Carbolic Spray used by Lister in his operating theatre.

While the introduction of ether and chloroform anaesthesia made oper⸗ ations more tolerable, the range of operations open to surgeons could not be extended until the problem of wound infection was solved and bleeding from cut vessels controlled. During the year he spent in Glasgow, I showed Engel specimens of the catgut that Lister had prepared by treating sheep intestines with carbolic acid. These he used to tie blood vessels to prevent fatal post⸗operation bleeding. Handing him the conical flask containing Lister's urine I told him this was how Lister taught his student about germs and their role in wound infection. Lister knew about Pasteur's work showing that germs were the cause of putrefaction in tissue and thought this could be the cause of wound infection in his patients. The technique he used to teach students his germ theory of infection was so simple. He excused himself from the classroom and passed a specimen of urine, which he then divided between two conical flasks and boiled the contents of both. One he plugged with cotton wool, sealing the top of the flask so that air could not gain access to the specimen of urine, the other flask he left open and exposed to the air. This was a simple replica of Pasteur's experiment and educationally very effective, since the students could compare the appearance of the two spe⸗ cimens each day as they came to the lecture. They found the contents of the flask exposed to the atmosphere became more and more cloudy and smelly and reminded students, as Lister intended, of the foul-smelling infected wounds they saw in patients in the surgical wards.

Engel picked up the carbolic spray and the carbolic dressings and looked at them. 'How did they come about?' he asked. I told him Lister had discussed Pasteur's work and his own experiments with the Professor of Chemistry at the university and heard from him about a sanitary officer in Carlisle who was using carbolic acid as a disinfectant for drains. Lister, with the help of an engineer, developed the spray, and a fine mist of carbolic vapour was sprayed into the atmosphere of the theatre. This caused great discomfort to the theatre staff and was discontinued. Instead carbolic dressings were used to cover the wound and prevent germs gaining access to wounds.

Lew was interested in the students' testimonial which he had picked up. 'How did this come about?' he asked. I explained that Lister had no beds at the Glasgow Royal Infirmary although he was Professor of Surgery. In 1861 he gave his first series of lectures in systemic surgery, which must have been very stimulating. At the end of the course the whole class signed this testimonial and expressed their appreciation of Lister's ability as a teacher and the hope that the managers of the Royal Infirmary would see fit to appoint him in charge of wards in the hospital. This must be one of the early examples of student power since the managers gave him beds soon after they received this testimonial.

Lister established the new antiseptic treatment and in 1865 published in *The Lancet* a report of the successful treatment and recovery of patients with compound fractures and a form of tuberculosis abscess (PSOAS) which in the past was usually fatal. Dr Collins Warren must have read this article and when he arrived in Glasgow, although Lister's position in the University was established, his antiseptic treatment was by no means universally accepted. Warren could see, for the first time, a scientific approach to the problem of infection; carbolic acid was not a cure but a method by which open wounds covered by carbolic dressings could be protected from germs and allowed to heal. Warren was well received by Lister, dined at his home in Woodside Street near Charing Cross and saw the experiments on which his antiseptic concept was built, indicating how treatment should be carried out with meticulous care. Lister realised it was through young surgeons like Warren that his new treatment would be used correctly, since the old surgeons who held power either could not or would not comprehend the germ theory or apply the antiseptic treatment at meticulously as Lister demanded.

The introduction of anaesthetics allowed surgeons to operate in the absence of pain but they still wore the same blood-stained, filthy jacket for every operation; the catgut used as ligatures was grossly infected and for convenience was rolled round the buttons of their operating jacket, or held temporarily between their teeth while they carried out some surgical ma-noeuvre. If a swab fell on the floor during an operation it was picked up and used, and even those surgeons who tried to follow Lister's methods would still use carbolic dressings which had been lying on the floor of the operating theatre. It was only after an operation, not before, that the surgeon would wash his hands. Dr Collins Warren realised that all this had to change, as he returned to Boston armed with carbolic dressings given to him by Lister and enthusiastic to apply the antiseptic treatment carefully, as explained and demonstrated by Lister. It was many years before he was allowed to do so, but eventually he established Lister's practice and later the aseptic surgical treatment as we know it today.

Lew was looking at the testimonial given to Lister by his first class of students and I drew his attention to the name D. Campbell Black which appeared on the list. Could this be the same person who in 1891 vehemently attacked 'The Germ-theory of Disease' in an address to the Glasgow Medical Literary Society? The author tells us,

> I entered the medical profession about the time Sir Joseph Lister was patiently elaborating what I conceive to be the absurd theory with which his name has been identified for more than twenty years. Suppuration according to the antiseptic theory was, Lister said, caused by certain spores (germs) from the atmosphere, but everyone knows that suppuration can and does occur in parts of the body to which atmospheric air can never have access.

I took Lew into the museum and showed him a specimen from the William Hunter collection of acute osteomyelitis and pointed out the area of suppur-ation lying between the bone and the overlying covering of periosteum. When the science of bacteriology was established and bacteria could be identified, it became clear that the germs (spores) had come from outside the body and were carried by the blood to settle under the surface of a bone causing an area of suppuration. Likewise it became clear why Lister insisted on soaking instruments and rinsing his hands with carbolic acid solutions as well as using carbolic acid dressings during operations. The use of carbolic acid was not without its ill-effects and danger. The carbolic spray in the operating theatre was uncomfortable and soon discontinued, and carbolic acid solution on dressings could affect the patient's skin. I showed Lew two specimens from the Burton collection in my museum, where the patients had been treated by Lister and had developed skin cancer. It was inevitable, as Lister expected, that advances would be made and the antiseptic method replaced by modern aseptic techniques. It was clear from his article that Campbell Black had been overtaken by developments in Germany towards aseptic surgery, for he concluded,

> I did not then anticipate that in the year of grace 1890 the high priests of this fetish in Germany would perform their operations in special galoshes, special cloaks, special antiseptic skull caps, if indeed there are any skulls to cover, after special corporeal aquatic purification and special tonsorial adjustment.

A visit to the Worcester Foundation Research Institute, outside Boston, brought me into contact with adrenal perfusion techniques, which I would use on my return to Glasgow. After a short visit to the Memorial Hospital and Sloan-Kettering Institute in New York, I took the train back to Montreal and sailed to Britain. I had made contact with clinicians and scientists in the United States and Canada who would become lifelong friends and with whom members of my staff would work to their benefit and that of the department.

CHAPTER 8

The Adrenal Steroid
Assembly Line
and Adrenal Disease

CHANGES TOOK PLACE in the medical staff of the department in the three years which followed my return from the United States and Canada. Colleagues who had been with me since my return from the army had gained experience in some of the departments I had visited in the United States, and left Glasgow to take over senior appointments in England.

Bob Curran was in the department when I returned from the army and had spent three months in the United States on a Royal Infirmary travel grant. He introduced into the department the technique of autoradiography which he used in his radioactive isotope studies of bone and cartilage in tissue culture medium. After a period as a senior lecturer in the University of Sheffield with Professor Douglas Collins, he was appointed to the Chair of Pathology in St Thomas' Hospital in London and latterly the Chair in that subject in Birmingham. He was secretary of the Royal College of Pathology in London for many years and later became President of the College.

Willie Crane, after the year he spent with Dwight Ingle in Chicago, went to Sheffield as a senior lecturer and then Professor of Pathology. His progress and success gave Margaret and me great satisfaction; we had known him as a delightful, good-looking, dark-haired young medical student who was in the first class I took when I joined Professor Blacklock, and he was clinical clerk with Margaret in Cleland. He kept in touch during his National Service in Malta where he met and married Yvonne, and after demobilisation I induced him to return to the Royal and make his career in pathology. He began his research career with a study on peptic ulcer and the role of the adrenal gland; later, with Professor Ingle in Chicago, he carried out some fine work on the permissive role of steroid hormones in experimental hypertension. He was an excellent lecturer who had a sense of humour that made him popular with

123

students. On occasions when we discussed teaching I would remind him, 'Try to be like Alistair Currie, and get to know the names of the students. If you do they will pay more attention to what you are saying and respond when you direct a question to them.' Alistair Currie had a remarkable gift of remembering the names of all the students in the class. Some time later after a post-mortem teaching session I asked Crane how he was getting on and had he mastered the names of the students in his class.

'No,' he said. 'You may have seen Mr Christie talking to me just now. I was conducting a post-mortem class with students from my tutorial group, pointed to some pathological feature and decided to ask one of them to describe it.'

'Who will I choose?' I said, and looked round the class for someone whose name I remembered. 'Mr Christie, you describe the specimen,' I said, and he did it very well. I would repeat the process during the next week or so, and after looking round the collection of faces would choose Mr Christie. As time passed I became very friendly with him and today, as you saw, he was waiting for me at the end of the tutorial. 'Well, Mr Christie, can I do something for you?' I asked.

'Yes, sir,' he replied. 'Would it be possible for you to learn someone else's name?'

I remember with pleasure the week in 1970 Margaret and I spent with Willie and Yvonne in Sheffield when I was invited to be a Visiting Professor to the university. I could see at first hand the excellent department he had created, and his untimely death in his mid-fifties was a great blow to us all.

Alistair Currie and I had been together in the Royal Infirmary for many years; he had established his own pituitary research unit in the department and through it had developed extensive scientific contacts in North America. When the Edinburgh and Glasgow medical journals amalgamated to form the *Scottish Medical Journal,* Alistair became its first editor. He was an outstanding teacher, popular with the students and as I said previously, had the rare facility for remembering students' names. During the class of systemic lectures to ninety students, he would refer to them personally, sometimes to their astonishment but never to their embarrassment. Currie was a first-class diagnostic pathologist whose opinion was eagerly sought and appreciated by all of us.

He moved with Professor Guy Marrian, to the Imperial Cancer Research Fund in London where he established a scientific unit in pathology. His contact with scientists of different disciplines at the Fund was excellent training and preparation for the years he would spend as a member of the Medical Research Council and the Cancer Research Campaign. However, his forte was in academic pathology where he would have close contact with students and clinicians. He moved to the Regius Chair of Pathology in Aberdeen and later was invited to the Chair of Pathology in Edinburgh. In both departments he introduced young pathologists to the important role science could play in elucidating the nature of disease, and at the end of his distinguished career he was knighted and became President of the Royal Society of Edinburgh.

Robert Patrick was the fourth member of the group. After a long war service he held a clinical appointment in the Infectious Diseases Unit in Belvedere Hospital, Glasgow and became intensely interested in the liver changes found in children with severe gastroenteritis. He carried out liver biopsies and developed new frozen section techniques to study the pathology. I arranged for him to spend a year with Arnold Lazarow in Minneapolis where he eagerly assimilated the newer technology Lazarow had developed in his study of diabetes. On his return, Patrick used the new techniques to advance his studies on liver cirrhosis. He quickly developed an international reputation as an authority on liver pathology with his highly acclaimed book on the subject (with Jim McGhee). He attracted a number of bright young pathologists to his unit: two of them occupy Chairs of Pathology in this country. Jim McGhee is Professor of Pathology in Oxford, while Eric Walker holds the Regius Chair of Pathology in Aberdeen. Patrick was, in addition, a highly respected and experienced histopathologist and a perfectionist in everything he did. He had only one standard and that had to be the highest. This may be why this self-effacing introvert was not a favourite with the students. It was certainly to the advantage of the department and to the university that he stayed in Glasgow, and he was rewarded with a Personal Chair. He certainly deserved it.

This was the exciting group of young academic pathologists with whom I worked in the early days of nationalised medicine after I returned from the army. It was largely through their research, presented at meetings in this country and abroad, that the department at the Royal Infirmary would emerge from the shadow of Sir Robert Muir and Western Infirmary pathology and become a force in British pathology.

The departure of those colleagues left vacancies in the department and I initiated a training programme which would vary to some extent as the years passed and National Service ended. The early replacements were graduate students who had excelled in the undergraduate course of pathology, had completed their residences in medicine and surgery as well as their National Service, and who came to the department on my invitation. Some spent a year in pathology in preparation for a career in medicine or surgery and, with a little encouragement during that year, many became attracted to the department and a career in pathology. All took part in teaching and in diagnostic pathology and those who became interested in a career in academic pathology were encouraged to take evening classes in chemistry where they received an excellent grounding in science enabling them to work confidently with the scientists I had introduced into the department.

Willie Duguid was one of my new recruits who, with me, had developed a close liaison with Jim Grant when he was still in the biochemistry department in Edinburgh. Fresh human adrenal glands, removed at operation from women with breast cancer, were preserved on ice and sent on the forty-mile journey to Edinburgh for Grant's biochemical work which was done in conjunction with our morphological and histochemical studies. While the collaboration progressed well in spite of some travel problems, it became more satisfactory when, with approval and support from the Principal and Professor Norman Davidson, I was able to induce Grant and his group to move to Glasgow and establish a steroid unit in my department. Later his unit was reinforced by the two young steroid chemists I had brought over from Heard's department in Montreal. As time passed and the work progressed, Grant would attract many chemists from abroad to work with him.

The research grants I won from the National Institute of Health in America and the Medical Research Council in this country enabled me to finance invited medical students to work with us on a research project during the summer vacation. The selected students had a good undergraduate record and many had, in addition, graduated with an honours degree in biochemistry, physiology or physics and mathematics. After completing the compulsory residency in medicine and surgery, some of them would come to the department as senior house officers, then registrars and senior registrars paid for by the National Health Service. Others would be financed from my research grants and given honorary contracts at the appropriate health service grade. In time both groups would qualify for lecturer and later senior lecturer posts in the university when vacancies occurred, but those academic appointments had to be won in open competition. In this training programme a period of four years would elapse before the selected undergraduate student would join the staff and another eight to ten years in the department before they would leave to take up a senior appointment in pathology in this country or abroad. During that period most of them spent a year abroad in one of the departments I had visited. This training programme brought together a group of talented and dedicated young men and women eight of whom, in time were appointed to chairs of pathology in this country, in the USA and Canada; one became vice-president of advanced scientific research and development at the world's largest healthcare company.

During those ten years, significant advances were being made in knowledge of the human adrenal gland and it is interesting to look back on our efforts with this information in mind. Organic chemists had synthesised the important steroid hormones and determined their structure. Steroid biochemists showed how naturally occurring hormones were inactivated in the body and excreted in urine, and they developed chemical methods to determine the concentration of steroids in blood and urine. We were interested in and learned a great deal about the group of enzymes which played an important role in the synthesis of the steroids and the site of each enzyme within adrenal cells. This process is complicated but important for an understanding of our research effort and in an attempt to simplify it, I have used the analogy of what happens on a motor car assembly line, thinking of it as the steroid hormone assembly line. Reference to Figures 1–4 will, I hope, help the reader understand how the four different steroid models are formed and the cells, in the adrenal cortex where the models are produced.

Cholesterol, which is present in the clear cells of the adrenal cortex (Figures 1A, B) or brought to the compact cells by blood, would represent the initial steroid chassis from which the hormones are made. It has twentyseven carbon atoms in the molecule and Figure 2 shows the numbering system used for the carbon atoms in a steroid nucleus and the main enzymes involved in the steroid assembly line. It should be noted that each enzyme acts in a well coordinated manner at a precise stage in the assembly line. This process of steroid biosynthesis can now be followed in Figure 3 which starts with cholesterol and ends with a series of steroid models such as *cortisol, testosterone* and *oestrone*, all formed by the cells of the zona fasciculata and zona reticularis and *aldosterone* which is produced by the cells of the zona glomerulosa.

The car chassis can only move along the assembly line when electric power is turned on, and it is the entrance into the adrenal cell of ACTH from the pituitary gland which sets the steroid assembly line in motion. At the first halt the side chainsplitting enzymes break the chain between C–20 and C–22 (Figure 2) to produce a steroid with 21 carbon atoms called *pregnenolone* (Figure 3). At the next halt (3) the enzymes bring about changes in Rings A and B to form *progesterone*, a C–21 steroid hormone also formed by the ovary. The assembly line up to this stage is the same for cells of the three zones of the adrenal cortex; now it diverges and we can see what happens to progesterone in the assembly line of cells in the zona fasciculata and zona reticularis. The sequential action of the hydroxylating enzymes add OH groups at (17), (21) and (11) positions to form *cortisol*, a C–21 steroid and the main hormone formed in this assembly line.

At the same time a minor assembly line exists at the *17(OH) progesterone* halt where enzymes remove two carbon atoms from the C–21 steroid to form a C–19 steroid which is an *androgen*, one of the illegal anabolic steroids used by athletes to build up body muscle to improve performance. At the next halt (19) another carbon atom is lost and a C–18 steroid or *oestrogen* is formed. It will now be clear that the cells of both the zona fasciculata and zona reticularis have the same enzyme systems and can form three biologically distinct steroid models — cortisol, testosterone and oestrone, whose structure is shown in Figure 3.

If we return to progesterone in the main assembly line we can see what happens to it in the cells of the zona glomerulosa which, unlike the other two zones, has no 17 hydroxylase. Progesterone progresses to halt (21) and is changed to DOC which, as we saw, was the hormone used by Selye in his animal experiments on which his adaptation syndrome was built. After halts at (11) and (18) the very potent salt-active hormone, *aldosterone* is formed. It is also a C–21 steroid, but unlike cortisol is formed in small quantities by the cells in the zona glomerulosa.

With this background we can look at the continuing research efforts of our group and examine the results and conclusions we reached and the theories we proposed. In my final undergraduate year in medicine, I had been with Sir Charles Illingworth in surgery at the Glasgow Western Infirmary. Illingworth had gathered together a very research-orientated group of young academic surgeons who were destined to fill many Chairs of surgery in Britain, and with encouragement from Sir Charles, Grant and I developed a close working relationship with Pat Forrest, later Sir Patrick Forrest, whose research interest was breast cancer. At the end of the nineteenth century, George Beatson, a Glasgow surgeon, found that removal of the ovaries from patients with breast cancer seemed to improve the patients' condition. Beatson's success was attributed to the loss of oestrogens which were necessary for the continued growth of the cells of the breast cancer. When it was discovered that the adrenal glands could produce oestrogens it appeared logical to remove both ovaries and adrenals and for a time this became an established from of treatment for breast cancer, although the patient had to be maintained for the rest of her life on cortisol.

Forrest was a valuable member of our multidiscipline research group and a two-stage operation was carried out, with the patient's permission, during which the adrenal glands were removed. First the right gland was exposed, a cannula inserted into the adrenal vein and blood collected over a fixed time interval, then the adrenal gland was removed. The patient rested for a period of three weeks, when we knew from experience that the left adrenal gland would be normal. ACTH in varying degrees of purity had now become available and four days before the second operation, the patient received intramuscular injections of ACTH to stimulate the remaining gland to produce steroid hormones. The same operation procedures were carried out before the left gland was removed. In this way the patient's first gland acted as a control and the effect of different strengths of the newly developed ACTH preparations was assessed by morphology and chemical techniques.

Following ACTH the left gland was heavier than the right and the thin compact cells of the zona reticularis seen in the normal gland (Figure 4A) had broadened at the expense of the clear cells of the zona fasciculata (Figure 4B), to occupy most of the adrenal cortex as had occurred in the post-mortem adrenals of patients who died in severe stress (Figure 1B). The chemists examined the nature and concentration of different steroids in the adrenal vein blood and, with histological control, prepared pure separate slices of clear cells from the zona fasciculata and compact cells from the zona reticularis. They studied the ability of those separate slices to form steroid hormones, using *in-vitro* cell culture conditions, and determined the steroid production of the slices when ACTH was added to the cultures.

On the basis of our histological and chemical studies I put forward the theory that the zona fasciculata and zona reticularis were indeed one single zone in which the *compact cell zone* produced the daily requirements of steroid hormones and the *clear cell zone* was a storage zone for the steroid precursor, cholesterol (Figure 1A). In time of stress or after injections of ACTH, cholesterol in the clear cells nearest the zona reticularis, would be utilised in the steroid assembly line (Figures 4A, B) and the clear cells would become compact bringing about the widening of the zona reticularis that we had found.

The chemists were not impressed with this concept. They pointed out that slices which I had confirmed histologically as clear or compact cells produced the same amount of steroid hormones when examined in their culture media. When ACTH was added to the media, increased amounts of hormones were produced from the cholesterol-rich clear cells but there was little response from the cholesterol-poor compact cells. Since the cells of both zones, they argued, behave similarly in their *in-vitro* system in the absence of ACTH, how could I hypothesise, as I had done, that the zona fasciculata was a resting or storage zone? This was indeed, quite a challenge. Could the results of an *in-vitro* experiment truly reflect what was happening *in-vitro*, and if not, how could I show what was taking place normally in the human gland and in times of stress when increased amounts of ACTH would get to the adrenal? The answer came from a completely unexpected quarter. Jim Dobbie was one of the undergraduate medical students I had invited to work with me during the university vacation. He used the simple technical methods available in all departments of pathology to construct a three-dimensional model of the human adrenal gland. When the model was examined carefully (Figure 1A) it was seen that blood would pass from the capsule of the gland down perpendicular capillaries, bypassing the clear cells of the zona fasciculata to reach and circulate among the main compact cells of the zona reticularis.

Dobbie's model showed that the blood entered the main adrenal central vein between thick muscle bundles which were present in the wall of the vein (Figure 1A). Intermittent contraction of those muscle bundles would hold up blood around the cells of the reticularis long enough for ACTH to diffuse into them. In severe stress (Figure 1B), with longer contraction of the muscle, blood would be dammed back to reach the inner clear cells of the zona fasciculata when ACTH could gain access to them, set in motion the steroid assembly line (Figure 3) and result in a broadening of the compact cell zone (Figures 1B, 4B).

Having established that the zona fasciculata and zona reticularis are parts of a single zone in which cells have all the enzymes required to form corticosteroids, androgens and oestrogens in the steroid assembly line, it was now possible to understand the histological appearance of the adrenal glands and adrenal tumours we encountered in patients with adrenal disease. I have selected the two adrenal conditions, adreno-genital syndrome and Cushings syndrome, to illustrate how our studies of the normal adrenal helped to explain the histological appearance of the first condition and the cause of the second.

The *adreno-genital syndrome* results from the production and liberation of large amounts of C–19 steroids, androgens, and the clinical effect of these masculinising hormones depends on the age and sex of the patient. In young girls there is marked enlargement of the clitoris to resemble a penis, young boys become stronger and muscular and the term 'infant Hercules' is used to describe them. Women affected by the illness become more muscular, the breasts atrophy, they grow a beard, become bald and indeed some bearded ladies found in circuses in the past suffered from the adreno-genital syndrome. This fascinating condition had been described as a syndrome 'in which little girls become little boys and little boys, little men. Those little men pass through the seven ages of Shakespeare in as many years'. Interest has been shown for many years in the adult form of this condition and Hippocrates described two examples in adult women.

The main cause of this illness is a defect in the enzyme which acts at halt (21) in our steroid assembly line (Figure 3). Cortisol, as we remarked, is the main hormone formed in the assembly line and it is the level of this hormone in the blood that controls the output of ACTH from the pituitary. If the level of cortisol falls, a message is sent to the pituitary to produce more ACTH and when the cortisol level rises above requirement, the output of ACTH is shut off. In the adreno-genital syndrome, an enzyme defect at halt (21) means the output of the cortisol model drops; and to maintain normal production the level of ACTH in the blood will rise to high levels and in our assembly line there will be a build-up of the C–21(OH) progesterone at halt (21). Excess amounts of this compound will be shunted into the subsidiary androgen assembly line to produce the excess androgens which cause the symptoms of the illness.

Our study, in which ACTH was administered to patients, allowed us to predict that in nature's experiment in patients with the adreno-genital syn-drome (Figure 4D) there would be a broad compact zone and a small or absent clear zone in the adrenals and the glands, even in young children, would weigh as much as 20–30 gms, instead of a normal weight of 1.5–3 gms. In the past, surgeons removed large adrenals as part of treatment, and the histological appearance of the excised adrenal was as we expected, a gland that was being subjected to high doses of ACTH. A look at the steroid assembly line will demonstrate why surgery should not be used and indeed, what form of treatment is indicated and why it should be carried out when the illness is at an early phase in its development. The patient should be treated with cortisol as early as possible so that the feedback mechanism of cortisol on the pituitary reduces the formation and liberation of ACTH to normal levels. This slows the production of the C–21 steroid at halt (21) and reduces the amount of androgen produced in the androgen assembly line. As a result, the patient, particularly the child, if diagnosed and treated with cortisol early in the illness does not suffer the effects of this masculinising hormone.

The second adrenal disease I wish to refer to is *Cushing's syndrome* which is named after the well-known brain surgeon Harvey Cushing. It presents in patients with such features as insulin-resistant diabetes, muscle weakness and osteoporosis of the spine. The patient bruises easily, shows striae, particularly in abdominal skin and has low resistance to infection. Moon-face, buffalo hump, hypertension and cardiovascular disease are usually present. This clinical picture is caused by overproduction of cortisol by the adrenal assembly line and many of the features are seen in patients who receive cortisol as part of immuno-therapy in transplant surgery. The adrenals in this condition are increased in size and weight between 10–12 gms. On histological examination we found the compact cell layer occupied about half the width of the cortex (Figure 4C) and it was this observation that induced us in 1960 to study the level of ACTH in the blood of patients with Cushing's syndrome who showed a three-fold increase of this hormone in the blood. There was no defect in the enzymes in the steroid assembly line. Cortisol was formed in excess amounts, but the pituitary was failing to respond and turn off the supply of ACTH. Treatment of the syndrome is removal of most of the two adrenal glands.

Like other organs in the body, the adrenals on occasion are the seat of malignant tumours which might weigh up to 2,000 grms, and in all instances they consist exclusively of compact cells. Again a look at the steroid assembly line (Figure 3) illustrates that enzyme defects could exist at almost all halts and the amount of steroid models formed by each tumour cell is very small, yet because of the great number of cells in the tumour, large amounts of one or all four steroid models are often produced. The assembly line in those malignant adrenal tumours is out of control, grinding along slowly to produce the models. If large amounts of oestrogens are produced by the tumour in a female before puberty, isosexual precocity will occur, feminisation will be found in the pre-pubertal male, while the adult male will seek medical aid because of the development of large, well formed breasts. When, in addition, androgen and corticosteroid models are produced in large amounts, the symptoms will vary with the age and sex of the patient. A knowledge of the structure and function of the normal human adrenal cortex has helped us to understand what is happening to patients with adrenal disease.

CHAPTER 9

The 'Path' Society
and other Lectures

THE RAPID ADVANCES being made worldwide were providing answers to the scientific and clinical problems of the adrenal gland and it was difficult for any one person to keep abreast of progress in all fields of adrenal research. Accordingly, with the help of a local organising committee of university and health service colleagues, and financial support from 'Red Hackle Whisky', arranged by Sir Hector, an International Conference on the Human Adrenal Cortex was held in Glasgow in July 1960, with the proceedings published in book form in 1962. The invited participants came from the United States, Canada, France and Great Britain and represented all sections of adrenal research. In their introductory talks the chairmen reviewed current thought and drew attention to existing problems. We departed from the usual custom of reporting verbatim discussions and sent the speaker's manuscript and a recording of each discussion to selected participants who were asked to assess the significant data that had emerged.

Over a period of years our research efforts were presented at meetings in this country and abroad and many papers were given at meetings of the Pathological Society of Great Britain and Ireland. This was an excellent forum for young colleagues to present their work and where I was keen to show how they could study problems in pathology using modern technology. The 'Path' Society, as it was called, met twice yearly in early January in one of the medical schools in London, Oxford and Cambridge, and in summer at one of the medical schools in Scotland, Ireland and the provincial schools of England. Later when Dutch pathologists joined the Society, the medical schools of Holland were included in the circuit for summer meetings and occasionally joint meetings were held in Oslo and Bergen with the Norwegian Pathological Society. The Path Society was used as a platform for young and old pathologists to present their work and sessions were held in histopathology, bacteriology and experimental research. In recent years the scope of the

133

sessions has been extended to cover other subjects. The Society also published the *Journal of Pathology and Bacteriology*.

I attended the January meetings from the time I joined Professor Blacklock's department. There were no grants to cover expenses and the group from the department travelled by night train to London, sitting upright in a crowded third class compartment. On arrival in London we walked to Lyons Corner House in Tottenham Court Road to breakfast in the Restful Tray, then made our way to the meeting which began about ten o'clock. I listened enthusiastically to the presentation of papers, each one scheduled to last not more than fifteen minutes. At the end of this period an alarm clock, which sat on the platform, would ring, the chairman would rise from his seat and approach the platform. This was the signal for the speaker to wind up and finish his talk. This manoeuvre was usually successful, if not, the audience showed their displeasure by stamping their feet, when the chairman would order the speaker to stop.

Members of the committee of the Society, professors and senior pathologists, would occupy the front two rows of the lecture theatre and invariably one of them would open the discussion on the paper which had been delivered. Mostly the questions were to the point, often constructive and helpful to the speaker, even complimentary. On occasions the questioner would be derogatory of the speaker's presentation, the contents of the paper or the quality of the slides.

'Dr X,' he would say, 'describes this as a rare or unusual tumour. I myself have seen many and did not think it fit to waste the Society's time by giving a paper. If the speaker had taken the trouble to read the old German literature on the subject, he would have found it described beautifully and illustrated with clearer photomicrographs than the poor lantern slides which the speaker has inflicted on us.' I was shocked and surprised at the venom of the attack and sorry for the young speaker, since I had never heard of the tumour he described and had learned from his paper. Surely, I thought, one of the functions of the Society was to draw the attention of young pathologists like myself to the existence of rarer tumours, as well as learning what research was going on.

When it came to papers on bacteriology I was feeling drowsy from a lack of sleep and the heat of the lecture theatre and had to make a determined effort to listen to the presentation. One paper I remember, was on erysipelothrix insidiosa, about which I knew nothing. The speaker read the paper in a monotonous and inarticulate voice, his lantern plates were full of detail and the lettering so small it was impossible to read them. I tried hard to understand this paper but from time to time my head would drop and I would nod off to be aroused by the noise of the alarm clock heralding the end of the presentation. I had learned nothing about erysipelothrix from this paper when a very irascible Scottish professor of bacteriology rose slowly to his feet, turned his back on the speaker and facing the audience said, 'I wish to point out to members that the rules of the Society do not allow speakers to read their papers. If this speaker had followed the rules and delivered his talk from the slides, poor though they were, I would have heard more than the word erysipelothrix.'

The papers on experimental cancer were difficult to follow, especially when the speaker glossed over the complex nomenclature used to describe the different strains of mice used in the experiments. It was impossible to read, far less understand the detailed lantern slides which they would flash momen- tarily to the screen with little or no attempt to use or describe them.

I learned a great deal about paper presentation from those visits and began to appreciate the honest and constructive comments made by many older members, designed to ensure a standard of excellence which, over the years, has been the hallmark of 'Path' Society meetings. I learned that a great deal of preparation goes into a fifteen-minute paper, that the lantern slides should contain only sufficient material to illustrate a point and to enable the contents to be read by the audience, who should be given sufficient time to do so. This has the advantage that the speaker can talk from the slides, use both auditory and visual impressions in the talk and obviate loss of memory which sometimes occurs. The speaker should have no more than fifteen slides for a fifteen minute paper and less if many slides have written material or diagrams which need to be described. This attention to detail ensures the speaker does not overrun the allotted time and obviates the need for notes. It is important, I learned, to anticipate questions and have slides available, appropriately num- bered and given to the projectionist, so that if required the question can be answered from the appropriate slide. However, to achieve this the research work must be six months ahead of the material presented. On a number of occasions speakers, even senior ones, get their slides in the wrong order and it is inexcusable in those circumstances to blame the projectionist, as happens quite often. I find it is important to check the slides carefully beforehand with the projectionist and make myself familiar with the light panels on the lecture desk. It is surprising how many speakers, even experienced ones, find a fifteen-minute presentation very harassing when the mouth gets dry and articulation is difficult. If, as sometimes occurs, water is not present on the lecturer's desk, it is of value to carry some vitamin C tablets and, if required, one can be placed under the tongue with beneficial effects.

My first paper to the Society was at a meeting in Glasgow when I presented my work on phaeochromocytoma. Later at a meeting in Birmingham I described the studies on the adrenal reaction to stress and found myself in confrontation with Sir Roy Cameron. I am glad to say this ended happily for me and began a long friendship with this distinguished gentleman. Sir Roy was one of my referees when I applied for the Chair of Pathology. We would meet at the Society for many years and on each occasion he would take me into a corner and I had to relate progress in our adrenal research and the contribution made by the young men working with me.

I gave a number of papers to the Society because I felt a strong allegiance to it and, as I said previously, I was trying to illustrate the role basic science could play in solving problems in pathology. Our young research group regularly presented their work to the Society and in every instance demonstrated the role of basic science. Munro Neville and Jim Webb, our steroid chemist from Montreal, showed how their radiochemical studies were used to determine the enzyme defects present in adrenal tumours removed from patients with the adreno-genital syndrome. Willie Duguid described how he was using densitometry to find a qualitative method which would indicate malignancy in an adrenal tumour. David Murray reported on the biochemical techniques he used to detect the high levels of cortisol in the blood of dying patients, especially in those with meningococcal meningitis and adrenal haemorrhage. The papers by them and other members of our group were complemented at meetings of the Society by others on liver pathology from Robert Patrick and his assistants.

We made regular visits to meetings of the Path Society and on every occasion the papers were prepared meticulously and carefully rehearsed. About five weeks before the meeting the person presenting the paper talked to the department, dealt with his material, how he proposed to present it, the relevant literature, what he would have on the lantern plates and the conclusions he would try to draw. At the first meeting he would listen to suggestions from colleagues and in the next two weeks prepare his slides and present them to colleagues at the next department meeting. On this occasion he would be subjected to the type of criticism he might expect at the Society meeting, and listen to suggestions for improving the slides and their content. Once the content, calibre and number of slides were agreed, future meetings would be restricted to presentation and delivery within the allocated fifteen minutes, and at this stage criticism was still allowed. This type of preparation could be quite traumatic and on one occasion one of my best assistants said he had had enough and wished to withdraw his paper. I refused, told him there would be no more criticism during the last ten days before the meeting, rather the time would now be spent in listening and giving him encouragement. I was delighted at the Cambridge meeting in January 1965 when five papers were presented by our young research group and all were complimented from the floor of the meeting for the calibre of their research and presentation.

No one ever complained again and I have no doubt they all used the same technique to prepare their own young assistants for scientific meetings.

Often I think of and compare the cost and travel arrangements of my early visits to Society meetings with those of my younger group. After medicine was nationalised, the university paid a third class rail and sleeper, and a contribution to hotel accommodation for a visit to one meeting per year. My former colleagues, now running their own departments, would meet up with us at the Society meeting in London, after which we would all attend the Society dinner. As time passed and our numbers increased, we would organise our own Royal Infirmary Reunion Dinner with old and new members of the department. Those were rare moments I would always treasure.

During the period I was developing the group in pathology, Professor Leslie Davies and Dr Joe Wright were attracting a talented group of young clinicians to their separate departments of medicine at Glasgow Royal Infirmary. Many of those young clinicians had gone abroad on Royal Infirmary travel grants and some had spent a year in scientific departments in the United States. On this occasion in 1962, Dr Wright came to see me; he had had a visit from Mr John MacFarlane, a well-known businessman who wished to establish a Chair in memory of his father Sir James MacFarlane, who had been Chairman of the Board of Managers of the Royal Infirmary. His portrait hangs in the Board Room of the Infirmary. Dr Wright was not impressed by some of the suggestions that had been made, and said he would like to discuss the matter with me.

'What do you think we should do?' he said to me. 'There will be a legacy of £90,000,' which at that time was a very considerable sum of money. I reminded Dr Wright that he had been a member of the Infirmary Board when medicine was nationalised and that £250,000 of the hospital's endowments had helped establish the Scottish Hospital Endowment Research Trust (SHERT) which was now financing the research of some of his young clinicians. I reminded him again that he was a member of the Board that used endowment funds to create travel grants to send our young men abroad to work with distinguished scientists.

'Surely,' I told him, 'the next step is for us to bring those distinguished clinicians and scientists to the Royal to spend a year with us. This can only be to the benefit of Glasgow medicine and particularly of the Royal Infirmary,' He agreed we should set up the MacFarlane Chair in Cancer Medicine for visitors and I should go to the Principal and put the proposal to him. As I expected, Sir Hector was very enthusiastic; the Faculty of Medicine agreed and the MacFarlane Chair for visiting professors was established. The Royal Infirmary Board sold some property, and purchased and elegantly furnished a new flat in the west end of Glasgow for the visiting professor and his family.

In addition the Board allocated to the professor the McGhee Cancer Research Fellowship for an assistant to work with him; and through the good offices of Sir John Erskine and Dr J. M. Johnstone, the Scottish Hospital Endowment Research Trust agreed to provide technical help, equipment and running costs for the professor's laboratory which was located in the pathology department. An appointment to the Chair was made every second year by the university and the first incumbent was Professor Rupert Willis, the distinguished tumour pathologist. He was succeeded by Professor Gyorgy Ivanovics from Szeged in Hungary, Professor Lewis Engel from Harvard and Professor David Glick from Stanford. The young doctors who worked with them had a stimulating year, the visiting professors delivered a series of lectures in the university and Glasgow hospitals and at the end of their terms of office the Board of the Royal Infirmary gave a dinner in their honour and invited the Principal and representatives of the University, Western Infirmary and SHERT. The cre-ation of this post did much to cement a good relationship between the Royal and Western Infirmaries and this was not always the case. Sadly the concept Dr Wright and I created with the MacFarlane Chair seems to have been lost, as happens on so many occasions with a worthy cause.

As our adrenal research progressed I received invitations to present the work at universities in this country and abroad. In 1960 I lectured at the University of Perugia in Italy, and in 1968 in Milan gave a slide seminar on the adrenal at a meeting of the International Academy of Pathology. This was a three-hour session during which I had to present twenty-five case reports, with lantern slides, of patients with all forms of adrenal disease. During the previous year my young technician, Wendy Smith, prepared two hundred sets of slides, along with a case history and biochemical studies on each patient. Each set represented a comprehensive review of adrenal pathology and was sent to the Academy for sale to participants who had the opportunity to study the slides and read the case histories before the meeting. Slide sessions entailed a great deal of preparation but it was rewarding since, in the international arena, I was able to illustrate how scientists and pathologists working together had been able to clarify many problems of adrenal disease.

David Murray accompanied me to the meeting and the organisers had arranged a Sunday visit to Streza on Lake Maggiore. It was a lovely early September day when we left Milan by bus, and on arriving at the hotel for lunch I was delighted to find Helen Polozopoulos waiting for me. Helen was a lecturer in pathology at the University of Salonika in Greece and had come to Glasgow on a British Council scholarship to work with me on the adrenal gland. She had seen my name on the list of speakers and come to Milan to renew our acquaintance and hear about my family and the members of the department. As time passed the British Council asked me to take overseas

Author with Professor Severi during a lecture at the University of Perugia, April 1960.

graduates from Hong Kong, Egypt, Hungary and India and it was gratifying to meet many of those young men and women in later years.

In 1964 I was invited to visit the medical school of the University of Szeged (Hungary) and was very impressed with what I saw. The anatomy department had a museum with beautifully dissected specimens of all the organs of the body displayed in such a manner that encouraged the students to learn. It was in the department of biochemistry in Szeged that Szent-Gyorgyi carried out the research on vitamin C which led to his Nobel Prize. Professor Gyorgyi Ivanovics' work on bacteriological biochemistry was impressive and I arranged for one of my assistants, Tom Anderson, to work with him in Szeged and later in Glasgow, when Ivanovics was appointed to the MacFarlane Chair. In time two Hungarian biochemists, Dr Arpad Fazekas and Dr Imre Faradin spent a year in our research group in Glasgow.

During the visit to Szeged I lived in the Semmelweiss hostel which housed medical students during university term. It was named after Dr Ignaz Semmelweiss, an obstetrician in the Szeged medical school who showed in 1861 that

Author giving a seminar on adrenal pathology at the International Academy
of Pathology, Milan 1968.

child-bed fever (puerperal sepsis) which occurred in women after delivery, was commoner in labour wards where students were in attendance. He found that the students brought in the infection on their unwashed hands and clothes from the post-mortem room where they were dissecting. The University of Szeged authorities arranged for me to visit the medical schools in Pecs and Budapest. I shall never forget the lecture I gave in the medical school in Szeged. As was my custom, I went to the lecture theatre to see the projec-tionist and hand him my slides for testing. The lantern was very old and when it was switched on, no image appeared on the screen: there was no condenser in the lantern. The projectionist left the room and returned a few minutes later with another condenser which he attached to the lantern. Now a quarter of the image projected onto the screen was in focus, but when I protested, was told that the condenser had been taken from a lantern in another theatre where a French professor was due to lecture and now he had no condenser in the lantern he hoped to use. I did not protest further but gave the lecture which I amplified by illustration on the blackboard; fortu-nately some white chalk was available and the audience was a tolerant one. This type of experience happens to most lecturers and it is wise to realise it can occur and be prepared to improvise.

I maintained a close link with the University of Szeged. Professor Petri, head of surgery, visited me in Glasgow and scientists from the departments of biochemistry and medicine worked in our research unit for one year. In 1965 Professor Ivanovics spent a year in Glasgow as the MacFarlane Visiting Professor.

In 1971 the University of Szeged celebrated the fiftieth anniversary of its foundation which followed the dissolution of the Austro-Hungarian Empire after the First World War. The Franz-Josef University was moved from Transylvania and established in the southern Hungarian town of Szeged. Along with twelve professors from universities in Russia, Germany, France and Italy, I was awarded the honorary degree of Doctor of Medicine by the University. This was quite an impressive occasion to which my wife was invited. On the eve of the celebration there was a firework display followed next morning by a procession of civic and university dignitaries, the honorary graduands and their wives, starting at the university and passing through the streets which were lined with schoolchildren on holiday for the occasion, and members of the public. I was sitting with the other graduands in the front row and invited guests were immediately behind. The ceremony was conducted in Hungarian, which I did not understand. At one particular part of the citation I heard each name of the honorary graduands mentioned, and those who understood the language rose, approached the platform and received from the Rector of the University the beautiful illuminated scroll of Doctor of Medicine. When my turn came I stood up and when my name was mentioned approached the platform and received my scroll.

After the ceremony I met the British Ambassador who had come from Budapest to be present at the ceremony. 'Do you speak Hungarian?' he asked me, and when I said I did not, he remarked, 'I thought you did since you moved up to receive the degree at the correct moment.' After lunch the honorary graduands had to present a thirty-minute paper on their research to an invited audience who seemed to speak four or five foreign languages, for they could all understand the talks each of which were given in the language of the speakers. I was glad to find that on this occasion the projector worked perfectly.

In the evening a buffet supper and dance was held in the university, followed next day by a visit to some of the departments to meet the professors and renew acquaintance with the scientists who had worked with me in Glasgow. The professor's room was furnished with the customary bookcases and large desk, and invariably in the corner of the office was a table covered with a typical Hungarian red tablecloth, and four chairs. Black coffee was served and even during a morning visit, a glass of Tokaji Aszu was always on offer; after which we got down to scientific discussions on some aspect of adrenal research.

Procession through the streets of Szeged (Hungary) as part of the ceremony to mark the 50th Aniversary of the founding of the University of Szeged, 1971.

In the evening we were taken to a theatre and then to the home of one of the professors. This was the only country in the Eastern European bloc where I was ever invited to the family home; it certainly never happened when in later years, I visited Poland and Russia.

In the years between 1951 and 1959 the British Post Graduate Medical Federation in London published a series of lectures on the Scientific Basis of Medicine and in 1961 this was altered to the Scientific Basis of Medicine – Annual Review. The governing body of the Federation was advised by medical scientists who selected a wide range of subjects to cover several disciplines and fields of interest. The subjects were chosen to show the role science could play in advancing knowledge and understanding of problems in medicine and surgery. I was invited to deliver the second lecture in the 1964 series, when I discussed the work our group had done in the patho-physiology of the human adrenal gland and how the results had led to a better understanding of the pathology and treatment of adrenal disease.

A few days before I was due to give the lecture I received a phone call from Dr John Sloper, who became Professor of Pathology at Charing Cross Hospital in London. I had known him when he was in charge of an army skin research group in Hong Kong and he had visited me in Kuala Lumpur where we would have a round of golf at the Selangor Club. John had a keen interest in the pituitary gland, but it was in the important though difficult field of muscle regeneration that he was to build an international reputation. He had a consuming interest in research and was one of the few pathologists in the country who had basic scientists in his unit to help with his muscle regeneration studies.

'I see you are giving one of the postgraduate lectures,' he said on the phone. 'Well, bring your golf clubs and we'll have a round over Moor Park.' I caught the night sleeper from Glasgow, complete with lantern slides and golf clubs and on arrival at Euston Station at 7.30 a.m., John was waiting for me. In no time he had driven me to his home in Rickmansworth where his wife Sue, an obstetrician, had a delightful breakfast ready. We played round this fine course, with the very impressive, stately clubhouse, returned to a late lunch and on to London where I delivered my lecture. Over a drink I listened to John's recent results, after which he put me, complete with golf clubs, on the night sleeper back to Glasgow. I am not sure how the lecture was received but thanks to John and Sue I could not think of a better way to give a guest lecture.

The National Health Service had been in existence for sixteen years when, in December 1964, I was invited by the Royal College of Surgeons of Edinburgh to give their Honeyman-Gillespie lecture. I chose as the title 'Research Past and Present' to highlight my views and concerns in this area. In the relatively short time since the health service began, the practice of medicine had changed. It had become more scientific, the doctor had at his disposal new equipment and technical aids for diagnosis and more remedies for treating disease. The health service provided reasonable financial security for those holding senior posts in hospital services, who wished to spend more time on research without recourse to private practice. Indeed it had become fashionable for everyone to carry out some form of research, and to publish papers in order to obtain higher university degrees in addition to the higher college diplomas which were mandatory. This research effort was commend-able and worked in most academic departments where the Chief ensured the staff received a proper training in research techniques. Many young physicians and surgeons did not receive this training, yet they became obsessed by the need to publish in the hope of improving prospects of promotion, and there appeared in the medical literature an ever-increasing volume of papers on medical subjects, much of which was of doubtful value.

In this new era the artists of medicine found their natural ability to practise good medicine and to care for patients was not always recognised in the manner they might have expected. The clinical scientist on the other hand could be judged by the number, but alas not necessarily the quality, of the publications. Some blame for this must rest with selection committees consisting of lay and medical members, who interviewed candidates for promotion.

I attended many selection committees to appoint National Health Service consultants and invariably most questions addressed to the candidate would enquire about his/her research. This inevitably led to caustic comments such as 'publish or perish' or 'the committee doesn't read the publications, it weighs them'. It became clear to me that some method should be found whereby the clinical skill of the artists of medicine could be assessed and their efforts suitably rewarded. I felt this would become more essential in future as more and more technical advances affected the care of patients.

At those interviews it was customary for candidates to be asked about their surgical or medical training. What I found revealing was their response when asked to tell the committee what interesting clinical problems they had encountered in their ward round that morning and what investigation and treatment were proposed. I would ask what advance in anaesthetics, biochem-istry, bacteriology or pathology or in other basic sciences had helped them to provide a better understanding of the problems of patients under their care. Their response gave me an insight into their knowledge of the literature and whether they kept abreast of the advancing field of medical science. I firmly believe that every clinical department, whether academic or not, must have consultants who are first and foremost clinicians who will provide a high-quality service to the patient. They should be able to understand and talk the language of the scientist and if, in addition, they have the training and ability to undertake research, this is a bonus.

I concluded my lecture by saying that most discoveries have come from people who have the capacity to recognise the problems, the ability to use the tools currently available, and the patience and determination to tackle the problem. Research today should be encouraged, but it is important that the clinician or scientist who does it, believes in it, wants to do it and can be trained to do it. Nevertheless one should never forget there remains a need for some degree of empiricism in medicine, and above all it must not be forgotten that sick people need both help and understanding. This is best achieved by the artists of medicine, provided they do not hide behind the cloak of ignorance and fail to appreciate the importance of advances in scientific medicine. It is the artists who will appreciate and pose the problems of clinical medicine and surgery, and while they may not tackle them, they must be equipped to understand how scientists approach the problems and the value of the results which emerge. It is only in this way that artists and scientists in medicine can come together, each performing the role for which they are best suited.

In 1965–66 I was a Visiting Professor of Pathology at Stanford University in California and took the opportunity to complete the preparation for the book I was writing on *The Functional Pathology of the Human Adrenal Gland.*

I made use of the excellent facilities of the Lane Library of the university and was able to check the references directly from books and journals on the library shelves. The book, completed and published in 1969, represented twenty-five years of research on the adrenal gland and I hope illustrated a dynamic approach to adrenal disease, based on the knowledge acquired of the normal structure and function of the adrenal gland.

In May of that year I was invited by the Royal College of Pathologists in London to deliver the Sir Roy Cameron lecture, and was able to tell how I relived the excitement he had experienced in exploring new pathways in the pathology of the cell. Sir Roy and his colleagues were dissatisfied and often discouraged by the purely morphological outlook on cellular pathology, and turned to biochemistry and biophysical techniques to answer many of the problems they encountered. Sir Roy's approach was similar to my own and I was delighted to have the opportunity to pay tribute to his approach and the contribution he had made to cellular pathology.

CHAPTER 10

The Changing Face
of Medical Teaching

WHILE RESEARCH CAN BE stimulating and at times rewarding, responsibility for teaching and diagnostic services in pathology can provide a valuable break from research and an added stimulus to return to it. The Chiefs with whom I trained used the term pathology to describe the changes found in patients with disease or abnormalities and to them pathology was synonymous with pathological anatomy or morbid anatomy. The word is now used by different people to mean different things and a brief look at the history of medicine will show how this came about.

The study of disease, divorced from dogmatism and theism, is believed to have originated in Greece around 400 BC during the time of Hippocrates and the teaching school of Cos which flourished in the island at that time. Naturally I found it very interesting during a holiday visit to the island of Cos, to dine on the terrace of the small taverna near the large old planum tree, in the shade of which Hippocrates is said to have taught his students the concept of humoral pathology. According to Greek philosophy there were four elements, air, water, fire and earth, and in humoral pathology the blood was warm and moist like air, phlegm was cold and moist like water, yellow bile warm and dry like fire and black bile cold and dry like earth. The sources of the humours were carefully defined. Blood was formed in the heart, phlegm in the brain, yellow bile in the liver and black bile in the spleen. In health there was normal mixing of the four elements and disease occurred when the mixing was faulty. When excess phlegm from the head reached the abdomen, oedema was produced. However, the Greeks attributed to black bile the greatest power for evil and the stage of medical history from Hippocrates to the Renaissance was aptly referred to as the period of the atra bilis. Nevertheless, the Greeks were well-informed in medical and surgical practice, although their descriptions of disease dealt only with symptoms and external changes found in patients.

146

Religious objections prevented post-mortem dissection, and descriptions of internal organs were based on animal dissection. The greatest authority on humoral pathology was Galen (AD 129–201) who believed that blood would ebb and flow like the tide, and it is difficult to appreciate that real advances in our knowledge of disease began only in the fifteenth and sixteenth centuries when dissection of human bodies was permitted and autopsies carried out in medical schools in Europe. Descriptions of normal organs led to the teaching of anatomy and when diseased organs or abnormalities were found during dissecting, the terms pathological anatomy or *morbid anatomy* were used and the diseased processes seen by the naked eye described as *macroscopic* changes.

Medical knowledge in the eighteenth century advanced by careful and thorough post-mortem dissection by Scotsmen like John and William Hunter, who will be remembered as famous teachers of normal and pathological anatomy and as lifelong collectors of specimens for teaching purposes. Due to their guidance, enthusiasm and industry, museums of morbid anatomy (pathology) were established throughout medical schools in this country. As I mentioned earlier, museums play an important role in the teaching of pathology to undergraduate and postgraduate students of medicine; the John Hunter collection can be seen in the Royal College of Surgeons in London, and the large collection by William Hunter is on view in my former department of pathology at Glasgow Royal Infirmary. The work of assembling and recording the William Hunter collection of more than 1,400 specimens was undertaken by Professor John Teacher and updated in 1962 by Dr Alice Marshall and Professor J. Burton who published the work in book form. This collection provides us with an insight into diseases which existed in the eighteenth century and includes many fine examples of bone, uterine and lung pathology, though none of the lung cancer which is so common today.

The creation of museums of morbid anatomy by clinicians was the first attempt to correlate the function of an organ, as seen in a patient by the clinician, with the changes he found at autopsy, and understandably the first pathologists were also clinicians. In spite of this and the earlier description of the circulation of blood by Harvey in 1628, the concept of disease was still based on humoral pathology and the faulty mixing of humours.

The development and use of the compound microscope in the early part of the nineteenth century was to rank as a major discovery and the means by which the concept of humoral pathology would end. Johannes Muller, a German pathologist, was one of the first to recognise the importance of the microscope and it was largely due to the efforts of his pupils Virchow and Cohnheim that the era of humoral pathology, which had lasted for two thousand years, should end and be replaced by cellular pathology in which the existence of the cell and its alteration in disease was established. When tissue taken from the patient was properly fixed, cut and stained to produce sections which were suitable for histological examination, it was discovered that every organ in the body was made up of cells which altered from their normal appearance in disease. Now the pathologist could not only look at the diseased process in an organ with the naked eye and describe the macroscopic features, but also, with suitably stained slides, describe the microscopic changes; and so the words *macroscopic* and *microscopic* became everyday terms used by pathologists when describing the disease process in an organ.

Initially specimens were taken from organs at autopsy, but in the middle of the nineteenth century the introduction of anaesthetics and antiseptic surgery allowed pathologists like Virchow and Cohnheim to obtain fresh material from organs in the operating theatre and to describe the changes seen in them. As a result, German pathologists and German literature led the field in pathology. Cellular pathology progressed along two lines. On the one hand, the changes found in the cells of patients with acute and chronic infections, disturbances of circulation and nutrition as well as in simple and malignant tumours were referred to as *general pathology* while *systemic pathology* dealt with the cellular changes found in the diseased organs of a particular system such as the alimentary, bone and joint and renal systems.

Thus theism and dogmatism were replaced by humoral pathology and in turn by cellular pathology. Once the macroscopic and microscopic appearance of disease was established, attention inevitably turned to the cause of disease and it was in this context that Virchow at the age of seventy-eight said in his presidential address to the German Pathological Society in 1889, 'We must not be content with the existence of a pathological process, we must strive to understand it.' It is therefore surprising that Virchow did not appreciate the role bacteriologists like Pasteur, Koch and others, would play in elucidating the cause of some diseases. Cohnheim on the other hand did, and in 1875 he met Robert Koch in Breslau where he examined his cultures of the anthrax bacillus. This work so impressed him that he wrote 'Robert Koch, a country practitioner, has made a magnificent discovery which, for simplicity and the precision of his methods, is all the more deserving of admiration, as Koch has been shut off from all scientific assessors. He has done everything by himself, there is nothing more to be done. I regard this as the greatest discovery in this domain and believe Koch will again surprise and put us all to shame by further discoveries.' This was indeed prophetic. The meeting with Koch convinced Cohnheim of the role bacteria played in infective diseases and it was a source of great satisfaction to Cohnheim that he lived to see Koch's discovery of the bacillus which caused tuberculosis and cholera. The science of bacteriology was born and in the ensuing years bacteriologists have played a major role in identifying the organisms responsible for infective diseases.

Chemical techniques were developed later to detect changes in the composition of body fluids in disease and in time departments of chemical pathology or clinical chemistry were created. As studies of the cellular components of blood and bone marrow progressed, independent departments of haematology, and later of immunology were set up. The group consisting of bacteriology, clinical chemistry, haematology and immunology, is often called *clinical pathology* and the term pathology restricted to mean morbid anatomy or cellular pathology. My English colleagues, particularly those in chemical pathology, tell me this is using the term pathology in the restricted Scottish sense and strictly they are correct if we accept the definition of pathology as the study of diseases or of abnormalities.

When I became Professor in 1954, haematology was done in the department of medicine whereas bacteriology and clinical chemistry were part of the department of pathology and, although I had administrative responsibility for this subject, each department ran as an independent unit with its own staff under the control of a university senior lecturer who had consultant status within the health service. Dr John Ives was in charge of bacteriology, Dr Jim Eaton of clinical chemistry, and we worked together to organise undergraduate teaching and post-graduate training in the three branches of pathology.

My responsibility was to ensure the young assistants received a proper training in morbid anatomy, which would in future allow them to provide a diagnostic service for the clinical staff of the hospital. As I mentioned, during my own training most specimens which arrived in the pathology department came from surgical and gynaecological operations, and some from skin and ear-nose-throat departments. The naked-eye or macroscopic appearance of the specimen would be recorded by the pathologist on duty, and those from cancer patients carefully dissected to assess the extent of the lesion and note the presence of any enlarged lymph glands. A simple diagram to record the position of the tumour and the appropriately numbered lymph glands is useful. Representative slices taken from the tumour and lymph glands were fixed and prepared in the usual manner and slides stained for histological examination.

Sometimes surgeons perform a biopsy on a patient and remove a small piece of tissue for histological examination. This is done to identify the histological appearance of tumours of lung, bladder, bowel, skin or other organs and help the surgeon to decide if more extensive treatment is necessary. Even smaller pieces of tissue may be obtained by needle biopsy, a technique used by surgeons to detect early breast tumours, and by physicians for liver and bone marrow examinations. The specimens received by the pathologist in training are very variable in size and one of the first lessons he or she learns is to ensure that specimens are carefully marked and recorded and small biopsies are not lost during their preparation. This was one of the first lessons I learned from Professor Blacklock.

I appreciated the importance exfoliative cytology could have as a diagnostic tool and created a unit, under Dr Helena Hughes, in this rapidly developing field of pathology. Cells are shed or exfoliated continuously from normal organs in the body and from cancers which affect them, and with experience, detection of exfoliated cancer cells can be used to diagnose the tumours. Exfoliative cytology is admirably suited to detect cancer of the cervix at a very early curable stage of the illness, provided the doctor takes the smear accurately from the endocervical region of the cervix where the cancer starts. The pathologist or cytologist can verify this by looking for and identifying endocervical cells. If those normal cells are found and no cancer cells detected, the smear has been taken properly and the patient can be assured she does not have cancer. If neither endocervical nor cancer cells are seen, the smear is faulty and must be repeated. If cervical cancer is to be eliminated as a fatal illness smears from all women must be taken properly by clinicians and prepared and read carefully by the cytologist. Exfoliative cytology is used to detect cancers of lung and bladder.

The trainee pathologist on routine duty will learn to report on a wide variety of specimens removed at operation, small surgical and needle biopsies and smears of exfoliated cells. Since much of this will deal with tumour diagnosis, training is scrutinised by a senior pathologist who sits with the trainee, preferably with a 'double head' microscope so that both can examine the slide, and discuss the histological appearance that allows them to arrive at a diagnosis. The supervisor may draw attention to some feature in the slide and refer the trainee to literature on the subject. Eventually the supervisor has to decide when trainees can be left to report on their own and does so with the strict understanding, particularly with tumours, that they will seek help if they are unsure of a diagnosis. Sometimes the senior himself will be puzzled by a lesion and will seek the advice of other members of the department. After this, if no diagnosis is made, the difficult slide may be sent to an acknowledged authority on the subject in this country. If there is a delay in reporting, it is always important to keep the clinician informed about what is being done to arrive at a diagnosis of a difficult section.

Sometimes a surgeon will request a frozen section biopsy on a breast swelling when the patient is in theatre and under anaesthetic, to help him determine the nature of the tumour and whether a local resection or a more radical operation is required. The pathologist and laboratory technician set up their equipment in a room adjacent to the theatre where they prepare the frozen section, examine it and pass the diagnosis to the surgeon who can proceed with the operation if the tumour is malignant. Frozen sections can help surgeons when they have to ensure complete removal of a tumour from a restricted space, as occurs when ear, nose and throat surgeons try to remove completely cancers of the larynx. The pathologist will receive biopsies from the edge of the resection and can tell the surgeon when the edges are free from tumour. Initially the trainees accompany the senior to the wards and learn to prepare and examine the frozen sections and express an opinion. Only when the supervisor is satisfied with their progress are the trainees allowed to report frozen section biopsies on their own.

The Emergency Medical Service (EMS) hospitals which were built during the war were retained when the health service was introduced. Those hospitals had units of clinical pathology but no histopathology services, which were supplied from the teaching hospitals by pathologists who carried out autopsies on request. Surgical specimens were sent to the pathology department of teaching hospitals and reported by their consultant staff. As the health service became established, departments of histopathology were created in most EMS hospitals and trainee pathologists seconded to those departments for periods of six months to one year. Now they would meet the hospital consultant clinicians, discuss clinical problems with them and have the responsibility to report histological sections on their own. It was an excellent training in dealing with and helping clinicians with their problems and if any diagnostic difficulties arose they could call on their supervisor for help. As time passed and trainees attained consultant status, appointments were made in histopathology to the peripheral hospitals which still maintained their link with the teaching hospitals.

While some trainees would become consultant pathologists in the health service in this country or abroad, others would aspire to a career in academic pathology. Irrespective of future intentions all took part in undergraduate teaching, all at some time attended meetings of the Pathological Society and all were encouraged to take an interest in some problem in pathology. Because of my association with Mr Arthur Jacobs, Chief of Urology at Glasgow Royal Infirmary, I saw and reported most of the bladder tumours he removed at surgery. Drs Jean Scott and Catherine Girdwood assisted me with this work and together we published our findings along with a review of British and American classification of bladder tumours. This study gave them an insight into research and experience in writing scientific papers.

About the same time the urologists and radiotherapists in Britain set up a clinical committee to study testicular tumours and I was invited to become a member of the Testicular Tumour Panel of pathologists who worked in conjunction with the clinical group. Professor Douglas Collins of Sheffield University was the chairman of the panel, and Dr Roger Pugh of St Peters and St Pauls, London, the panel secretary. In addition there were on the panel, five senior consultant pathologists who were attached to medical schools in London, Bristol and Manchester. I represented Scotland. Each of us, with the exception of Roger Pugh, would see about three patients with testicular tumours. By advertising at meetings the role and interest of the panel, coupled with the stimulus and enthusiasm of Roger Pugh, the panel received clinical data and specimens from all over the country. In time we were able to establish a working classification, which could be used by all pathologists in the country, and an assessment of the outlook for patients with different types of testicular tumour. The panel published two books on the subject and on the untimely death of Douglas Collins in 1965 appointed me as chairman where I remained until it was disbanded in 1970. Little did I think that my own son would fall victim to one of the most malignant forms of this illness. Dr Catherine Cameron worked with me, looked after the panel slides, made the diagnosis of the tumour slides we received from Roger Pugh, and with me wrote the chapter on endocrine tumours of testes, which appeared in the panel's second book.

In addition to the training at the Royal, our trainee pathologists had the opportunity to gain experience in skin, eye, bone and joint pathology and also neuropathology which Professor Cappell had established at the Western Infirmary. This training was to prove invaluable when the College of Pathology was established and our assistants had to sit the final examination for the membership diploma of the Royal College of Pathologists. Cappell donated to the College the gold medals he had won during his undergraduate and postgraduate career, and they were melted down to form the badge of office of the first President, Sir Roy Cameron. It was Cappell's fondest hope that he would succeed Sir Roy as President of the College, but sadly this honour never came his way. He talked to me on numerous occasions of his disappointment, and in my view he deserved this recognition by the college for his early research on vital staining, his pioneering work on blood transfusion and his development of many branches of special pathology. This all helped to maintain the international reputation of the department, which had been created by his mentor, Sir Robert Muir. Pathologists in Scotland owe him a debt of gratitude. He sacrificed his research on blood transfusion when the health service began, to ensure the status of pathology and make it financially as attractive as medicine and surgery to the best students in the medical faculty.

The training programme I established in pathology was more intensive than in my time with Professor Blacklock. There were more assistants to be trained and the consultant supervisors were committed to training at a crucial period in their own research careers. Accordingly, with the approval of the hospital and Health Board, I appointed to the department a full-time consultant who would supervise the trainees, organise the autopsy and histopathology service and run the weekly clinical pathology conference when the clinicians would have the opportunity to discuss their problems and see projections of slides prepared from their patients. Dr Hector Cameron, an experienced histopathologist, took over this appointment and ran the service with great distinction until he left to develop the laboratory service in the medical school in Nairobi.

Undergraduate teaching was given a high priority by Professor Blacklock and I tried to maintain the standard he set with some slight modifications. Permanent demonstrations were established on the ground floor of the museum; two new display cabinets stood in the centre of the museum and illustrated the macroscopic and microscopic features of the general principles of pathology.

The diseases of every system in the body were illustrated by a series of pathological specimens mounted in Perspex jars kept in glass cabinets, which lined the walls of the museum floor. Attached to each specimen was a printed card which described the pathological changes the student should see and a summary of the clinical history of the patient. In this way the student could compare the clinical and pathological features of each disease. Glass-covered display panels projected towards the centre of the museum to form a series of alcoves in which a desk and chair were placed for the use of the student. Information on the cause, nature and complications of each disease process was typed on the display panels and from time to time this was changed so that information on the disease was kept up to date. The museum was available at all times to the student who could refer to the demonstration to clarify a problem that might arise from the systematic lecture and was used by tutors to conduct their weekly tutorials.

The lecture course in pathology was integrated with that given in bacteriology by Dr Ives and his staff. Students would be told in pathology that exudates in the throat in children could be either fibrinous or purulent and would learn from the bacteriologists that the fibrinous exudate was caused by the diphtheria bacillus, whereas purulent tonsillitis was due to the staphylococcus. The integration of lectures on pathology and bacteriology continued throughout the year when diseases of the different systems were taught. During lectures on the respiratory system, the pathologist would deal with the cellular changes in the lung in pneumonia and the bacteriologist would talk to the students about the pneumococcus, how it was isolated from a patient, cultured on media and identified.

Just as the student could review the lectures in pathology from the museum demonstration, Dr Ives had established (on the second floor of the museum) a permanent comprehensive demonstration of all aspects of bacteriology, from which the student would learn how to sterilise surgical instruments, gowns and swabs, make culture media, identify different bacteria in culture, see what they looked like under the microscope and understand how the organisms could be isolated from a patient and identified. Most students made good use of the museum and many would return to study there in preparation for the final examination in medicine, or for the primary fellowship of one of the Royal Colleges of Surgery.

My experience with Professor Blacklock taught me the value of post-mortem room teaching, but first I had to get rid of the morgue appearance of the dissecting room and make it resemble a surgical operating theatre. No one was allowed on the floor of the autopsy room unless suitably attired in rubber boots and gown. As usual the preparation of specimens had to be ready for student teaching at 11 a.m., the dissecting bench cleaned and the body covered by a white sheet. Sometimes student nurses and physiotherapy students came to the autopsy room and they appreciated this arrangement, as indeed did the medical and dental students who became regular attenders at those sessions.

Regrettably only a few senior surgeons and physicians maintained the tradition of the great men of Guy's Hospital in London who followed their patients to the autopsy room to ensure their diagnosis was correct. Nevertheless my senior colleagues were co-operative when I asked them to nominate a senior registrar or lecturer from the unit to come with the students to an autopsy on a patient from the unit. This proved a successful exercise and I gathered together a group of fine young surgeons and physicians to help with clinico-pathological teaching at autopsies. One of this group I remember, was George McNicol who was attached to Professor Davis's medical unit. George was appointed later to the Chair of Medicine in Leeds and then became Principal of Aberdeen University. During their first year in hospital, medical students began clinical studies in surgery where they were taught to take a history and learn how to examine a patient. As a student in the first term of clinical surgery I was unfamiliar with the pathological terms used repeatedly by surgeons and decided in my first systematic lecture to the new students to give a précis and a typed sheet of what they would study in the ten-week course on general pathology and the meaning of the terms they would hear surgeons use during clinical rounds. In this way, from their first week on the wards, students could understand the terms used by clinicians. They learned about acute and chronic inflammatory conditions, what was meant by the term *thrombus* or blood clot, how it could form in a vein and become dislodged and carried in the blood as an *embolus*. They learned that the embolus could block the blood supply to an organ and cause an *infarct* or area of dead tissue in the organ. They would hear from the surgeons a great deal about *tumours*, that some were *simple* and named after the tissue of origin. They would now understand, by adding *oma* to the tissue of origin, that a simple tumour of muscle was a *myoma* and of cartilage a *chondroma*. When the tumour arose in epithelial tissue the terms *adenoma* and *papilloma* were used. Cancer, they would learn, was a name used to describe all *malignant tumours* and the student would remember from anatomy that muscle, bone, cartilage and fibrous tissue were all examples of connective tissue, and a malignant tumour which originated in connective tissue was called a *sarcoma*. When the surgeon referred to a tumour as a myosarcoma, they would understand he was referring to a malignant tumour of muscle, and a chondrosarcoma as one which arose in cartilage. Whereas simple epithelial tumours were either papilloma or adenoma, the term *carcinoma* was used to describe malignant tumours which arose in the epithelial cells of organs like lung, bowel, prostate, or endocrine glands, to mention but a few examples. The students would learn later that not all tumours could be fitted into this simple classification, but they would adjust later to the anomalies they would encounter. I explained on this first meeting that sarcomas would be spread by ulcerating into blood, whereas carcinomas would be spread, or in strict terms *metastasise*, by the lymphatics and in some instances by blood. They learned that simple tumours spread locally and do harm by pressing on vital structures, or liberate powerful chemicals as in endocrine tumours. Malignant tumours are life-threatening and spread to form *secondary deposits*.

This introduction to common medical terminology in my first lecture helped the student understand from their first week in hospital the terms used by the clinicians and the pathological changes they would see at autopsy. At the end of each autopsy I would select a student and ask them what general principle of pathology could be demonstrated. In this way autopsy room teaching was correlated with the systematic lectures and practical class teaching, and the student referred to the appropriate section of the museum demonstration in pathology or bacteriology.

When, by the beginning of the third term, the students had covered much of the systematic lecture course, the approach to teaching in the post-mortem room changed. The clinician began by giving the age and sex of the patient and the complaint that brought them to hospital. It was up to the students now to ask the relevant clinical questions. These were dealt with by the clinician who guided them to the system and organs mainly involved and the type of investigation carried out. Eventually the students, with help from the clinician, would make a differential diagnosis and finally, by elimination, a specific diagnosis of the patient's illness. The pathologist would now take over and ask the students what organs they wished to see and the pathological changes they would expect. In this manner the clinical and pathological findings would be correlated and the cause of death proposed by the clinicians was invariably confirmed. The resident doctor from the clinical unit would ask what he should write on the death certificate, and here again the students would be involved, thus gaining valuable experience for the time when they would be required to issue a death certificate. Whereas in the wards students would learn the art of examining a patient and the role of bacteriology, clinical chemistry, immunology and radiology as diagnostic measures, on the other hand morbid anatomy would teach them to look through the patient in the hospital bed and try to visualise the changes which were occurring in organs to explain the patient's symptoms. Thus pathology, when used in its broadest sense, is the bridge which links what the students have learned in anatomy and physiology with what they have found on clinical examination of patients.

The academic year 1965–66 I spent as Visiting Professor of Pathology to Stanford University in California and I took an active part in their undergraduate teaching programme. Stanford, like Harvard Medical School in Boston, could attract the best American students who wished to study medicine and it was an extremely talented and confident group of young men and women with whom I would be involved. The medical course at Stanford lasted four years and many students would extend their course by a year to receive a university grant to help faculty members with their research.

The pathology department was responsible for the hospital autopsy service but there was no organised post-mortem room teaching as in Glasgow, and no responsibility for diagnostic histopathology which was done by a separate department of the medical school. However, there was an active research programme and full responsibility for undergraduate teaching. General pathology was studied in the second year of the course and systemic pathology taken in the third year. In any one year the department was responsible for around 120 students. Unlike Glasgow Royal there was no collaborative teaching of pathology and bacteriology.

My first assignment was to lecture on acute inflammation in the course on general pathology. 'We can read the textbook to find what happens in acute inflammation,' they would say. 'What we want to know and discuss is the recently published work on the subject.' This was the type of material I would discuss with those Glasgow students who had completed the course of pathology and had been selected for the honours degree in science pathology. It was fascinating and indeed stimulating to lecture to the Stanford students who were, on the whole, about two years older than my students in Glasgow.

Their third year course in pathology dealt with disease in different systems and, unlike my course in Glasgow, only a selected number of systems were covered so that students were expected to and indeed did familiarise themselves with the rest. On many occasions they would tell me, 'We come out top in the Board's examination in pathology, in spite of the teaching.' I suppose this supports the view that any form of teaching is good, provided the student wants to learn and at Stanford, students were there to learn. In view of my interest in endocrine pathology I was asked to arrange a course on this subject and prepared a permanent demonstration with photomicrographs and question-and-answer sheets which I used to amplify my lectures. The course included up-to-date studies on the pituitary, thyroid, pancreas, adrenals, ovary and testis and students in the second and third years course were joined for the endocrine series, so that I talked to 120 students. The lectures were delivered during a three-hour period on one day per week. This concentrated lecture course was, I felt, unrealistic and decided I would give three lectures of fifty minutes each with a coffee break of ten minutes during which I could clarify any difficulties that arose. It was a enjoyable and gratifying experience to work with this group of students.

The arrangement at Stanford University for written examinations was a new experience for me. I met the students in the lecture theatre, handed out the examination papers and waited for ten minutes during which I answered queries about the wording of a question, then left the room. Some students followed me, went to their room or to the library where they wrote their paper; others remained in the examination hall. They were on their honour not to discuss the paper with anyone or consult books and if they broke this honour code they were reported, not to the faculty but to fellow students who dealt with the infringement. However, the students jealously guarded their honour code in the way one might expect from the mature persons they were.

Often I would wonder how those Stanford students would react to our teaching programme in Glasgow. I suspect they would have benefited greatly and most, but by no means all of them, would have qualified for and taken our honours course in pathology, which led to a degree in science as well as the medical degree. My experience at Stanford made me think of the quality of the Glasgow students, the need to stimulate them to read more and become self-reliant. After consultation with my colleagues on my return to Glasgow, the course was modified in an attempt to achieve this.

When I met the class on the first day of the new term in October 1966, I explained there would be a progressive assessment of their work during the year. Those who obtained an average of 60% during the year would be excused the professional examination in June. Students who failed to achieve this would be required to sit the examination, provided they achieved 40% on the year's work. Students who failed to reach this mark would be required to repeat the year.

Tutorial groups were reduced to ten students per two tutor; this was made possible by offering honorary teaching appointments to young pathologists who were attached to Stobhill Hospital and Victoria Infirmary, where some of our students had clinical attachments and attended post-mortems. Those students were placed in the tutorial groups of the young pathologists who took a personal interest in their progress. This tutorial arrangement allowed us early in the course to pick out and help any students who were having problems which affected their performance.

I arranged for the librarian at the Royal Infirmary to take each tutorial group and show them how to do a literature search. Each student was allocated a topic in either pathology or bacteriology and given six months to write a dissertation, complete with bibliography. This was submitted to their tutor who assessed it and gave a mark which counted for exemption from the professional examination. Since there were ninety students in the class, most subjects were covered in the dissertation and in time each student became quite knowledgeable on their topic. Systematic lectures were cut from five to three per week and they focused on problems the student would meet in the prescribed text book they were obliged to use. As each system was completed and discussed in tutorials, an objective examination was held and the student credited with a mark. Progressive examination throughout the year replaced the customary class examinations. I kept a note of the different topics which had been allocated and during my lecture on one of them, would call on the student involved. Slowly and rather diffidently, a hand would be raised and I would ask if what I said in my lecture was correct. Not quite, they would say, and refer to a recent article I had not read. This was exactly what I wanted and to the great delight of the rest of the class, I would invite the student to come to the lecture desk and talk to the class on the article.

My surgical and medical colleagues were very supportive of the scheme, since the students were no longer absent from the clinics, as previously, in a last minute preparation for the term examinations which I had abolished. 'What are you doing with those students?' one of the surgeons asked me. 'On one occasion,' he said, 'I was talking to the students about the differential diagnosis of swellings of the liver and happened to mention hepatoma as a rare cause and asked if anyone knew about the condition?' Apparently a rather shy young lady student who had kept discreetly at the back of the class, had this topic for her dissertation and, my colleague remarked, 'She talked for twenty minutes on the subject and referred to the most recent publications on hepatoma.' The scheme was going well and the students were responding and gaining in confidence.

At my request the surgeons arranged for each pair of students in their clinic to be attached to a patient. They would learn to take a case history, carry out and write up the clinical examination, go into the operation theatre with the surgical team and assist at operation. At the end of the operation the students would bring the specimen, complete with case history, to the pathology department. The pathologist on surgical routine would help them record the naked-eye or macroscopic appearance of the specimen and cut representative slices for histological examination. At the next meeting of the practical class the two students presented the clinical history, details of the operation and the naked-eye description of the specimen. Each student in the class received a microscopic slide which had been prepared from one of the representative blocks and this, with the clinical history, was discussed by the tutors and recorded in a notebook kept by the student. Similarly they kept in a notebook the clinical details and pathological features observed in patients at autopsy. At the end of the year the tutors allocated to each notebook a mark which counted towards the professional examination exemption scheme. In this way the student built up a personal record of disease and learned how pathology and bacteriology could help them gain a better personal understanding of a disease.

The techniques of the carrot and the stick certainly worked. The students responded to the challenge and emerged as more mature individuals. More than 60% of the class gained exemption from the professional examination and only one student had to repeat the year. He was a particularly gifted student who had family problems. Once they had been dealt with and since he had qualified by virtue of his first and second professional examination results for the combined honours course in science, done in conjunction with medicine, I awarded him one of my student research grants to work in the department. In the following year he joined our honours course in pathology and is now a very successful consultant.

The top 10% of medical students in the year, judged by results in the first and second professional examinations, were offered places in the honours science course. Between one and four students per year would choose pathology or bacteriology and begin the course on successfully completing the third year studies in pathology. This first or junior honours year was taken in conjunction with the students' fourth year studies in medicine. They spent Tuesday afternoon, all day Wednesday and Thursday morning in the department. The emphasis during this period was for the student to learn and become proficient in a series of techniques which could be used in the small research project they would undertake in the next or final year of the course, when they would suspend medical studies for a year and be full time in the department.

There would be six five-week sessions in the junior honours course. In the first the student would carry out a complete autopsy, learn to use different fixatives for different organs, process the fixed material and prepare it to cut 6μ sections. They would learn to use the different histological and histochemical stains used by the pathologist. The next five weeks were spent in the animal house where they were taught the care of laboratory animals and how to conduct animal experiments. In preparation for the third five-week block, the student obtained fresh animal tissues and human specimens from the operating theatre and fixed them for study by the electron microscope. They would learn about the sub-microscopic particles present in the cell and the functions they perform. In the remaining three blocks the student worked in the research groups of members of staff and thereby gained experience of radio-chemical techniques, gas liquid chromatography, protein analytical methods, autoradiography and other technical methods used in the department. They kept a notebook of their experiments and this was used in the viva with the external examiner at the end of the academic year. This was a difficult year for the student who, in addition, had to cope with fourth year medical studies. They were all talented students and certainly of a calibre of the top students in Stanford Medical School.

The students took a year out of medicine to complete the honours science course, when they carried out a small research project which allowed them to use the techniques they had learned. They were given prescribed reading in textbooks of general and special pathology and the two examination papers they took were based on the prescribed reading. The thesis and written papers were assessed by the external examiner and I sat with him during the students' viva. This course in pathology proved popular with the selected students and it was from this group that future academic pathologists, physicians and surgeons would be drawn.

Medical students are kept busy during the academic term and most worked conscientiously. However, they were not averse to having fun at the expense of the medical staff. I was not exempt from their pranks and learned, on most occasions, to play along with them.

I reflected on some of the things that happened in my student days and invariably it was the insecure teacher who could not deal with student pranks. Sometimes the students were merely spectators and not initiators of the events but they were always willing to participate, often to the embarrassment of the teacher, as will be seen from the following amusing incident which occurred in the anatomy dissection room. Six students were watching a senior demonstrator carry out a dissection on a particular part of the body. The demonstrator, who was preparing for the primary fellowship examination in anatomy, was a hefty well-built surgeon. He was seated on a small circular stool, supported by three legs. It was customary during the dissection to tilt the stool forward so that it was balanced on two legs with the third suspended in mid-air. A student at my dissection table drew my attention to a second demonstrator who was walking slowly up and down the dissecting room. As

Author with Dr Alistair Currie, Donald Hay Jr and Donald Hay Sr in front of the Pathology Department, Glasgow Royal Infirmary, 1958.

he passed the table where his colleague was conducting the dissection, he paused momentarily and looked at the stool perched precariously on the polished floor. 'He's going to whip that stool away,' said my partner. As the message passed from table to table there was an air of expectancy throughout the room; the demonstrator however, kept walking up and down, pausing momentarily each time he passed his colleague. Eventually the temptation proved too much and next time, he flicked the legs of the stool, his colleague fell backwards onto the floor and, in an attempt to save himself, tried to grip the dissecting table, missed, but caught hold of the body which fell on top of him. Angrily he rose, lifted the body and replaced it on the table to the hilarious amusement of the students. He approached his colleague with a threatening gesture, suddenly changed his mind and left the room in great embarrassment.

Students will always remember when a teacher is embarrassed and often it is the reaction of the teacher to those moments, as much as the fun they cause, that determines the relationship which develops between student and teacher. If a good relationship is built up it becomes easier for the teacher to be firm if, as sometimes happens, students get out of hand.

During the fifteen years I was in charge of the department I had many amusing experiences and sometimes embarrassing moments at the hands of the students. On 4 November 1954 my daughter Esther was born and I was due to lecture the following day. As was his custom, Donald Hay, the Chief Technician, came to my room, collected the slices for the lecture and went ahead to the lecture theatre. On this occasion when I opened the door of the lecture theatre everything was in darkness, there was no sound from the customary boisterous students. I groped my way around until I found the switch and as the lights came on, the theatre erupted to cries of 'daddy', the students had, apparently, been forewarned of our new arrival and were well prepared; potties rattled, baby bottles filled with beer were being sucked and nappies waved from all parts of the theatre. On his seat at the projection desk sat Donald Hay who was enjoying the antics and I'm sure helped to set me up. The women students occupied the front two rows of the lecture theatre and took no part in the din but enjoyed it nevertheless. The blackboard was covered in message of congratulations and after reading them I held up my hand. The noise suddenly ended and the students waited for my reaction. I thanked them for their felicitations and said I thought they were due some explanation. Dr Marshall, one of the older lady doctors in the department, was well known to the students, and I explained that for years she had been responsible for making morning coffee and, unknown to the medical staff, had been recently engaged in a research project involving an aphrodisiac drug which she put into the coffee. She had assured me, I told the students, that the professor was in the control group but like many research projects, things did not work according to plan and I found myself in the test group. I suspected that Dr Alistair Currie as well as Mr Hay had been in on the act and informed the students that they would receive a progress report on Dr Marshall's research in a month's time, and proceeded to give my lecture.

A month later Alistair's son Alex was born, and when Alistair entered the lecture theatre he was met with the same noisy show of congratulations and the same display of baby utensils. Afterwards he told me he had never experienced anything like it, and later as the noise subsided and he began to lecture, the theatre door burst open and in came one of the tallest male students dressed in a nurse's uniform. He was pushing an invalid chair in which sat a very hirsute student who was nude except for a baby's nappy which covered his lower abdomen. The invalid chair was pushed up and down in front of the ladies in the class and the 'baby' was happily sucking a beer-filled baby bottle and crying 'daddy, daddy'. The theatre was in an uproar once more, as the 'nurse' wheeled the baby up and down. In a flash Alistair held up his hand; the noise stopped suddenly as he said, 'Nurse! Your baby's nappy has come off,' and in full view of the lady students the naked 'baby' complete with beer bottle was wheeled out of the room. This was the first class of students I taught after my appointment as professor and they responded to the efforts of the staff with outstanding results at the professional examination.

Donald Hay always had a good rapport with the students and was involved with them in most of the pranks they would play. Unknown to the students, Donald usually kept me informed when something was going to happen and indeed he was often the instigator.

'They are a bit lethargic,' he would say, 'I think we had better do something to liven them up.' He would talk to the students and get from them some amusing but perfectly respectable slides of the students and their nurse girlfriends on picnic. These would be interspersed with the slides for my lecture, during which I would illustrate some point from the slide when it was projected on to the screen. As I turned towards the class Donald would show the student's slide to the great amusement of the class. I never knew if Donald told them I was in on the act.

I was keen to give the students some experience of talking before a large class, since this was something many of them would have to do later in their careers. On occasions I would select a student, bring him or her to the lecture desk and ask them to describe the features of the slide which had been projected on the screen. If they had problems I would help them and in time they enjoyed the experience once they realised they would not be made to look foolish in front of their colleagues. As they became more confident, I would ask for three volunteers to deliver one of the lectures I set aside as part of their training. This involved a great deal of preparation, as each student was given a part of the lecture and shown how to use slides to illustrate different points. They took the slides, studied them at home and each student rehearsed their part with me in my room, using a projector. They gave a confident performance and from time to time questioned their colleagues who in turn questioned them. Some years later I met a general practitioner who was actively involved with post-graduate education. One of those students had delivered a paper on some aspect of his work and after being congratulated on his presentation was asked where he had learned to prepare and deliver papers. Proudly he announced he had been one of the students in my class at Glasgow Royal Infirmary.

Like most teachers, I get great satisfaction when a former student comes to speak to me. On one occasion, when on holiday in Crete, my wife told me a man approached her in the hotel where we were staying and asked, 'Was your husband a professor in Glasgow? My wife says she was one of his students, but he won't remember her.' When next we met the lady, I looked at her and said, 'Yes, Evelyn, I do remember you.' She had been a very good student and in a class of ninety I got to know the very good students, as well as the weaker ones. These I would see regularly, try to discuss their problems and, with some students, even threaten them. The middle-of-the-class students worked away conscientiously, had good contact with their tutor, passed the examinations and had contact with me only through the lecture course. I was always delighted when, in later years, I would meet and talk with them when they would inevitably relate some of the amusing incidents that happened.

'I was in the year,' they would say, 'that arranged for a salesman to sell you an island off the west coast of Scotland,' or 'that asked the brewery to deliver two barrels of beer.' However I never found out who submitted my application form to the doctors' hobbies exhibition. On this occasion I received a phone call from a secretary at the exhibition, who said they were interested in my application form and wished to talk to me about my proposed exhibit. Immediately I sensed this was the students' work, asked what I said in the application form and explained this could be the time the students tried to outdo their predecessors. The young lady on the phone was highly amused and proceeded to read the letter describing my exhibit. Apparently I said I was interested in and involved in the technique of head-shrinking and after many years had been successful and wished to exhibit two examples of my work at the doctors' hobbies exhibition. This incident in 1959 was reported in the *Daily Express* under the headline 'Hunt is on for Shrunken Head Hoaxers', but I never learned anything further about the secret that was passed on from generation to generation of medical students.

I hope the instructions given and lessons learned in the department taught the students what help pathology could give them when faced with problems they would encounter in clinical practice. Equally I hope they remember there may be, on occasions, a need for some empiricism and that sick people need both help and understanding. The relief of pain in the terminal cancer patient, or the simple act of visiting a lonely old person even for a short time, can give an element of satisfaction which can never be measured in terms of finance. That is the satisfaction a good doctor will receive and learn to value.

CHAPTER 11

New Medical Schools
in East Africa

THE SIXTIES DECADE was a busy, exciting one and I became involved
with the new medical schools in Kenya and Tanzania, served on the
scientific committees of the Cancer Research Campaign and the Medical
Research Council in London, as well as spending a sabbatical year as Visiting
Professor to the Medical School of Stanford University in California. All
this was possible since I now had working with me an experienced group of
pathologists who could accept responsibility, yet keep me informed of what
was happening when I was away from the department.

During this decade about 2,500 medical students graduated annually from
the universities of Britain, yet only 10% of them came from the developing
Commonwealth countries; a number quite insufficient for the needs of those
countries. Sir Arthur Porritt was invited by the British government to assess
their needs of medical manpower, and the 1962 Porritt Report on Medical
Aid to Developing Countries decided it would be better to train most of the
graduates in their own country and receive financial and technical aid to do
so. The British government accepted the report and invited universities in
Britain to consider the possibility of establishing links with universities in the
developing Commonwealth countries.

At a meeting of the Faculty of Medicine of Glasgow University, the
University of East Africa was selected as a possibility since our veterinary
faculty had already established a link with the Universities of East Africa
Veterinary Faculty, which was now in Chiroma in Nairobi. The Glasgow group
was actively engaged there in an intensive retraining programme of Kenyan
veterinary surgeons.

The University of East Africa at that time was a confederation of universities in Uganda, Kenya and Tanzania: the medical faculty was in Uganda,
the science faculty in Kenya and the faculty of law in Tanzania. Along
with Professor Charles Fleming, the Dean of the Faculty of Medicine,

Glasgow, Sir Edward Wayne, Professor of Medicine and Roland Barnes, Professor of Orthopaedic Surgery, I was a member of the delegation selected to visit the constituent colleges of East Africa, examine the medical requirements of each country and report back with our recommendations. In February 1964 we flew from London to Entebbe in Uganda and thence to Kampala where we spent a week visiting each department in the Medical School in Makerere University College, which was founded in 1924. It was granting a Licentiate in Medicine by 1951 and the MB, ChB degree of the University of East Africa in 1964, the year we were there. The university was located on a beautiful campus and the medical school housed in a modern hospital with excellent, well-equipped buildings for pre-clinical research and teaching. The professors of both pre-clinical and clinical subjects were British or Commonwealth expatriates, and the standard of teaching and excellence of patient care was on a par with that of any British medical school. However, there were only forty-five students in each year and this was not sufficient to cope with the medical needs of the three countries. Naturally the medical staff of Makerere were unwilling to lower their standards to increase the numbers required by the three countries. We spent the second week in Nairobi which impressed me as a town with its bougainvillaea-lined main streets and beautiful cool, sunny climate, in contrast to the clammy, uncomfortable heat of Kampala. We met the senior consultant surgeon and physician with whom we visited the wards of Kenyatta National Hospital, which was built before the First World War and named George VI Hospital in 1951. There was some post-graduate activity and a training programme for junior hospital staff who hoped to get higher medical qualifications.

I found the laboratory cover in morbid anatomy and clinical pathology very poor and in marked contrast to what I had seen in Makerere. I did learn there was a centre in Nairobi and in Dar-es-Salaam where male medical assistants received three or four years' training to allow them to carry out a variety of medical procedures. Some of these men were very good and able to handle surgical emergencies such as caesarean sections and strangulated hernias. Their presence and value to the community had to be, but was not always, recognised when assessing the medical needs of the East African countries. I had the opportunity to see a small community dispensary in the country outside Nairobi and met the medical assistant in charge. He had with him at the clinic a nurse, midwife and sanitary officer and was able to diagnose and treat most of the outpatients who came. If he thought it necessary he would refer them to the district hospital or the Kenyatta Hospital for investigation and treatment. Once weekly an ambulance would tour the surrounding villages when the staff could examine and treat sick people or send them to the district hospital. An active immunisation programme was offered.

In 1963 the 16th Assembly of the World Health Organisation (WHO) agreed that one doctor for 10,000 of the population was the lowest acceptable ratio. In Britain and in most countries of Western Europe this ratio is about one doctor per 800 patients and in Kenya, with a population of twelve million and approximately 1,000 doctors, the ratio of 1 per 12,000 people would appear to be within the WHO lowest acceptable rate. When this is examined for urban and rural areas, the ratio in the main towns like Nairobi was one doctor per 1,500 whereas in the vast rural areas of the country the ratio was 1 in 37,000. The need for more doctors in Kenya was obvious, since nearly half of them were involved in private practice. It was left to the remainder to provide the scanty medical service for the rest of the population through the Ministry of Health, mission hospitals and city councils. This problem was re-emphasised later in the week when Professor Iain McIntyre, leader of the Glasgow University veterinary group in Nairobi, arranged for us to meet Dr Njorge Mungai, the Minister of Health, who was a medical graduate of Stanford Medical School, and keen for us to help create a medical school in Nairobi.

Each night our delegation would meet, discuss the day's work and consider the pros and cons of Kenya and Uganda. Since the medical and technical staff we would send would in most instances be accompanied by their wives and families, we considered the climate, housing and schools as well as working conditions for the staff. It was our opinion that Makerere was an excellent medical school, capable of training doctors for the community hospitals of Uganda. However, there was a genuine need to establish a medical school in Nairobi, which could be run initially by senior and junior staff in surgery, medicine, obstetrics and laboratory medicine seconded from the Glasgow University Medical School. There was a need for a new modern hospital in which future medical staff could be trained to a high academic standard so that in time they would assume clinical control of the medical school and train the necessary personnel to staff the district hospitals in Kenya.

We had decided to recommend Kenya to the medical faculty of Glasgow, but felt a duty to visit Tanzania and so we rose early on the Saturday morning to fly to Dar-es-Salaam and return that evening. It was an interesting flight to Mombasa and along the coast of East Africa to Zanzibar and Dar-es-Salaam. During the flight I recalled the days I spent as a general practitioner in Cleland, Scotland, with Dr Sanderson who had been a regional medical officer in Tanganyika, as the country was then called. I remembered the stories his wife told of the receptions they attended in the State House, and the visit of the Prince of Wales to Dar-es-Salaam. I appreciated the beauty of Oyster

Bay as we drove to the home in the Ocean Road Hospital, of the British
Medical Director, Dr Evans, whose tour of duty was finishing. We had lunch
in his house and later met the senior surgeon, a Scotsman, and a young
Australian physician, Dr Rankine, who made a great impression on us all. We
visited the wards in the hospital which was built originally by the Germans
and was used now for maternity patients. The clinical laboratories were old
but still functional and were run by an expatriate pathologist, Dr Mackie,
who was also responsible for the bacteriology, haematology and blood transfusion services for the Muhimbili Hospital. This was the main general
hospital, a few miles away, and known formerly as the Queen Elizabeth
Hospital. The distinguished German bacteriologist, Robert Koch, about whom
I have already written, brought staff from Germany to the Ocean Road
Hospital to work with him on malaria and sleeping sickness. A personally
signed photograph of Koch sat on the desk in the Ocean Road laboratories
and years later Dr Ruthven Mitchell, one of the young men I sent to
Dar-es-Salaam, arranged for it to be gifted to the local museum before, as he
said to me, it disappeared into some visitor's briefcase.

Our delegation visited the Muhimbili General Hospital which was quite
modern, and went with Dr Rankine to see the lecture rooms and laboratories
which had been constructed to take the thirty young African students who
had already begun training in the Medical School of the University of
Dar-es-Salaam. The surgeons taught them anatomy, the physician physiology,
but there was no one to teach pathology and since the clinical pathologist in
the Ocean Road Hospital was due to return to Britain, Dr Rankine informed
me their teaching programme next year was in jeopardy.

Our delegation returned to Nairobi that evening, now fully convinced that
the Glasgow effort had to be in Nairobi, but I knew within myself that I was
going to help Dr Rankine create his medical school in Tanzania and provide
a pathologist who would help him achieve this.

The Faculty of Medicine in Glasgow accepted our report, which was
received with enthusiasm by the medical staff of the University and Health
Board. This was followed by a visit to Glasgow by the Minister of Health,
Dr Mungai, when proposals for Glasgow's participation in a new medical
school in Nairobi were discussed. A WHO group then reviewed the situation
on behalf of the Kenya government and recommended a medical school
should be established in Nairobi with an initial intake of thirty students,
building up to at least one hundred per annum. Glasgow was expected to
shoulder the main teaching responsibility. It would start initially as an
extension in Nairobi of the Makerere Medical School and develop a teaching
programme for half the students who were in the final year of their studies
in Makerere and were willing to make the transfer to Nairobi.

In March 1965 the first group from the Glasgow Medical School were seconded to Nairobi and consisted of senior and junior physicians, surgeons, obstetricians and anaesthetists. The senior clinicians were professors of me- dicine and surgery and health service consultants, who had charge of wards in the Glasgow Medical School, and they remained in Nairobi for periods of three to six months.

During the period 1965–67, the Glasgow clinicians were attached to the Kenyatta Hospital as part of the Makerere College extension, and as such were guests in the wards of the local government clinical consultants, sharing with them the responsibility for student teaching and patient care.

I took over responsibility for pathology and seconded, for a period of two years, a senior lecturer, Dr Stuart Kennedy and Dr George Frank, a senior registrar, along with two technicians. Kennedy became clinical sub-dean whilst Frank upgraded the laboratory services for the clinicians and took part in the teaching programme. The Kenyatta Hospitals had not been designed for teaching and space for offices and laboratory work, as well as teaching, was at a premium. Nevertheless most of the government clinical and laboratory staff were enthusiastic participants in the teaching effort and indeed, in some specialities like ophthalmology and ear, nose and throat, teaching was carried out exclusively by local consultant staff. There were abundant patient ad- missions for teaching purposes and for the students to learn patient care. The Glasgow clinicians were all experienced teachers of undergraduate and post- graduate students and it was not surprising that the final examination performance of the first Nairobi students was the same as those who chose to remain in Makerere.

About a month after I returned to Glasgow from the delegation's visit to Dar-es-Salaam I received a letter from Dr Rankine expressing his sorrow that we had not selected Tanzania. He informed me of his determination to develop the medical school and asked for my help with pathology. After discussions with my senior colleague Hector Cameron, it was decided I would approach the Regional Health Board and ask for their help. The Board were interested in and had commitment to the Nairobi school and they readily agreed to fund a senior registrar appointment for Dar-es- Salaam. I appointed to the post an extremely talented young pathologist, Dr Slavin, who had been trained by Cameron in Stobhill Hospital, Glasgow. Slavin's appointment brought an extra bonus when I discovered his wife Brenda was a biochemist and interested in a laboratory appoint- ment in Dar-es-Salaam. During the first year the Slavins worked hard to establish a laboratory service for clinicians in the Muhimbili and Ocean Road hospitals and by the second year were ready to start the under- graduate teaching programme in pathology, bacteriology and clinical chemistry for the thirty students who were now in the third year of the medical course.

Cameron and I agreed on the need to train young Tanzanian doctors to take over, in time, the department of pathology and we proposed this to Mr Austen Shaba, Minister of Health, and Dr Charles Mtwali, the Principal Secretary to the Ministry of Health when they came to see us in Glasgow. They agreed and four young Tanzanian doctors, graduates of Makerere Medical College, were selected for this purpose. Dr Shaba, brother of the Minister, would specialise in histopathology and Dr Singh in bacteriology. They would come immediately to Glasgow and be trained to a standard that would allow them to take the primary and final examinations of the Royal College of pathologists of Britain. At the same time the other two Africans, Drs Lema and Mitoka would work with the Slavins who would prepare them for the primary part of the college examination in Dar-es-Salaam.

At the very moment Shaba and Singh were due to come to Glasgow the government of Tanzania decided not to support Singh who was not a citizen of Tanzania, and only when I appealed directly to President Nyerere was he allowed to come. Shaba and Singh in time passed the primary and final part of the college examinations and I allowed them to remain an extra year with us to learn something about research techniques which I felt would help them tackle local medical problems when they returned. At the end of the fourth year of our association with Dar-es-Salaam, Mitoka and Lema came to Glasgow, passed the primary examination of the college and after a further two years took the final examination and returned home. Unfortunately when the time came for Singh to return, he refused, and in the end it was left to Shaba, Lema and Mitoka to run the department and teach the students when my responsibility ended in 1972.

Early in my association with the medical school in Dar-es-Salaam the Minister of Health asked me to advise on the training of medical assistants and laboratory technicians and in 1966 Hector Cameron went to East Africa to look at this problem. He discussed the subject with Professor Hutt in Makerere and familiarised himself with the laboratory needs of Nairobi before proceeding to Dar-es-Salaam where, along with Slavin, he made an assessment of the laboratory services. Cameron was now intensely interested in the East Africa medical project and, when Kennedy and Frank completed their two-year tour in 1967, he was the ideal choice to develop the department in Nairobi, be available for discussion with the young pathologists in Dar-es-Sa-laam and collaborate with Hutt in Makerere in developing a common technician training programme for the three countries in the East Africa community. The scheme was based on the pattern of the old British Institute of Medical Laboratory Technology (BIMLT) diploma. Classes were held in each of the three medical schools and the examinations conducted in the three centres in turn. The scheme worked well; it was a stimulus of co-operation and an assurance of a unified standard of competence in the laboratories of the three countries. In Dar-es-Salaam it provided encouragement for both Mr Robert Mkandu, the laboratory manager, and Mr Sandau who made an outstanding contribution to running the laboratories.

In Kenya, between 1965 and 1967, planning for the new Kenyatta National Teaching Hospital was in progress. A series of Medical School Planning Committees was established and in July 1967 the Faculty of Medicine of the University College in Nairobi was inaugurated. An Australian Professor, Gordon King, was appointed Acting Dean. The first intake of twenty-six medical students began training that year. Due to the shortage of pre-clinical teachers in the medical faculty, the students were taught and shared classes with veterinary students until the new pre-clinical medical faculty building at Chiromo was opened in 1968, when practical help in biochemistry and anatomy came in the form of staff from the University of Padua in Italy.

Dr Cameron arrived in Nairobi with his family in time to see the creation of the new Faculty of Medicine. He took with him from our department in Glasgow a young pathologist, Douglas Bremner, who would continue his training in Nairobi along with the Kenyan medical graduates of Makerere whom Cameron attracted to pathology. One of our senior technicians, Alistair Reid, went with him and in due course Cameron appointed an expatriate, Tom Pringle, to be laboratory manager. Pringle had been in the forensic laboratory of the Nairobi police, had good contact with suppliers of laboratory equipment and was a valuable asset when the new temporary accommodation was hurriedly built and opened in time to receive the first group of locally trained students, when they entered the clinical stage of the medical course in 1969. In July 1968 Hector Cameron was appointed to the Foundation Chair of Pathology in the University Medical School of Nairobi. Each year I visited East Africa and as external examiner, took part in the professional examinations in pathology in Makerere, Dar-es-Salaam and Nairobi, where Cameron was training young pathologists to staff the district hospitals in Kenya. He selected two, Dr Kungu and Dr Gatei, to take over the department when he left. It was a proud moment for him towards the end of 1971 when Phase I of the New Kenyatta Hospital was opened and he showed me the new buildings. There was an extensive outpatient department with admissions hall, emergency and consultant clinics, a radiology department and students' residence and an impressive clinical science building. Hector talked to me about the excellent facilities for pathology as he showed me the new teaching laboratories he had designed to hold 100 students, the museum and medical illustrations department, and a spacious autopsy room which, he told me 'even the clinicians enjoy visiting'. The laboratories for the different branches of laboratory medicine were housed on two floors of the building and were under his administrative control. He had the responsibility of recruiting suitable staff to head the departments of clinical chemistry, haematology and bacteriology, and brought a research scientist to help him with his studies on liver and oesophageal cancer. In time he established a WHO Immunology Research and Training Centre, which became a regional centre for research into problems of importance to Kenya, such as schistosomiasis, malaria and the relationship of malnutrition to the high mortality of children with measles.

The African government staff he recruited, unlike those in the clinical disciplines, were always part of the University Faculty of Medicine and in time they became associated with the research activities of the department. Since Cameron was responsible administratively for all branches of laboratory medicine he would, as in Glasgow, integrate the teaching of all branches of pathology to medical students.

Cameron's appointment to a Chair in Pathology was followed by the creation of a Foundation Chair in Medicine to which Professor Wm. Fulton, one of the Glasgow team was appointed, and some time later, Professors Douglas Roy and Donald Gebbie respectively took over the Foundation Chairs of Surgery and Obstetrics. The medical school had more stability following those appointments and the completion of phases two and three of the New Kenyatta Hospital complex provided a tower block with 1,800 beds to meet the teaching and service requirements of the medical school.

As early as 1963, a delegation from the medical faculty of McGill University in Montreal, Canada, visited Nairobi to look at postgraduate education, and following another delegation in 1964 it was decided that McGill would help with the Nairobi project. In 1968 the first Canadian contingent arrived in Nairobi and contributed to the academic strength of the department of medicine with specialists in internal medical. In addition, McGill took over responsibility for a busy unit in paediatrics where the acute observation wards were dealing with between 3,000 and 4,000 seriously ill children and infants each month.

Medical teachers had come from many universities, motivated by their desire to help create a Kenyan medical school and brought their skills and dedication to achieve this. Indeed, in the next few years a fine medical school was developed and in spite of the frequent staff changes that occurred and the increasing numbers of students that had to be dealt with, an excellent medical training programme was carried out.

The course consisted of two pre-clinical followed by three clinical years, and was planned essentially along the same lines as in Glasgow, but adjusted to train general duty doctors to develop and run the medical services of Kenya. Community health had an important place in the curriculum when subjects relevant to the major health problems in East Africa were taught. The students had to perform many practical procedures seldom encountered now by general practitioners in Britain. They were trained to give anaesthetics, perform the type of operations they might be required to undertake later and conduct complicated deliveries and caesarean sections. In pathology they learned to be competent parasitologists, to work with the trained laboratory technicians and to be able to supervise the more straightforward laboratory investigations they might need in remote hospitals. At times they could find themselves as the only authority capable of dealing with public health problems, or in the position of having to carry out an autopsy and give help to the police on fiscal matters. Thus, in addition to an essential training in patient care, the student had an active involvement in the laboratory and mortuary as well as in the wards and clinics.

Their training following graduation continued with a compulsory year of internship under supervision in the Kenyatta or in one of the district hospitals. Professor Fulton, in an enlightened inaugural address which followed his appointment to the Chair of Medicine, emphasised the need for consultants in district hospitals to have an attachment to the professorial departments in the medical school and take part in the undergraduate and postgraduate training programmes of the departments. In this way, he argued, they would provide the standard of training required during the compulsory year of internship. If a standard of excellence in patient care and graduate training was to be established in the district and Kenyatta hospitals, the university, Fulton argued, must be represented on any committee dealing with consultant appointments which, until then, had been in the hands of government medical services.

After the intern year was completed successfully, the doctor was registered to practise medicine independently. Since the government financed the training of most graduates, they were bonded for a further three years to serve the government who could post them to any hospital in the country. In addition, the few graduates who had government support for postgraduate studies abroad had their bond extended for two additional years and on their return could be posted as the government authorities decided.

Although great progress had been made, the difficult part lay ahead if the excellence of the school was to continue when overseas help came to an end and Kenyan academic staff were trained and ready to assume responsibility for the school. I wrote to the Inter-Universities Council and suggested they should create four Commonwealth Professors, for the senior Glasgow professors who had been appointed to the Foundation Chairs in Nairobi. This, I felt, would provide more stability for the school and allow my colleagues more time to select and train suitable African graduates to take charge of the departments. Since the four had voluntarily given up secure posts in Britain they could, when their mission in Kenya was completed, be posted to any medical school in the Commonwealth where their experience grained in Kenya would be invaluable. Unfortunately my proposals were not accepted and the four stayed in Nairobi, where they selected and trained Kenyan graduates to replace them before returning to Britain.

In Britain it is customary for the best students in the year to be invited by professors to embark on an academic career, and invariably the student looks on this as a privilege. The same would apply in Kenya once the medical school had been established with Kenyans in charge, but in the beginning, without the tradition of academic medicine, this did not necessarily apply. Indeed it did take time before the government and university worked together to achieve this. Naturally the government regarded the new emerging medical graduates as vital in meeting the needs of the country, and it was essential for the university to impress on the government that an apparent superfluous staffing of the academic departments of the Kenyatta Hospital was necessary, not only for patient care but to teach the future doctors of Kenya and train the young graduates who were emerging from the medical school. Likewise, those young graduates would find the training laborious and the remuneration of academic medicine vastly inferior to what they could earn in private medicine once their bond period was over.

Professor Fulton continually emphasised the need to train future academics and deplored the fact that in 1970 only two Kenyans were in training in each of the departments of medicine, surgery and obstetrics and one in paediatrics. Since the first Kenyan graduates would not qualify until 1972, the seven under training graduated either in Makerere or in Britain. His warning must have had an effect, and in 1973 Nairobi graduates had begun postgraduate training; two Kenyans were now professors, six held positions as senior lecturers and twenty-seven were lecturers or research fellows. The Nairobi medical school was well on the way to controlling its own destiny and each year would produce ninety doctors for the country, yet both Cameron and Fulton were emphatic that the increase in population in Kenya in the ensuing years would mean that the doctor-to-patient ratio would remain at 1:12,000. Economically there is little justification for another medical school, but there is every reason to develop and enlarge the medical assistant and technician training programme which could, with minimal medical help, play an important role in the care of the population in the rural areas of Kenya.

In Tanzania, unlike Kenya, the medical school had been created before I became involved and here the staff I sent were government, not university employees, who nevertheless were responsible for undergraduate teaching as well as their numerous government laboratory responsibilities. Dr Slavin carried out those duties to great acclaim. After two years he returned to my department in Glasgow, remaining until 1969 when he became head of the pathology department in the Medical Research Council's (MRC) Hospital at Northwick Park in London. A few years later he was appointed Professor of Pathology at St Bart's Hospital in London. He was succeeded by Dr Ruthven Mitchell, another of my excellent young pathologists. Mitchell had taken an honours degree in physiology, worked with me each summer when he was taking the medical degree and later became a member of the staff. As an experienced pathologist with training in physiology he was an ideal candidate to take over the laboratories in Tanzania and teach in the medical school.

When the teaching programme and diagnostic laboratory services were running to his satisfaction, Mitchell was able to turn his attention to the laboratory requirements of hospitals in other parts of the country. On one of my visits we flew in a small Cessna aircraft to Arusha where we met the Regional Medical Officer who took us to see the magnificent site and some of the buildings of the new Kilimanjaro Medical Centre which, I understand, has now been opened and is an outstanding success. Mitchell was always available to doctors from the up-country hospitals and mission hospitals who sought his help, and his house in Oyster Bay was a haven for them when they visited the capital.

There was a need for a new pathology centre at the Muhimbili Hospital and it was during Mitchell's tenure of office that Professor Geigy from the Geigy Foundation in Switzerland induced the Swiss government to commission architects to build the new department. Dr Herman Lehman, the WHO adviser in haemoglobinopathies spent some time with Mitchell and on his return to London wrote to me in glowing terms of the work 'this young man was doing and the help he had been'. Mitchell in turn had met someone who had excited and inspired in him an interest in blood diseases. At the beginning of the health service in Britain my young assistants learned to accept responsibility when they helped to develop the emerging laboratory services in Lanarkshire. Now it was a delight for me to see the incredible achievements of Slavin and Mitchell in developing the teaching and laboratory services of the medical school and assessing the needs of the hospitals in Tanzania.

As Mitchell's two-year tour was coming to an end, I had to find a replacement for him. The morning I was due to fly to Africa to take part in the professional examinations in Nairobi and Dar-es-Salaam and meet

President Nyerere to discuss future developments, my wife discovered a swelling in her breast. I examined her, found the tumour was moveable and made her promise to see a surgical colleague that day. I knew she was worried but would not let me cancel my visit which was one of the least pleasant I made to Africa.

When I arrived in Dar-es-Salaam, Mitchell and his wife informed me there was now a great deal of anti-British propaganda in the local papers and they felt this would not make it easy for me to induce the next member of my staff to come with his family to Tanzania. 'I think,' said Mitchell, 'you should take this up with the President when you meet him.' I had met Nyerere in the State House on many occasions and, after discussing the progress of the medical school and the need for a new laboratory in the Muhimbili Hospital, I took up the question of the newspapers with him.

'You don't want to pay attention to what the papers say,' was his reply. 'You know what happened to the Archbishop of Canterbury when his ship docked in New York harbour. The American press came on board to interview him and the first question they asked was, 'Archbishop, will you be visiting a night club when you are here?' to which he replied, 'Are there any night clubs in New York?' Next morning the headline in the New York papers read, "Archbishop's first question on arriving in New York – are there nightclubs in New York?" 'Now,' said the President, 'you don't take too much notice of the papers' comments.' I was to learn from this that it is not what you say to the papers, but what they say to you. Nevertheless, news of anti-British publicity had reached the department in Glasgow and the bacteriologist who was interested in a period in Tanzania informed me he was unwilling to go with his family.

During my visits to Tanzania I had never visited any of the game reserves and on this occasion the government authorities had arranged for me to spend a few days in the Serengeti. I explained to them about my wife and returned to Glasgow as soon as my business was completed. On arrival in London I phoned home to find Margaret was in hospital, the operation scheduled for that afternoon and a frozen section had been arranged. I went immediately from the airport in Glasgow to the hospital and was very relieved to find the tumour was a simple one and Margaret was well; the week I had been out of the country was a great worry for her. She had seen the surgeon who was non-committal about the nature of the tumour and refused to operate until I came home. 'You know what this could be and the operation I might be required to perform,' he told her.

She had read all about breast cancer in the books in our house and if the tumour was malignant, was worried about what would happen to our daughter Esther, who was only fourteen. Those are the thoughts that haunt women when they find a swelling in the breast so it is essential that an early diagnosis of the lesion should be made and, if the tumour is malignant, the patient can be prepared to meet the problem. Women are not only concerned about their own illness and future, but how their illness will affect the family and whether they will be spared to see their family grow up and be settled in life.

I was having difficulty finding a replacement for Mitchell when Dr Colin Anderson, one of my assistants told me he would like to help in Tanzania. Colin was born in Argentina of Scottish parents who went from Paisley in the early twenties to work in Buenos Aires. Colin graduated from medical school there, became interested in pathology and spent five years training in our department. He had passed the final examination of the Royal College of Pathology and was due to return to Argentina when he offered to help in Tanzania. Like his predecessors, Colin was a great success. He ran the diagnostic laboratory, taught medical students and, with his wife and young family, spent three years in Tanzania. He saw the three Tanzanians return to take over the new pathology centre that Professor Geigy had organised in the Muhimbili hospital. Since the Germans had controlled Tanzania at one time, Anderson made contact with the West German government and induced them to provide the finance to equip the new laboratories. Thus although Dr Geigy had built the pathology centre with help from the Swiss govern⁄ ment, the West Germans equipped it. I trained the Tanzanian staff in Glasgow and my three assistants, with great distinction, helped to create the new medical school in Dar⁄es⁄Salaam.

Whereas the senior expatriate academic staff in the medical school in Kenya were given professional titles, the young pathologists I sent to Tanzania were in the employment of the government. Although they all carried teaching responsibilities in the medical school, they were given no recognition for their efforts by the university. Indeed on my last visit to Tanzania to take part in the professional examination in pathology I was disturbed to find the university had appointed a young inexperienced pathologist from Bulgaria to run the teaching, and although Anderson helped him, he no longer took part in the examinations. By then the first batch of medical students had graduated, the young Tanzanian doctors had returned to take over the department and my commitment to the medical school I helped to create was ended. Dr Rankine, the driving force and creator of the school had departed, his task completed. Of my three assistants, Slavin is now Professor of Pathology at St Bart's Medical School, London; Mitchell conti⁄ nued his interest in blood diseases and is now Director of the Glasgow and West of Scotland Blood Transfusion Service, while Anderson is Professor of Pathology in the University of London, Ontario, Canada. It was a great disappointment to me that the University of Tanzania had not shown its gratitude to those three men by conferring on them an honorary degree; it is not too late to do so even now.

CHAPTER 12

The Marsden Hospital and Institute of Cancer Research Site Visit

ALTHOUGH THE University and Health Board were responsible for the salaries of clinical, technical and secretarial staff of the department, I was very dependent on winning support from grant-giving bodies in this country and in the United States to finance much of my research. Consequently, in the 1950s and 1960s I gained a great deal of experience in writing and submitting grant applications.

My first success was winning a project grant for three years from the Scottish Hospital Endowment Research Trust (SHERT). This was extended for another three years and was complemented by a project grant from the Cancer Research Campaign (CRC) in London. As my research progressed, a lucrative five-year programme grant was awarded by the National Institute of Arthritis and Metabolic Diseases of America. This allowed me to purchase an expensive high-resolution electron microscope as well as radioactive counting equipment and provided me with sufficient money to pay the salaries of new young scientific and technical staff. Our adrenal research had progressed to such an extent that in the mid-1960s I applied for and was awarded substantial group support from the Medical Research Council (MRC) in London. This was a very important five-year grant since the MRC would not consider an application for group support unless the university agreed at the end of five years to accept responsibility for funding it, if the group application was successful. In my case the University of Glasgow was not required to fund my group, since the MRC extended support for another five years when I moved to London.

In the late sixties and early seventies I served on the scientific committees of the Scottish Hospital Endowment Research Trust, the Cancer Research Campaign and Medical Research Council and gained valuable insight into the working of those committees, how grant applications were assessed and what constituted a good and a bad grant application.

I was appointed to the Medical Research Council in the final year of Sir Harold Himsworth's tenure of office and became a member of the Council's Biological Research Board where grant applications were assessed. The members of all grant-awarding bodies are senior academics and the appointments made so that most fields of biological science are covered by someone on the research board who can speak with authority on each grant application. In addition, the permanent medical officers of Council will send a copy of the grant application to one or two acknowledged authorities on the subject of the grant and his or her report is available when the Board meets. The Biological Research Board met once monthly and about ten days before the meeting I would receive a copy of each three-year project and five-year programme application, along with a request to talk at the meeting on one or two of the applications. Two and sometimes three members of the board were detailed to express an opinion on the same application, after which the rest of the committee would be free to give their views or question any point. The Secretary of Council would read the external experts' comments and opinions and, after further discussion, members of the board would decide whether to recommend or reject the application. However, it was up to Council, at their next meeting, to decide if the successful application could or could not be funded.

The Medical Research Council has an outstanding record of encouraging young biomedical scientists to develop their creativity and has established many research units directed by outstanding men and women in hypertension, virology, reproductive biology, endocrinology, molecular biology and many others throughout the country. Some of those units are situated in medical schools and universities and all are financed exclusively by Council. The units are visited on a quinquennial basis by council members, when the research work of the unit is assessed and a decision taken to recommend continued support or terminate the unit. I took part in a number of site visits to Medical Research Council units when the scientists were given the opportunity to talk about their work, elaborate on certain aspects of it and describe what they proposed to do. They, in turn, were questioned on their research and on how productive it was; sometimes they had to justify why a particular line of study should be continued.

In June 1969 I was a member of the committee which represented the interests of the Medical Research Council and Cancer Research Campaign and spent three days on a site visit to the Institute of Cancer Research whose departments were located at Fulham Road, London, at Sutton (Surrey) and Pollards Wood, Chalfont St Giles, Buckinghamshire. The Institute was supported by a block grant from the two bodies and in 1969 the grant was in excess of two million pounds. I knew the Institute began as the department of pathology and cancer research when Dr William Marsden created his Free Cancer Hospital in 1851, and I was interested to discover why the Institute was now on three sites and what had brought this about. On many occasions I visited the pathology department of the Royal Marsden Hospital for meetings of the British Testicular Tumour Panel. We dined in the boardroom of the hospital and on each occasion I was attracted by the fine illuminated portraits by H. W. Pickersgill of the man, Dr William Marsden, who had founded not one, but two hospitals which would become famous in the world of medicine and science. I learned there was a picture in the entrance to the Royal Free Hospital and Medical School in Grays Inn Road, which Marsden had founded in 1828 for poor sick women. The painting depicts him holding in his arms a sick young woman who was dying of acute syphilis. At that time London slums rotted with depravity and disease and admission to hospital was in the hands of the governors who doled out letters to the unfortunate patients. Without the letters, hospital admission was impossible and death would often take place in the street. Although Marsden was trained in St Bartholomew's Hospital, he had no subscribers' line and was unable to gain admission to the hospital for the girl. He found her lodgings for the night but she was dead when he returned to see her the following morning. Incensed by such inhumanity he decided to create his own free hospital and carried out his task with skill, enthusiasm and determination, against opposition from colleagues who were envious of his success and took every opportunity to try to discredit him and his successful free hospital. He faced up to opposition from influential surgeons and from the College of Surgeons, in striving to maintain a standard of service and ethics for his Free Hospital, and on very many occasions he made considerable financial sacrifices for its success. In all this he had great support from his wife, who saw less and less of him, until her health began to fail. Although she was seen by surgical and medical colleagues, the cancer she had developed was diagnosed late in the illness and her pain had to be dosed with laudanum until she died in 1846. He brooded over his wife's suffering and the lack of information on the nature, cause and cure of the disease that had taken her. While he married again the following year, his attention turned inexorably to cancer and he determined to set up a new free cancer hospital; this he achieved with less frustration, though at times with limited financial resources.

A number of influential friends met in his home in Lincoln's Inn Fields in February 1851 and agreed to help him create what was to become the first specialist cancer hospital in the world. It was devoted to the free treatment of poor people with cancer, and to attempts to find a cure for the ravages of this distressing illness. Cancer patients at that period could be admitted to the wards of general hospitals where provision to treat them was inadequate, yet most surgeons saw no need for a specialised hospital. When Marsden requested Queen Victoria to become a benefactor, she refused. Nevertheless within three months of the initial meeting in his home, the Free Cancer Hospital opened at 1 Cannon Row, Westminster, where only outpatients were seen. A year later six in-patient beds were provided, but so great was the demand that an in-patient facility to accommodate twenty patients was opened at Holywood Road, West Brompton in October 1852. Again for lack of funds, only six beds were filled initially.

The year 1856 was an important one in the history of the hospital when the committee purchased and built on part of the hospital's present site in Fulham Road. The hospital was a very beautiful building with six wards and eighty beds, but only half of them were used, until the public became conscious of the need to support this special hospital which was providing much needed help, care and support for cancer patients. The Queen, noting the hospital's success and popularity, now became a benefactor and donated one hundred pounds. This encouraged others to subscribe and in 1864 finance became available to allow all eighty beds to be used. Marsden, who died in January 1867, had lived long enough to see his Free Cancer Hospital established in Fulham Road, where his philosophy of care for the poor with cancer would be carried on by his son, Alexander, and by the generations of successors who would become part of the staff of his cancer hospital.

In 1878 another part of the hospital site was acquired and a year later all outpatients were seen at Fulham Road. Two new wings were added on either side of the original central hospital building so that by 1883 there were one hundred and twenty beds. The following year the administration offices and boardroom were sited in the Fulham Road Hospital; all necessary activities of the Free Cancer Hospital were now on one site.

Since its creation in 1851 the name of the hospital has undergone a number of changes. Marsden was determined that patients with cancer would receive treatment free of charge and the word 'free' was included in the name of the hospital – Free Cancer Hospital. In the short period when letters of introduction were needed the 'free' was dropped from the title but was revived in 1864 to read 'Cancer Hospital (Free)', and this name was used until 1910 when King George V granted a Royal Charter of Incorporation and the hospital became known as 'The Cancer Hospital (Free)'. In 1936 King Edward VIII commanded that thenceforward the hospital should be 'The Royal Cancer Hospital (Free)'. It was a fitting tribute to the vision, compassion and industry of its creator that one hundred years after Marsden had established it in Fulham Road, the name should be changed once more to become the 'Royal Marsden Hospital' in his honour.

The annual surgeon's report signed by Marsden gives some idea of his philosophy on the treatment of the sick poor afflicted by the disease. Nothing was withheld if it was for the benefit of the patient, who was watched carefully to the end of the illness. Although most patients were seen when the disease was well advanced, all received medical care and attention was paid to their diet. Some patients had surgery in an attempt to eradicate the disease and a few cures were recorded. If, as usually happened, those measures failed, efforts were made to alleviate any severe pain experienced by the patient. Marsden's philosophy and care of patients is the basis of modern holistic or whole body treatment of patients with terminal cancer, and the concern that he showed for the care and dignity of those patients still persists to this day in the hospital he founded.

Marsden travelled, at the hospital committee's request, to several larger medical and surgical institutions in Paris and Brussels where he found no general agreement on the treatment of cancer. Patients were treated either by surgery or medicine and if neither was relevant, the illness was considered incurable and they were sent home to die. Since Marsden was qualified both as a physician and surgeon, this was contrary to his belief that surgery and medicine could, in some patients, be complementary and he paid attention to patients' dietary needs which were neglected completely in the institutions he visited. The medical treatment he used was entirely empirical and the multiple obscure, alleged medical cures submitted to the hospital by the public were tested. One 'cure' used by cancer quacks was the application of caustic paste to growths whether they were benign or malignant. The tumours would swell up, turn black and slough, leaving a large, raw, ulcerated area. In time the area, from which a simple tumour disappeared, healed and this was regarded as a cure for something that in fact was simple and needed no attention. The cancer quacks charged extortionate fees, sometimes hundreds of pounds for this treatment. For the unfortunate victim whose cancer was malignant, the patient in the end suffered protracted torture, and those lucky enough to come to the free newer hospital were treated for the pain with drugs and compassion. Eventually the hospital committee had to decide against testing so-called cures.

Whereas medicine had little to offer as a cure, surgery was used sparingly, being in its infancy. However, it was ready, as we shall see, to explode onto the scene as a potential cure for cancer. In those days when patients had surgery without an anaesthetic, many died from post-operative shock. Those who survived would succumb later to haemorrhage from bleeding vessels and worst of all from hospital gangrene. Surgery in the free cancer hospital was used reluctantly. Indeed no surgeon was allowed to operate on a patient in the hospital without the written consent of one of his colleagues, the consent being recorded in a book kept for this purpose. This rule was repealed only in 1911 when 'each surgeon was made responsible for the treatment, operative or other, of every patient under his care'.

When in 1846 ether anaesthesia was introduced in America by Morton, the first step was taken to prevent post-operative shock, and in that year Morton anaesthetised a young man who had a large tumour removed pain-lessly from his neck. A year later in Edinburgh, Simpson introduced chloroform as an anaesthetic and now the limiting factor to surgical progress was not lack of anaesthetic, but post-operative haemorrhage and hospital sepsis, which was caused by fulminating wound infection followed by septi-caemia, the feared hospital gangrene. Indeed at that period it was safer to operate in a patient's home rather than in hospital, and so patients were reluctant to go to hospital for surgery.

During the period in which Marsden was building his cancer hospital in Fulham Road, scientific research was being carried out in Paris by Pasteur and in Glasgow by Lister, and their results could have revolutionised the surgical approach to cancer. Joseph Lister, who became Professor of Surgery at Glasgow Royal Infirmary in 1860, had from 1854 been working on methods of preventing fatal post-operative haemorrhage and hospital gangrene. Be-tween 1857 and 1867 when Marsden's hospital was being built, he wrote a detailed account of inflammation, and how infection occurred during oper-ation from microbes or germs carried by the surgeon on his hands, his clothes, the surgical instruments he used, or from infected air in the hospital wards. Lister's work was based on studies by Pasteur, the distinguished French bacteriologist, and on his own experimental work which he demonstrated to his class of medical students.

During that period Pasteur proved that putrefaction, so common in the wounds of patients after surgery, was caused by microbes or germs and was not the result of spontaneous generation as was still believed by most surgeons.

Lister solved the problem of post-operative haemorrhage by using germ-free ligatures made from sheep gut which he treated with a solution of carbolic acid, and he controlled wound infection by excluding germs from the site of the operation. After washing, his hands were immersed in a weak solution of carbolic acid, and until they were required, his surgical instruments were kept in a carbolic acid solution. Initially during operation a carbolic acid spray was used to control infection in the air of the operation theatre, but this caused such discomfort to the skin and lungs of the theatre staff that the spray was discontinued. At the end of the operation the surgical wound was covered by a carbolic-impregnated gauze dressing so that germs in the air could not reach the wound. His dressing consisted of eight layers of clean sterilised gauze saturated with carbolic acid. A strip of mackintosh was inserted between the seventh and eighth layers to keep the germs from reaching the wound, and an impermeable silk protective placed between the skin and the bandage to control the irritant effect of the carbolic. The ability to control post-operative haemorrhage and infection allowed Lister to deal successfully with more extensive operations and to undertake internal operations, which until now had been impossible; and in March 1867 *The Lancet* published his classic paper on 'The Antiseptic Principle in the Practice of Surgery'. Although this was published two months after Marsden's death, I find it surprising that someone with Marsden's vision, who had travelled extensively abroad, was unaware of Lister's work and did not see the potential of antiseptic surgery in treating patients not only with easily accessible tumours but cancers within the body, from which his wife had suffered and whose death had caused him so much pain and anguish. He had a passion for cleanliness and his new wards and operation theatre would be ideal places in which to use Lister's antiseptic treatment and the new-found means of delivering anaesthetics. It is doubtful if Marsden in his younger days would have failed to exploit those new ideas. However, it must be remembered that London surgeons did not accept Lister's antiseptic techniques until he became Professor of Surgery at King's College Hospital (London) in 1876 and even in 1879 when he opened into the tissues of the knee to wire the two ends of a fractured patella, leading surgeons proclaimed he should be sued for malpractice. Four years later the same men acclaimed his work, when he demonstrated before them six patients whose patella operations had been successful.

Nevertheless the antiseptic technique had its defects, carbolic acid was a severe irritant to the surgeon's hands and older surgeons, unconvinced of the existence of germs, carried out Lister's antiseptic technique in a very unsatisfactory manner. Lister was adamant that his method had to be followed meticulously and decided it was by teaching and training young surgeons that his methods would be followed and advances in surgical technique made possible. Indeed this proved to be the case and the aseptic technique used today was developed in the latter part of the nineteenth century by the students Lister taught as well as by German surgeons. This antiseptic technique was short-lived but it opened the door to the scientific approach of modern surgery.

Marsden's cancer hospital, with certain well-defined conditions, did undertake cancer surgery and in 1869 a 'chloroformist' was appointed to the staff. It was only in 1897 that the name was changed to 'anaesthetist'.

In 1887 technical advances in aseptic surgery induced surgeons in the free cancer hospital to operate on patients with tumours in the abdominal cavity and so wards and a new operation theatre were designed and constructed to minimise hospital infection. The surgical work of the hospital increased. It became an important tool in cancer treatment and additional staff were appointed. Mr Charles Ryall (1897) was senior surgeon and Mr W. E. Miles (1899) assistant surgeon, and in time both men would become world leaders in cancer surgery, playing an important role in developing other hospital facilities. Advances in surgical techniques followed their appointment and in time specialist surgical units were created to deal with the different types of cancer now being seen in the hospital. Surgery could now effect a cure if the disease was seen and diagnosed at an early stage of the illness, and this led in 1902 to the installation of an x-ray diagnosis machine and the appointment of the first radiologist to the hospital. The surgeons wanted to know if the tumour they removed was simple or malignant, was it confined to the organ from which it arose, had it spread outside the organ and was there evidence of distant spread or metastasis? This was important in assessing the outlook or prognosis for the patient.

It was now time to see what was happening in the department of pathology and cancer research which Marsden had created in 1856 when he installed as the pathological anatomist, Dr Robert Knox, who had been associated with the notorious body snatchers, Burke and Hare, in Edinburgh. Marsden would have had no scruples about appointing Knox, since he himself had spent many hours in the Anatomical School of Joshua Brookes in London, where he dissected bodies which he must have known were procured by resurrectionists. At any rate, Knox was an accomplished anatomist and an excellent teacher who created a museum of specimens which he obtained at post-mortem or from the operations that were performed. He prepared drawings of the external appearance of the tumours he encountered. On his death in 1862, no successor was appointed and his duties in pathology were undertaken by the surgeons; this at a time when a virtual revolution was taking place in the concept of disease. For over 2,000 years disease was believed to result from faulty mixing of the four bodily humours; the concept of humoral pathology ended with the discovery of the microscope and its use both by the great German pathologist Muller and by Virchow, who showed that the organs of the body were made up of cells which were changed in diseases. This concept of cellular pathology offered a new parameter with which to study disease and many publications began to appear on the cellular nature of tumours and the tendency of some tumours to spread to adjacent lymph glands and elsewhere in the body. The logical question being asked was what made it a cancer cell, and many theories began to appear in the literature, of which two took preference. In the 'tumour germ' theory, cancer arose in a cell which had a tumour germ, the cells multiplied and spread by the action of an agent which excited the cells. The supporters of the tumour-germ theory believed the recurrence of tumour some time later at the site of operation and the occurrence of tumour many years later at a site distant from the original growth supported their tumour-germ theory. But what was the agent that initiated this change?

It would appear that the free cancer hospital made no contribution to this controversy until 1889 when Dr H. G. Plimmer became head of the department of pathology and cancer research. Bacteriology was recognised now as an important discipline in medicine, and infectious diseases such as tuberculosis, typhoid fever and others were found to be caused by bacteria. Naturally attention was directed to a 'cancer organism' as a cause of the disease and Plimmer was one of the main protagonists of a parasitic theory. He described round bodies about 0.004 mm in diameter found in the cells of tumours removed at operation, and in tumour cells that he kept viable in serum and examined under the microscope. Although Plimmer's parasitic theory stimulated interest in Germany and in America, the round bodies were never identified as any specific parasite. When he resigned in 1903 many members of the medical staff of the hospital became unhappy with the lack of progress being made in cancer research and questioned the role of the pathology and cancer research department in the hospital. In the ensuing years sometimes one man would be in charge of both parts of the department, then changes would be made and one person would head pathology and another direct cancer research. The death from cancer of two members of the Royal family and the increasing public awareness and fear of the disease concentrated the minds of members of the hospital committee. In 1909 they began to rebuild and adequately equip the department of pathology and cancer research within the grounds of the hospital. Dr Alexander Paine was appointed the first director of the department which was named the *Cancer Hospital Research Institute* and opened officially in 1911. It is generally accepted that the Institute of Cancer Research had its origin in this new department. Paine organised the building of the new Institute, saw to the equipment and, of equal importance, induced the committee to create appointments for assistants in those scientific disciplines he felt would contribute most to cancer research. He devoted many years to a study of the clinical and pathological manifestations of cancer in man and animals. He concluded that cancer is not a specific parasitic disease but is a disordered growth of the cell which follows a chronic inflammatory reaction produced when the cell is damaged by physical agents such as x-rays, or by the chemicals in pitch, petroleum or soot. In fact, Paine's contribution to cancer research was minimal, but he brought into the department men like Kettle and Nicholson who in time would become leaders in the field of tumour pathology and whose text books on the subject were still in use when I was training in pathology. Paine provided the surgeons with an expert diagnostic tumour service and the combination of x-ray diagnosis and tumour pathology improved the outlook for the cancer patient by drawing attention to the need to see the patient as early as possible in the illness when the tumour was more likely to be localised and a cure effected.

At the turn of the century another parameter became available for the treatment of cancer. The hospital received a small amount of radium and studies began into the effect of x-rays and gamma-rays on malignant disease. When Dr Robert Knox took over the radiology department in 1910 he controlled x-ray diagnosis, x-ray therapy and radium treatment. Due to his efforts radiotherapy progressed and a new form of treatment was added to that of surgery. Although a radium department was formed in 1929, the logical step of combining radium and x-ray therapy into a department of radiotherapy did not take place until 1944. X-ray diagnosis remained a separate department within the hospital and the Chair of Radiology which had been created in the hospital in 1930 and was the first of its kind in the University of London, now became the Chair of Radiotherapy.

Initially the therapeutic use of x-rays and radium was empirical and the part-time physicist Major C. E. S. Phillips was appointed, who carried out pioneer work on the measurement of x-rays and radioactive substances. The important role for physics in radiotherapy was established in 1926 when a full-time physicist, Mr W. V. Mayneord was appointed; within two years an international standard dose had been agreed. Initially medical physics was in the department of radiology until a separate department was created in the hospital under a university reader. In 1940 a Chair of Physics was formed by the University and Mayneord became Director of Physics applied to Medicine. In addition to his outstanding contributions to medical physics, he played an important role in determining the nature of the first chemical carcinogen which was now the main research interest of the organic chemists and biochemists in the Cancer Hospital Research Institute. We can now look at the circumstances which directed the scientists into this line of work which was to bring world acclaim to the Institute.

As far back as 1775, Sir Percival Pott, a surgeon at St Bartholomew's Hospital, London, attributed the high incidence of scrotal cancer in chimney sweeps to the soot the boys encountered while climbing the chimneys. Many years would elapse before the Japanese scientists, Yamagiawa and Ichikawa between 1915 and 1918 produced cancer on the ears of rabbits by repeated applications of coal tar. At this time Dr Paine was Director of the Research Institute and in 1920 his appointment was terminated. He was replaced by Dr Alexander Leitch who had been a house surgeon at the hospital and had gained experience in cancer research elsewhere before returning to the hos, pital. He was actively involved in studies on industrial carcinogenesis, published papers showing that lubricants derived from shale oil were carci, nogenic when applied to animal skin, and suggested that chemicals in the lubricants were possibly the cause of mule,spinners' cancer found in workers in the Lancashire mills. In 1922 he brought Ernest Kennaway into his department as a chemical pathologist and together they searched for the chemical substance in tar which could be responsible for cancer induction in animals. Could it be arsenic which was present in small quantities in coal tar? Indeed they published a paper showing that arsenic could produce animal skin cancers. At the same time Kennaway discovered that cancer,producing tars exhibited the property of fluorescence when exposed to ultraviolet light. Whatever the nature of the chemical compound it could convert the invisible short ultraviolet waves into large visible ones and the chemical responsible would fluoresce in the dark. Kennaway was now joined by his physics colleague Mayneord who showed that the ultraviolet spectrum of those tars was usually characteristic, and since arsenic did not fluoresce in the ultraviolet, it was not the culprit.

Just as Lister's antiseptic surgical technique developed from Pasteur's germ theory and a knowledge of the use of carbolic acid to treat the sewers in Carlisle, Kennaway's discovery of the first chemical carcinogen began when Bloch in Zurich adduced evidence that the chemical substance in tar might be a complex hydrocarbon consisting of three or more molecules. Between 1924 and 1929 Kennaway was joined in the Institute by a talented group of organic chemists who carried out an extensive programme of synthetic chemistry, and the pure hydrocarbons they prepared were tested for their fluorescence spectra and carcinogenicity in animals. During this period in the Institute, Hieger synthesised the compound 1:2,benzanthracene which had the characteristic spectra but was not carcinogenic in animals. However in 1929 Clar described the synthesis of the related hydrocarbon 1:2:5:6 dibenzanthracene and when this compound was prepared by Institute chem, ists, it was found to be fluorescent and carcinogenic. In June 1932 Kennaway and his colleagues Cook, Hieger and Mayneord reported to the Royal Society in London the first induction of cancer by a pure chemical substance. This polycyclic aromatic hydrocarbon showed undiminished carcinogenic activity even when highly purified. Now the logical step was to determine the nature of the carcinogenic compound or compounds in coal tar and this study began with alcohol extraction of two tons of pitch. In an article to the *British Medical Journal* in 1955, Kennaway describes the part each of his colleagues played in identifying the carcinogenic compound and the 'single thread that led through the labyrinth' was that those compounds would have the characteristic fluorescence spectrum of the benzanthracene compound they had synthesised. In 1933 Cook, Hieger and Hewitt isolated from pitch the compound 3:4 benzpyrene, established its structure by synthesis and showed it to be a potent carcinogen for mouse skin. I knew Cook, who became Professor of Chemistry in Glasgow when I was a student in chemistry, and Colin Hewitt when he was Director of the Organon laboratories in Lanark, shire. Colin became interested in my adrenal research and provided me with the crude and purified ACTH I used in my work. Dr Leitch, who had initiated the studies on chemical carcinogenesis, did not live long enough to see the work completed. He died in 1931, but two years previously the University of London recognised his experimental work and made him Professor of Experimental Pathology.

Ernest Kennaway was appointed Director of the Cancer Hospital Research Institute in 1931 and in the years that followed many hydrocarbons were tested for their carcinogenic activity. These substances are widely distributed in our environment, being formed when most carbon-containing substances are burnt, and so are present in the air we breathe, the tobacco smoke we inhale and in the cooked meat we eat. While the studies on hydrocarbons have helped clarify the cause of some occupational cancers, they did not provide the answer to the origin of human cancer. Kennaway's studies had led to a new era in cancer research when new carcinogenic chemicals were detected. Chemists attempted to relate the structure of a compound with its carcinogenic activity, biologists and biochemists studied the means by which the body might inactivate the carcinogen and render it safe, and experimental pathologists looked at the role of animals in testing for chemical carcinogens.

There was a need for larger premises and more sophisticated equipment for Kennaway to continue his work, and in 1939 the Cancer Hospital Research Institute moved about two hundred yards along Fulham Road to new quarters in the red brick building which had been the Freemasons' Hospital. This move was made possible by the benefaction of Sir Alfred Chester Beatty, whose name is now incorporated in the title. The inscription in gold letters across the face of the building reads 'Chester Beatty Research Institute' and, to show its origin from Marsden's hospital, are the words 'Cancer Hospital (Free)'.

When Sir Ernest Kennaway retired in 1946, Alexander Haddow became Director of the Chester Beatty Research Institute. Under him studies on chemical carcinogenesis continued, more scientists and technicians were employed and foreign research workers both from the United States and from countries in Eastern Europe came on scholarships to work in the Chester Beatty. In the jubilee year of the opening of the Cancer Hospital Research Institute in 1911, an extension was made into an adjacent building which was linked to the old one on four floors. The extension provided fine animal house accommodation and laboratories for biology, organic chemistry, physical chemistry, immunology and cytogenetics, as well as a conference hall to seat one hundred and eighty. The old building was remodelled to provide excellent library facilities. In addition, the Chester Beatty Institute had acquired an experimental station at Pollards Wood, Chalfont St Giles, Buckinghamshire where work on biological mutation, tracer biochemistry, nucleic acid and protein chemistry was done. Later a special germ-free animal colony was created and housed in a modern building.

The Chester Beatty, by which name it was well-known in the science world, had begun as a compact Cancer Hospital Research Institute in the grounds of the Cancer Hospital (Free) and was now widely dispersed, a move which would make effective control of the research difficult and lead to reduplication of effort. During Haddow's stewardship another important treatment parameter, in the form of chemotherapy, was added to surgery and radiotherapy in the treatment of cancer, and the Chester Beatty was ideally suited to play a prominent role in its development. Chemists in the Institute prepared new drugs and the department of biochemical pharmacology had the expertise to assess the toxicity of the drugs in animal models that had been developed in the Institute. Chemotherapeutic agents such as Myleran, Chlorambucil and Melphalan were prepared in the Chester Beatty and used in the treatment of different types of leukaemia. The introduction of chemotherapy increased the need to have physicians with an attachment to both Hospital and Institute, and in 1962 a small Clinical Research Department was created.

There was also a need to expand the accommodation for radiotherapy and physics. The equipment available to treat patients was becoming more and more sophisticated and expensive to run, and space for expansion at the Royal Marsden in Fulham Road was limited. Due to the drive and enthusiasm of Professor Sir David Smithers, the departments of radiotherapy, physics and the radiology unit moved to new accommodation in a large open site in the country at Sutton, Surrey, where Sir David built, with government funds, a modern hospital with one hundred and fifty beds. This allowed space for some redevelopment of radiotherapy in the hospital at Fulham Road, which still retained a radiology and physics department as well as pathology and biochemistry which remained there when the Chester Beatty Institute was formed in 1939. Over the years research was undertaken into the effects of radiation on normal and malignant cells to ascertain how radiation affected the delicate mechanism which controls the cell cycle during cell division. Departments of biophysics and radiobiology were created for those studies at Sutton. Just as the Cancer Hospital Research Institute of 1909 had become the Chester Beatty Institute in 1939 and was now separated on three sites from the Royal Marsden Hospital, so the hospital itself was now on two widely separated sites and it would be interesting to see if they could exist as two separate entities or would rationalise the patients with different forms of cancer into one or other hospital.

I was now better acquainted with the history and constituent parts of the Institute of Cancer Research. It consisted of the Chester Beatty Research Institute, created in 1939 from the Cancer Hospital Research Institute of 1909 with Sir Alexander Haddow as director, and included the academic parts of the hospital department of physics and radiotherapy, along with the more recent additions of departments of biophysics and clinical research; each of these four departments was run by a director. The Institute had for several years been recognised as a School of the University of London and when the National Health Service was introduced in 1948, the Institute of Cancer Research became affiliated to the British Postgraduate Medical Federation. The five directors were responsible to the Institute Committee of Management and in addition, those who had clinical appointments were responsible to the Board of Governors of the Royal Marsden Hospital. The Institute was supported by an annual block grant from the Medical Research Council and Cancer Research Campaign which in 1969 amounted to two million pounds. It received legacies from the public and was allowed to advertise twice yearly in a legal journal. The last source of income was from Institute investments. This then was the Institute of Cancer Research I was to visit in the summer of 1969 as a member of the Medical Research Council, Cancer Research Campaign three day site visit.

The Institute prepared a detailed report on the work of each department and a copy was sent to all members of the visiting team. Each section of the Institute was visited, members of the scientific and medical staff talked about their research work and in turn were questioned on it. The committee also sought information on the number of staff who had tenured or permanent appointments and enquired about the financial status of the Institute. A critical report of the Institute's research activities and financial status was prepared and submitted to Council, and some time later I would experience the reverberations of this report which was accepted by Council. Later in the year I was one of the representatives of both funding bodies who met at the home of Lord Heathcoat Amory in London to discuss future funding of the Institute. It was decided to cut the joint block grant from the existing level of two million pounds to one million, which would be used to cover the basic facilities and staff salaries of the library, photographic departments, animal facilities and administration. The other one million pounds would be needed to cover salaries of scientific, medical and technical staff and provide the equipment and chemicals needed for their research. It was decided this sum would require to be won by three-year project and five-year programme grant applications. A joint scientific committee consisting of representatives of the Medical Research Council and Cancer Research Campaign was appointed to assess future grant applications and a site visit would be made to each department in the Institute every five years. The same committee would be responsible for supervising the grants made by them to the Beatson Cancer Institute in Glasgow and the Christie-Holt Institute in Manchester.

In the autumn of 1969, the University of London declared a moratorium on all academic promotions and appointments to departments in the Institute. A committee of senior academic and lay members of the Institute under Sir Edward Hale was set up to examine staffing and administration of departments. As I pointed out earlier, the Institute had independent directors of the departments of biophysics, clinical research, physics and radiotherapy, as well as Sir Alexander Haddow who was director of the large Chester Beatty Research Institute. Sir Alexander had a distinguished career in cancer research but illness and ultimately blindness compelled him to relinquish his post as director of the Chester Beatty, although he remained Professor of Experimental Pathology until he retired. The Hale Committee recommended there should be appointed an overall Director of the Institute who would have administrative responsibility for all Institute departments, and this was accepted. In addition a committee of senior Institute scientists recommended a staff redundancy programme which involved the dismissal of twenty-five scientists. This understandably led to a great upheaval in the Institute.

During the next few months I heard nothing more about the Institute, but in the middle of December I received a phone call from the Chairman of the Search Committee asking me to go to London to meet Lord Halsbury, who was Chairman of the Institute Committee of Management. When we met he informed me the search committee had recommended me for the post of Director of the Institute and if I accepted, this would meet with his approval. When I asked about the reaction of the present five directors, he assured me they approved and would work with me. He agreed the Institute had financial problems, was using up its reserves and, unless the drain on reserves was reversed, it would be in severe financial difficulty in about seven years' time. I pointed out that half the two million pound block grant the Institute had been receiving would in future need to be won as project or programme grant support. He agreed that many of the staff, even senior members, had little experience in preparing grant applications. We discussed the editorial in *Nature* which summed up the situation: 'The problem facing the new Director is how to get rid of old staff and bring in new ones when there is no money to do so.' On the question of redundancy, Lord Halsbury agreed this had a devastating effect on the morale of the staff who had been informed that the new director would be asked to meet those members who had been declared redundant. After discussing some personal problems, Lord Halsbury agreed I should have time to think things over and talk only to my wife and the Principal of Glasgow University, Sir Charles Wilson, whose advice I could seek. He hoped he would hear from me within ten days that I would accept the challenge and come to the Institute.

CHAPTER 13

Decision Time

W HEN I RETURNED to Glasgow I made contact with the Principal and
was disappointed to find he would be out of the country for a few
weeks and I would be denied the benefit of his advice to help me come to
a decision. I had to rely on talks with my wife and family, when we discussed
the good times we had together and understandably considered the effect a
move to London would have for them, and for the group of young pathologists
I had attracted to the department, as well as my commitment to the East
Africa Training Scheme.

When I came home from the first visit to the United States in 1955 the
children were small. Robin was nine, Alan four and Esther one, and in the
ensuing years they grew up within the environment of a university family. In
1956 we built a new house, off the Switchback Road in Bearsden, Glasgow
which was convenient for the Glasgow High School which the boys attended.
In their new surroundings the children made many friends and for the first
time in my life I had to construct a new garden, lay cement pathways to the
house and garage and learn to work like an Irish labourer – ten minutes' work
and ten minutes' rest. During this period in the garden I was able to think
over departmental problems and try to come up with a solution. The garden,
created in this manner, became an enjoyable exercise and since the house was
on a large corner site, I became quite expert at preparing the ground for
sowing grass seed, which I learned was a mixture of bent and chewing fescue.
Around the periphery of the lawn I planted a border of Frensham floribunda
roses and a mixture of hybrid tea roses in a bed I had prepared in front of
the house. Over the next two years, at the back of the house, I made a patio,
rockery and a raised lawn which was separated from the neighbours' dividing
fence by a collection of flowering shrubs, spiraea, laburnum, weigela, philad-
elphus and flowering currant. The patio was sheltered from the road at the
front of the house by a six-foot buttress wall which extended from the garage
to the side of the back door, and tubs with tulips in spring and begonias in
summer added to the attraction of the patio where we would barbecue and

dine out in the summer days. The boys showed great interest in my activities but did not help much. Our house was separated by the busy dual-carriage Switchback Road from the beautiful Garscube Estate which had been donated to the University of Glasgow and was the site of the new Glasgow University Veterinary School and Farm. The children loved to walk with us in the estate and along the banks of the River Kelvin which flowed through it. When Granny Symington came to stay with us, Esther would take her hand and walk into the Estate along the woodland paths, lined in spring by rows of blooming azaleas and rhododendrons. They would stop at the small dog cemetery when Granny would read to her the inscriptions on the small tombstones which had been erected by a previous generation of owners of the estate in memory of their pets.

Robin had a lively daschund pup called Rudi who loved to go with us for walks in the estate. On this particular day he ran out of the house when the boys were at school and made for the estate when he was struck by a car on the busy Switchback and killed. Margaret had the painful task of carrying him home and burying him in the garden. When Robin returned from school she had to break the sad news to him. The little boy was in bed crying quietly when I arrived home, and between sobs he told me what had happened to Rudi. Then, looking up at me with tear-filled eyes, he said, 'Mum told me that Rudi, like the dogs in the estate cemetery, would be in heaven now, and if only I knew this was true, I would be happy for Rudi.' Margaret and her family were regular churchgoers and she saw to it that the children attended Sunday school. On one occasion when Robin was a very small boy and, learning about God and the Creation, he asked Margaret, 'If God created the world, where did he stand when he was doing it?' He was a thoughtful little chap and to him the knowledge that Rudi was in heaven was a great source of comfort. The thought was very much in his mind when a few months later he came into the room where I was reading. 'Dad,' he said, 'I've been looking at a television programme about the Universe by a man called Huxley and in it he said that the world is millions of years old. Is that correct?' Never thinking, I said it was, but I could see he was distressed and puzzled. 'In that case, if God created the world he must be a very old man. Do you really feel Rudi is in heaven?' I confess I didn't know what to say. I could see he was going to be disturbed no matter what I said, and rather weakly suggested that his schoolteacher Miss Ralston might be the best person to answer that question. I don't think he ever asked her for she was a stern, uncompromising but outstanding teacher who made her pupils work in class and at homework.

As the years passed some of the family summer holidays were spent at Professor Rupert Willis' cottage in Cornwall. The children were very fond of Rupert and had become acquainted with him when he came to Glasgow for a year as the MacFarlane Visiting Professor of Cancer Medicine. Rupert held the Chair of Pathology in Leeds and was an international authority on tumour pathology. He retired on ill-health to Cornwall where he had a small rat cancer research unit. When he knew the children were coming he made multicoloured conical paper hats which the rats wore at parties he gave for the children, to their obvious delight.

Many male and female doctors from Egypt, Germany, Greece, Hong Kong, India, Iceland and Thailand came to study with me, and Margaret would invite them to dine at our home when they would meet and talk to the children. Each one, in time, would bring Esther a doll dressed in the national costume of the country, and as the years passed she collected quite a number of them. I would add to this collection by bringing dolls from the different countries I visited.

The appendix in my family seemed to lie in a position behind the caecum and when it became inflamed, the retro-caecal appendicitis was difficult to diagnose. My sister and I had been so afflicted, as was Robin, but with Esther the diagnosis was confusing. She vomited a great deal then developed tetany which required treatment, and it was only after an exploratory laparotomy that the inflamed appendix was discovered and removed. When Robin was fifteen years of age he began to grow rapidly and unfortunately, due to a scrum accident at rugby, he developed a prolapsed disc and required surgery. The Fates dealt him a further blow five years later when he collapsed with a spontaneous pneumothorax, when small blisters or bullae on the surface of the lung rupture and air passes in to the pleural space causing the lung to collapse. Although he recovered from this attack, eventually he required surgery to close the hole in his collapsed lung. This series of illnesses at a critical period in his life had a profound effect on his career. Margaret and I expected the children to take university entrance qualifications and go to the university with a view to entering a profession. It never dawned on us that the family would do otherwise. What happened next to Robin led to a career in business and not in one of the professions.

One day I met a banker friend who had helped with one of our international conferences. He knew Robin well and having enquired about his health and what he proposed to do, suggested he would like to talk to him and discuss his future. Apparently he arranged for Robin to visit a number of business associates.

'Robin,' he said, 'they will all try to get you to come and work with them, but don't accept any offers until you talk to me.' When Robin returned home that evening, I was naturally keen to learn what had happened.

'I met a number of different businessmen and was offered a training post as an insurance broker with Stenhouse in Glasgow. I liked the man who interviewed me and I've accepted the post and start tomorrow.' Then, looking at me he said, 'I thought the banker was your friend, Dad, but he doesn't seem to think much of you.' I was surprised and amused at his comment and wondered what was behind it. Then, looking at me hopefully he continued, 'I thought you were an important man in the University,' and waited for my reply.

'What else did the banker say?' I asked. With a tinge of sadness and disappointment in his voice he replied, 'Your father is a backroom boy and could be done away with tomorrow and never be missed.' Now he felt his colossus had feet of clay. 'Is that so?' he asked me.

'I suppose it is,' I answered, and once again he expressed his faith in me and repeated his original comment, 'But I thought you were an important man in the University.' The banker had applied strong medicine and I was intrigued.

'Now we have established that I am not important, what else did the banker say?' I asked, to which he replied, 'The most important men in the country, he said, are the businessmen and if you concentrate and apply yourself to this work, you can become more successful and more important than your father.' The banker's psychology certainly worked. Robin became an insurance broker with Stenhouse and after a temporary setback, showed tremendous drive and enthusiasm for the work. He became very close to us and would consult me when drawing up a policy which involved radioactive isotopes, and seek his mother's advice when the policy had to deal with medical problems. About this time he became engaged to Sandra Brown who was an air-controller at Glasgow Airport. She gave him great support and encourage-ment in his business career. I have told Robin's story to many professional colleagues who, like me, had a limited knowledge of what careers are open to children who have no desire to follow the profession or career of their parents. The banker's psychology worked for us.

Alan was just fourteen and Esther ten when I had the sabbatical year at Stanford University, California in 1965. We rented a house in the beautiful village of Portola Valley where Esther went to the village school. Alan, who was a pupil at Glasgow High School and a good student who worked well and had little difficulty with studies, was admitted as a day student to Woodside Priory School which was near our home in Portola Valley. The school was founded by Benedictine monks who had escaped from Hungary during the 1957 uprising. There were four classes in the school, freshman, sophomore, junior and senior, and after an interview with the headmaster, Father Christopher, Alan was placed in the sophomore class with pupils who were a year older; his training at Glasgow High School had impressed Father Christopher. Woodside Priory set a high standard of academic excellence and

Wedding photograph of Robin and Sandra Symington, September 1970.

in mathematics Alan studied only Euclid geometry and covered the whole course in this subject in one year. Trigonometry and algebra would be dealt with in the two subsequent years. He took, in addition, English, Science, French, Latin and Social Science and the school certainly believed in the carrot and stick principle. Any student who failed to make a certain mark in the progressive examinations that were held, was dropped from the soccer team, no matter how good he was, and was not allowed to attend the monthly dances which the priests arranged. Girls from adjacent convent schools were brought in as partners.

Alan coped well with the pressure of work, made the Honor Society and was the first Presbyterian to attend the school. Later, on returning to Scotland, I was discussing the merits of the school with our friend Philip Flanagan, Rector of the Scots College in Rome, who said, 'What did you expect? The Benedictines have been educators for a thousand years.' The monks, coming from Hungary, were soccer enthusiasts and introduced the game into schools in the San Francisco area, Woodside Priory had its own soccer coach and Alan made the team which reached the final of the schools' cup. He had always been keen on soccer and for a number of years I took him to Wembley to see the Scotland versus England International Match. Usually we spent the Friday evening in the Blue Boar in Cambridge, motored to Wembley next day and returned to Cambridge in the evening. On the Sunday morning I took him through the different colleges and would say how wonderful it would be to study there. He wasn't impressed by my enthusiasm and invariably turned the conversation to some incident in the game the previous day.

When we returned from California, Alan completed his studies at Glasgow High School, took his entrance qualifications to Glasgow University and in October 1969 entered the Faculty of Medicine.

During the period when the family was growing up, Margaret gave up her medical work to look after them. She invited and entertained to dinner in our home the visiting doctors and scientists who came to work with me, as well as the numerous scientists and their wives who were visiting the department or spending a sabbatical year with us. As time passed and the children grew older, she would go with me on invited lecture tours of countries in Europe and sometimes when I was external examiner to a medical school in Britain and Ireland. During our sabbatical year at Stanford she took the opportunity to restart her career in medicine and spent three mornings of each week working voluntarily in the cytology department at Stanford Medical Centre. At the end of the year, on her return home, she obtained an appointment in cytology in the pathology department of Stobhill Hospital in Glasgow.

It is always a worry when parents are growing old. When the children were young we took them every Saturday evening to the farm in Bellshill to visit Granny Forsyth, who looked forward to their visit and would be very disappointed if we were unable to go. When she was eighty she died suddenly from a heart attack. Granny Symington, who lived with my sister in Ayrshire, was a regular visitor to our home and loved to look after the children on the occasions Margaret and I went abroad. When we returned from the United States in 1966 she was unwell and I had her examined at the Royal Infirmary, only to find she had an inoperable gastric cancer from which she died a few months later. This was the end of an era for us.

Indeed I was coming to the end of an era as well, in my department of pathology where, apart from two years in the army, three months in the United States in 1955 and the year at Stanford University, I had spent twenty-seven years of my life. Maybe it was time to move on. The young men and women I had recruited into the department were ready to move to more senior posts, the African training programme was going well and could be finished from London, my book on the human adrenal gland had just been published; and I could continue the adrenal research in London by taking two or three members of the staff with me, supplementing their efforts by seconding some senior and junior biologists and chemists from the Institute to work with us, although I would need to win support for their salaries. I did not think this would be a problem.

If I left now my successor would acquire one or two senior active medical staff and a number of vacancies he could use to recruit new staff or bring his own research group and so introduce a new line of research. There was no departmental reason for me to stay.

I could now reflect on what possible reason I could have to break up the family, for this is what would happen, and to leave an active happy department for a large Institute with severe financial problems, staffed by senior scientists, some of whom had lost their creativity and would have problems obtaining grant support by themselves. The fact that the Institute departments were located on three sites certainly added to the problem of reduplication of effort and there would need to be a marked reorganisation of many Institute groups into well-defined divisions with someone in charge of each one. I knew these changes could create problems and I would need to remove some senior staff with professional status and replace them as heads of divisions by younger, active scientists whom I felt could win grant support for members of their division. If I accepted the post I knew this move to create a proper and responsible divisional structure would win me no medals, but it had to be done and so I took a closer look at the work of the Institute with all those points in mind.

Kennaway's discovery of the first chemical carcinogen stimulated a vast amount of research on the subject. In the ensuing years many groups at the Chester Beatty and Pollards Wood laboratories were engaged in studies to determine how the changes in cells that followed exposure to the chemicals would lead to cancer. When Kennaway joined the Institute in 1922, Boveri was developing the theory that cancer was a result of a somatic mutation in the cell. Over the years scientists in the Institute and elsewhere had tried to discover how chemical carcinogens could achieve this whilst at the same time learning how the cells exposed to the carcinogen would attempt to protect themselves from its lethal effects. As expected, Kennaway's polycyclic hydro- carbons were used extensively in those studies, and later when the carcinogenic effect of Nitroso compounds was discovered, their role and that of other chemicals believed to cause somatic mutation was studied by a number of groups in the Institute.

When the carcinogen enters the cell, a series of enzymes in the cell cytoplasm reacts with the chemical to make it more soluble. In this activated form the chemical can combine with proteins or ribosenucleaic acid (RNA) in the cell cytoplasm, or enter the cell nucleus and become attached in different ways to the bases which are part of the two DNA strands. In this form the chemical can cause an alteration in the structure of the gene, and this altered gene structure, protagonists believe, results in somatic mutation, and cancer.

As time passed, scientists discovered in the cell nucleus a series of repair enzymes. During cell division, when the two strands of DNA separate, if those enzymes detect the presence of the chemical carcinogen, they remove that portion of the DNA to which the carcinogen is attached, make new DNA, and link up the two cut ends so that normal replication and cell division can progress.

In lay terms, the fate of a cell when confronted by a chemical carcinogen is like an attempt to derail a train by moulding a large obstruction to both rails of the track. However, regular examination by railway inspectors or gangers would detect the obstruction, remove it and the damaged rails and replace them with a new length of track.

If it was the intention not to destroy the train but to direct it permanently onto another line, it would be necessary to introduce a subtle change at the points, which would go undetected by the gangers but automatically direct the train onto another line. This could happen in the cell if the carcinogen is sited discretely between the bases or attached to a specific part of a base and, as with the obstruction at the points on a railway line, the repair enzymes in the cell nucleus would miss the change and misread the code on the altered base. During cell division, mutation would occur and cancer cells result. This change would continue in perpetuity.

However, if the cancer is the result of somatic mutation, then all carci- nogens should be mutagens and capable of causing mutation when bacteria in a culture media is exposed to the carcinogen. The fact that all known carcinogens did not cause mutation was a setback to the mutagen theory of cancer until it was discovered that those carcinogens had to be metabolised in the body before they were able to act as mutagens. This led to the development in the Institute of a number of independent groups looking for new techniques to test the mutagen effect of chemicals.

When reviewing the work on chemical carcinogenesis it was clear that numerous small, as well as large units, were involved and in two widely separated sites at the Chester Beatty in London and at Pollards Wood in the country. The scientists were well qualified, many were senior and well respected for this work. There was undoubted reduplication and a lack of overall control and co-ordination of effort. A division of chemical carcinogenesis was needed and someone placed in control, since a great deal of money was involved in its support. It was difficult to know how much of the research would be funded by the grant-giving bodies.

Although the view of most chemists in the Institute was that cancer caused by chemicals was the result of an altered gene structure, there were groups who were interested in the molecular aspects of gene control and cancer, and who believed that chemical carcinogens could exercise their effect by altering gene function and not gene structure. In our train analogy something would need to happen in the signal box which would set the points permanently in position to deviate the train onto a new track, but the change at the points would be missed by the gangers. This group of physical chemists had been involved for many years in identifying a specific group of proteins, named histones, whose composition had not changed for millions of years. These proteins were believed to play an important role in representing gene activity and I felt this group had an important role to play in understanding the cancer problem. Unfortunately the group had been severely depleted during the redundancy exercise and it would be necessary to reform it as a small division under a new leader.

There were separate groups in the Institute engaged in problems of immuno-biology, tumour biology and metastasis, and a large isolated department of electron-microscopy. They needed to be unified by creating a division of biology.

Sir Alexander Haddow, Director of the Chester Beatty Institute, had a great interest in chemotherapy and many new drugs were developed in the chemistry department. A variety of old and new animal models were used to test the toxicity of the drugs and assess their anti-tumour effects.

The biochemical pharmacology unit where those tests were performed had a number of senior scientists, but once more there was a need for more centralised control and the creation of a division under an active, younger scientist. There was a small but active department of epidemiology which I felt had to be expanded into a division. Likewise the small clinical research department in the Marsden Hospital under its Director, Dr Thompson Hancock, had to be expanded into a division of medicine under a university professor. This was one way of closely linking the Marsden Hospital and the Institute at Fulham Road which unfortunately had grown apart. There was no doubt that the Institute at Fulham Road and Pollards Wood would present many problems, as would attempts to bring the Marsden Hospital and Institute closer together.

The Institute departments at Sutton had well-established divisional structures run by senior scientists and medicals, all with professorial status. Three of them would relinquish the title of director following the recommendations of the Hale Committee to have one director for the whole Institute. It would be important to have the confidence of those men if I decided to take the post. I knew each one from my visits to the Institute earlier in the year, was familiar with the research of their divisions and so had some ideas of what needed to be done.

The physics division was very large, some staff were Health Board employees who worked with patients in the radiotherapy department, others were senior and junior research scientists on the Institute staff whose salaries would come from grant support. One group was developing chemical sensitisers which if successful would increase the sensitivity of tumours to radiotherapy. Others were trying to develop new equipment such as zero-radiography which, it was hoped, would in time replace x-rays. Other scientists were trying to improve existing ultrasonic scanners to make them more sensitive for clinical use. Even in this well-developed division there were some scientists whose work I feared would not receive grant support.

The Marsden at Sutton is a fine modern hospital with medical, surgical and paediatric units whose existence was the result of the drive and enthusiasm of Professor Sir David Smithers. His radiotherapy department was housed in new buildings which contained the most modern and up-to-date equipment. The large waiting hall for patients was tastefully decorated with murals painted on the walls of the corridors along which patients would pass on their way to the treatment rooms. These walls were covered by large pictures of attractive scenes of foreign countries, which proved comforting to patients who could look at them while receiving radiotherapy. While many forms of cancer were treated at Sutton, Sir David had established a multidisciplinary approach, with considerable success, in the treatment of patients with Hodgkin's disease and some, but unfortunately not all, varieties of testicular tumours. During the site visit Sir David's work had been well received and his multidisciplinary approach to those cancers had excited me. I wanted to learn more about it, see if it could be applied to the treatment of all patients with cancer and ascertain what help Institute scientists could give.

Hodgkin's disease is a cancer which affects the lymph glands of the body and the patient usually presents with a swelling in the neck. A surgical biopsy is done and the pathologist makes the diagnosis; the radiologist then injects radio-opaque dye between the toes of the foot. The dye passes along the lymphatic channels of the leg into those in the abdomen and chest. When an x-ray is taken, the injected dye will outline the spread of tumours along the lymphatics and tell the clinicians if the cancer is present only in the thorax or has spread to the abdomen, in which case the surgeon will remove the spleen and take a biopsy of the liver. An assessment of the extent of the disease can now be made and treatment by radiotherapy alone or with chemotherapy can be decided by group consultation. I was impressed to hear that, using this team approach, the five-year survival for patients under forty years of age with all grades of the disease, had risen from 45% to between 80 and 90%. If Institute scientists could be involved with clinical problems throughout the Marsden Hospital, I saw this as a means of drawing the two institutions closer together. Although basic research was being undertaken in the radiotherapy department, it did not impress the visiting site committee, and I felt more could be achieved by creating a closer link with some of the scientists in the division of biophysics which was directed by Professor Len Lamerton. His was a well-organised department, carrying out studies on the different phases of the cell cycle in normal and cancer cells, and I felt this department would benefit by the inclusion of an excellent but small group who were working in isolation in the Chester Beatty laboratories on the effects of ionising radiation on isolated mammalian cells. The effect of cytotoxic drugs on cultured blood cells was being studied and the relevance of this to patients with leukaemia demonstrated the close link that was possible and could be extended between biophysics and the departments of radiotherapy and clinical medicine. The last division at Sutton was tumour immunology which was centred in a new building there and was under the direction of Professor Peter Alexander. He had established a close liaison with clinicians and was involved with them in studies on patients with conditions such as leukaemia and melanoma.

During the ten days I had been given to consider the appointment I thought about the work of the Institute, the problems that existed and the great potential that was there if it could be harnessed to work effectively. There were 450 staff members of whom 125 were scientists and medicals. The Institute, as I mentioned previously, was a member of the British Postgraduate Medical Federation of the University of London and many of the senior staff had either professorial or reader status with, accordingly, tenure for life. The remaining senior and middle-grade scientists had no university appointments, but firmly believed their contracts with the Institute conferred tenure on them. Since 70% of the running cost of any institution covers salaries, it was painfully obvious that the Institute had to win full support from the granting bodies when the new system was introduced. If they failed to achieve this level of support there would be a drain on reserves with unthinkable consequences. It was rather a daunting prospect, and to meet the challenge I was now certain there was a need to create a proper divisional structure into which the numerous small isolated groups in the Institute could be placed. This would prevent reduplication of some of the research I had encountered.

Although there was a well-established divisional structure at Sutton, the departments were under the control of senior academics who had been directors and so answerable only to the committee management. They would continue to control the work of their department, but now would be answerable to the new director. I had seen some changes and improvements I felt were necessary and naturally wondered if they would co-operate with me to bring them about. The existence of the Institute on three sites put extra pressure on both staff and directors to bring about the co-ordination of effort I felt was needed.

While many of the senior staff were actively engaged in research that I felt would be supported, a number had lost their creativity and would find it difficult to gain support for themselves, and the junior scientists and technicians in their research groups. Nevertheless the scientific expertise and training of those senior men, and their ability to tackle problems presented to them, could make them valuable additions to other research groups to which they could be transferred. I could only hope they would agree to this, but I would need to wait and find out. The multidiscipline clinical group created by Sir David at Sutton had excited me and I saw the possibility of extending this concept to all forms of cancer research at the Marsden in Fulham Road as well as at Sutton. There was a need to develop academic departments of medicine and surgery and to redeploy some of the Institute scientists to work in them. Where was the money to come from? And would the Marsden clinicians co-operate? I was not sure.

However, my main worry was the effect a move to London would have on the family. A year after returning from the sabbatical year at Stanford University, we built our retiral home in Bearsden and this time the children had grown up and helped to get everything in order. Margaret was very fond of this house and enjoyed the work she was doing in cytology. Alan was now a first year student in medicine at Glasgow University and Robin had settled into a business career. Esther, still at school, was very supportive of a proposed move to London, whereas Alan, who never liked change, was non-committal. Margaret listened when I discussed the move and was concerned when I talked about the problems I would meet.

'Why look for problems when we are happy here, have our family with us and a new home for our retirement, and you have an active and happy department in Glasgow?' I knew she was not in favour of the move, mainly because it would split the family whom she had devoted so much energy to and had seen through many serious illnesses.

'However,' she said, 'you must make up your own mind what you want to do and whatever decision you make, we'll all support you,' and she added, 'and by the look of things you'll need our support.' However, it was Robin who was the deciding factor.

'Dad,' he said, 'this is a new challenge for you and if you don't accept you will regret it. Sandra and I will get married soon and it will be good for us to come to London. You always wanted Alan to go to Cambridge and maybe he will be able to manage this. Mum will get a medical post in London.'

It was a difficult decision to make, but in the end I decided to accept. I phoned Lord Halsbury, sent my resignation to the University of Glasgow and informed the pathology staff of my decision. Next day *Nature* published another editorial: 'What the Institute needs is a distinguished scientist, but it is doubtful if anyone of distinction would accept the post.' I had burned my boat. There was no turning back.

CHAPTER 14

I Meet Daniel K. Ludwig

I VISITED the Institute in the week prior to Christmas 1969 and met Mr
Neil Hadow, the Institute secretary who had retired from the colonial
service to take up this appointment; in the ensuing years I would learn to
value his help and advice. At first I found him difficult and provocative as
he would accept my plans for improving the Institute only after intense
questioning and a demand to justify my reasons for the proposals. Knowing
everyone in the Institute, he recognised their strengths and weaknesses and
knew whether a frontal attack or a more subtle approach was likely to be
successful to achieve my aim. It was not long before I began to recognise
he was being a devil's advocate and, if I could convince him of the value
of my plans I would have little difficulty putting them into action, depending
on his support with complete assurance. During my tenure as director we
would have weekly working lunches when I would talk aloud to him. If he
was not impressed, he would say so and I knew it would be unwise to proceed
further.

On the first visit he revealed his concern about the committee structure of
the Institute, and the composition of the large central division which consisted
of staff from the Director and Dean's office, library, photography and animal
units on three sites, as well as the staff responsible for buildings and stores.

We discussed the need for a divisional structure in the Institute and I
informed him I envisaged ten divisions each with someone designated in
charge, who would be responsible for the programme and project grant
submissions. He agreed the numerous small groups scattered throughout the
Institute should be allocated to an appropriate division and be responsible to
the head of the division, but indicated I could expect some opposition,
particularly from some of the older staff.

'Leave the divisional changes until we see the results of the new grant
submissions which they will have to make. They will be more willing to accept
the changes if they fail to gain support for their work,' was the good advice
I was pleased to accept. 'It will be necessary for you to meet the staff of the

Institute at the three sites and explain how important it is for them to win grant support and to start thinking about their submissions now.' The announcement of twenty-five redundancies of senior and junior staff and the decision by the granting bodies that the finance for salaries and equipment had to be won, sent a shock wave through the Institute.

I was due to take up the appointment in July 1970 and in the intervening six months visited the Institute twice monthly. Neil Hadow arranged for me to attend a meeting of the academic board when I was asked and agreed to meet any of the scientists who had been declared redundant who wished to see me. Some of the older men decided to retire completely, but some came to see me to discuss their work, and later, I was glad to find they had obtained posts in universities or industry. One individual became very abusive when I refused to rescind the redundancy notice and later he found a post abroad. Among my Christmas mail that year was a card from him saying he would open a bottle of champagne when he heard of my death. When my appointment was announced I met my good friend Professor Norman Davidson. 'Tom,' he said, 'I hear you are going to the Chester Beatty. That place will drive you mad.' By now I was feeling he might be right.

During the six-month waiting period I applied to the Medical Research Council for a new five-year programme grant for my adrenal tumour research and a new study on tumour markers which I hoped would help clinicians decide when treatment by chemotherapy could be stopped or needed to be restarted. Cancer, when established in a patient, is like an iceberg with only a small portion of the tumour showing. The tumour shrinks with treatment but it is difficult for the clinician to know how successful the treatment has been. In patients with chorio-carcinoma of the uterus, the tumour produces a chemical substance, or tumour marker (gonadotrophin) which can be measured in the urine. When the level of this substance drops to normal, treatment by chemotherapy can be stopped and, if regular urine checks show a rise of the hormone, treatment can begin again. It was my intention to try and find out if every tumour had the ability to form tumour markers and determine what they were. My application for programme support was accepted by the MRC and I was able to take one of my Glasgow assistants, Dr Munro Neville, with me. I built around him a new Institute division of endocrine tumour pathology, and drafted into the division senior and junior chemists and biologists already in the Institute to form a viable active group.

I was delighted when my secretary in Glasgow, Miss Nan Allen, agreed to come with me and take charge of the Director's office. She had extensive experience of grant applications and would provide the help needed by the Institute scientists with their grant submissions.

Grant applications from the Institute for one million pounds were submitted in September 1970 and duly assessed by the committee set up jointly by the Medical Research Council and the Cancer Research Campaign. Early in 1971 I received their critical report. Only £400,000 of the research would be funded, the remaining £600,000 they would not approve. However, the committee agreed to allocate the one million pounds for a period of seven years to allow me to redirect the research and win this support. How I did this would be entirely my responsibility, it was not up to the grant committee to tell me what should be done. In addition, the letter informed me the committee had decided the Institute should have a tenured establishment of thirty posts and it was left to me to allocate them. The Institute was top heavy with senior scientists and this was the committee's way of reminding me there were about forty-five senior scientists and medicals who would be supernumerary to the establishment. I was given seven years to retrain, redeploy or help them find new lines of research. At the end of this period the Institute was expected to have a proper pyramidal structure. In time the senior supernumerary scientists would retire, but in the meantime their salaries had to be won. It was now time to start creating the divisional structure and appoint someone in charge of each division.

The Professor of Biochemistry at the Institute retired and I took over his floor in the Chester Beatty laboratories, where I installed my endocrine pathology group under Munro Neville and brought in a number of technicians as well as senior and junior chemists and biologists from different parts of the Institute to work in the new group. I accepted responsibility for their salaries.

The scientific and technical staff of small isolated groups in cell biology, membrane biochemistry, immuno-biology and electron microscopy were incorporated into a division of biology under Dr Tony Davis who had an established reputation for his studies in immuno-biology. I allocated a senior chemist, Dr Walter Ross, to work with the group. Ross had for many years worked on the development of new drugs for chemotherapy which kill normal as well as tumour cells when administered to patients. Davis and Ross would try to find a method of attaching the drug to an antibody or some agent which would target the drug to tumour cells and so protect the normal cells of the body. This type of collaboration I found exciting. In addition, Davis took over responsibility for the animal facilities at both Fulham Road and Pollards Wood and I allocated to him a middle-grade tenured post for this purpose.

Organic chemistry had played a prominent role in Institute research from the days of Kennaway and Alexander Haddow, and the division was now under Professor Alan Foster, a carbohydrate chemist who was to play a prominent role in our research on tumour markers. He seconded one of his middle-grade scientists to work on the problem. Foster had a mass spectro-metry unit at Sutton under Dr Jarman, who collaborated with clinicians in their studies on the metabolism of the chemotherapy drugs when administered to cancer patients. This type of collaboration introduced scientists to the role they could play in clinical problems. It also taught the young clinicians to understand the language of science, how research should be conducted and, we hoped, how to improve patient care. The division of chemistry was providing an expert service to both Institute and Hospital and this service to patients would increase in the future. Initially the chemistry division was responsible for testing the toxicity of chemotherapy drugs on animals and their efficacy on animal tumour models. As time passed, a division of biochemical pharmacology was established under Dr Ken Harrop to deal with the synthesis and evaluation of new anti-cancer drugs, and another senior organic chemist, Dr John Stott, was seconded to the division. This was another example of the role an older chemist could play in a division run by a younger scientist who accepted responsibility for winning grant support for an older colleague. Harrop's division expanded and later moved to laboratories at Sutton, where they have played an important role with chemistry and later medicine in developing a drug development section. They became the first academic group to achieve the worldwide registration of the new anti-cancer drug, carboplatin.

Molecular biology was the next division to be established in the Chester Beatty. It was considered by the redundancy committee to have little relevance to cancer and most of the senior scientists in this department left the Institute. I reconstituted a small division under Dr Ernie Johns, with three young scientists and technicians and was delighted to find their submission to the grants committee was fully financed. They were studying the composition and function in the chromosomes of a specific group of proteins called histones. These have a role in deciding whether a gene is active or repressed and how those changes affect gene function and the development of cancer. The different histones are made up of a series of amino-acids, and Johns in his grant submission had requested and was awarded an expensive piece of equipment called a sequenator which would quickly characterise the arrange-ment of the amino-acids in the different histones he isolated. I drafted into the division a senior physical chemist whose grant application had been rejected and he quickly settled into the new surroundings, took over the sequence work and soon became an invaluable member of the group.

The division of chemical carcinogenesis formed at Pollards Wood had three well-established and respected scientists whose work had been fully funded, and I put Dr Peter Brooks in charge of the division. The divisional structure already existed at Sutton and only a few scientists failed to win support for their research. I knew Professor John Landon who was head of the department of chemical pathology at St Bartholomew's hospital, and with his help paid the salary of two of the scientists for three years. One was trained in clinical chemistry and the expertise of the other was used to prepare purified hormones for clinical use. This venture proved successful and both men obtained permanent posts in the health service at the end of the three-year period. One or two senior staff preferred to continue their research with a restricted staff of one research fellow and a technician and were accommodated with limited laboratory space in one of the divisions. One of them gave me valuable help when the time came to draft and submit the grant applications. The secondment and retraining scheme worked admirably. I experienced very little antagonism but I was dealing with highly qualified men whom I encouraged and treated with dignity. Very few men and women in science or medicine can perform at the same standard of excellence throughout their whole careers. Inevitably in the last five to ten years of their professional life many have acquired skills that can be put to some other and more productive use. This is what I did in the Institute and it is something that the authorities in universities and the health service have got to appreciate and utilise.

The grants' committee had limited the number of tenured posts in the Institute to thirty, and I distributed them to the ten divisions in accordance with their size. Most were given two posts, a few larger divisions had three, and small divisions like molecular biology and epidemiology, one. I insisted the Institute accept moral responsibility for those senior scientists who had been redeployed and were supernumery to establishment I had created, but I fully expected that subsequent quinquennial grant applications by the head of divisions would take care of their salaries.

My mind went back to that first editorial in *Nature*.

'What the Institute needs is to get rid of old staff and bring in new young scientists, but without the money to do it.' I did not get rid of old scientists, I had attempted to use their skill and experience; but it would be more difficult to deal with the second point. Nevertheless it was necessary for the sake of the future of the Institute, to develop in each division an establishment of three middle-grade scientists who would become the future leaders of the Institute. The only problem was, as the *Nature* editorial correctly said, where was the money to come from? At this time President Nixon of the United States had passed the 1971 Cancer Act which allocated vast sums for cancer research with the slogan 'The Moon in the Sixties, Cancer Cure in the Seventies'. In this country the Prime Minister, Edward Heath, asked Lord Zuckerman to look at the financial support for cancer. I knew Zuckerman from endocrine meetings we attended and he spent a day with me at the

Institute. I showed him the grants' committee report, pointed out that we were not justifying the money we were receiving, described the steps I had taken to win this money in the future and hoped the middle-grade appointments I needed would be won in the ensuing applications. He agreed it would be wrong for me to ask the government for more money until I had justified what I was receiving at present. His visits to other cancer centres in this country, he said, confirmed this view. Nevertheless, financial support did come from a completely unexpected source which allowed me immediately to finance a number of Grade I appointments and at the same time help to establish a Chair of Medicine which I hoped would help to bring the Institute and Marsden Hospital closer together.

In October 1971 I received a phone call from Mr Dick Kent, House Governor of the Royal Marsden Hospital, asking me to see two American businessmen who had walked into his office. When I met them, the younger man, Mr John Notter, said they represented a wealthy American, Mr Daniel K. Ludwig, who wished to establish a link with the Institute of Cancer Research in London; on his death most of his entire fortune of $53 billion would go to cancer research. Notter then asked how much money I wanted to set up this collaborative effort and on the spur of the moment I said $1 million over a period of five years. The two men looked at each other and without further discussion agreed to this sum and produced documents for me to sign. By now I was convinced they had escaped from a lunatic asylum, or this must be a hoax. Things like this didn't really happen. It was too good to be true. Notter than asked if he could phone New York, reversed the charges and spoke apparently to Mr Ludwig who asked some questions and agreed to the deal. It was beginning to sink in that this was real and that I had asked for $1 million. I took them home to meet Margaret and to talk over what I proposed to do with the money. I informed Notter that the agreement would need to be signed by Lord Halsbury who would be required to get the consent of the Institute's Committee of Management, the Royal Marsden's Board of Governors and the Department of Health. I am pleased to record that the assent of all three bodies was obtained in record time. I got the $1 million and could now proceed with the Institute developments which John Notter had made possible and for which the Institute of Cancer Research would be eternally grateful.

I had impressed on the staff that I would only agree to them applying to outside agencies or firms for financial support for the salary of senior supernumerary or junior staff. This I called 'soft money' which was useful as a three year project grant, but it was the type of support which could suddenly disappear and leave the Institute with further financial commitments. Indeed it was the withdrawal of a large American grant of soft money that had landed the Institute with financial problems and a large supernumerary staff. Neil Hadow was therefore conscious of this danger, saw it could happen with Ludwig and in masterly fashion arranged that Ludwig deposited stock to the value of £100 million in a Ludwig company established in London so that the income from this would take care of future Ludwig commitments which, like the Medical Research Council and Cancer Research Campaign support, was hard money on which we could build the Institute.

The divisional structure, under a senior academic along with one or two senior colleagues who had tenure, gave the divisions the basis for a much needed pyramidal structure. The next step was to create the middle grade layer of Grade I scientists who would become the future leaders of the Institute. It was my aim eventually to have two and in most divisions, three Grade I positions and the Ludwig award would allow me to make a start. I created what we called six Ludwig fellowships at Grade I level and awarded them to young scientists and clinicians whose research had been received favourably in the initial MRC/CRC report. The first Ludwig fellows came from the divisions of chemistry, physics, molecular biology, cell pathology and medicine and their support was for five years. Neil Hadow and I had regular meetings with John Notter, Ludwig's representative, and impressed on him the need to establish a Ludwig Advisory Committee of senior scientists and doctors who could liaise with the Institute and hospital and look after the Ludwig interest. We did not advise on the composition of this committee, but one was established and Dr Hugh Butt, a senior physician in the Mayo clinic who had had Ludwig as a patient, was made Chairman. He had Dr Carl Baker, Director of the National Cancer Institute, Washington USA, Dr Lloyd Old, Deputy Director, Sloan Kettering Cancer Institute, New York and Professor Henry Islicker, Lausanne Switzerland as members of the committee. They visited the Institute yearly, met the young Ludwig fellows and discussed their research. Those meetings continued annually for the next five years.

The Ludwig finance also helped me to develop an academic division of medicine from the small clinical research department which Dr Thompson Hancock had created in 1962. The University of London removed the moratorium on the Institute and once more allowed academic appointments and promotions. With the help of Sir Theo Crawford, Chairman of the CRC, the latter provided finance for a Chair in Medical Oncology (cancer medicine). The professor appointed, along with his staff, would have facilities in any of the Institute laboratories, the help of scientists in the Institute, and beds for patient care in the Royal Marsden Hospital at Fulham Road and Sutton. Dr Gordon Hamilton-Fairley, who was killed so tragically by an IRA car bomb, had an attachment to the Institute and hospital in Surrey. Along with Sir David Smithers he had developed highly successful multidisciplinary cancer treatment teams for Hodgkin's disease, certain testicular tumours and leukaemia. He had an attachment as a physician to St Bartholomew's Hospital, and over the years brought many young physicians from that school to work with him at Sutton. In the interval between the CRC providing the money to endow the Chair, the University ratifying it and the medical committee of the Marsden Hospital agreeing to give an honorary consultant contract to the professor, the Imperial Cancer Research Fund endowed a Chair of Oncology in the University of London, to which they appointed Dr Hamilton-Fairley. He set up a department of medical oncology in St Bartholomew's Hospital where he had already a consultant appointment. Now I had to look elsewhere for a suitable candidate for the Institute.

I had been at the Institute two years before I accepted an invitation to travel abroad, and at the end of this period Margaret and I attended a cancer conference in New Hampshire, USA. After this we spent a few days in Boston with our friends Lew and Peggy Engel, who were intensely interested in the developments in the Institute. Lew, it will be remembered, had been a MacFarlane Visiting Professor with me in Glasgow. In his youth he had been a post-doctoral fellow in chemistry at the Institute where he met Peggy, who was secretary to Kennaway. Peggy's family had a long association with the Institute. Her father was Robert Knox who established radiology and radiotherapy in the Cancer Hospital (Free). I told Lew about developments in the last two years, my plans for an academic unit in medicine and the need to appoint a professor who would attract young doctors to a career in cancer medicine. In time they would be seconded to one of the Institute divisions where they would have contact with scientists, learn from them new emerging technology, as well as how to plan, execute and assess the research project. This in time would lead to a higher degree in science or medicine. In return the scientists would be introduced to the problems of cancer in patients. The department of medicine, like pathology and radiotherapy, would become another bridge linking the Institute and the Hospital closer together. What I needed was an experienced clinician with an acknowledged reputation in research. Our discussions took place in Engel's office in the Collins laboratories of the Massachusetts General Hospital. Suddenly he said,

'Phillip Bondy's your man.' I knew Bondy very well. He was Professor and Chairman of Medicine in Yale University Medical School and highly regarded as an excellent clinician and scientist who had published a large number of scientific papers on endocrine problems and edited a very well-respected and comprehensive textbook, *Diseases of Metabolism*.

It was not uncommon for American professors of medicine to come to Chairs of Medicine in England. Sir William Osler left the Chair of Medicine in Philadelphia for the Regius Chair in Oxford and his valedictory address 'Equanimitas' was delivered to his students on leaving for England. Phillip Bondy's predecessor at Yale was at that time holding the Regius Chair of Medicine at Oxford and, since Bondy was giving up as chairman of the division of medicine at Yale, he might be persuaded to come to London; at least I could sound him out. I talked to Bondy from Engel's office in Boston and invited him and his wife Sally to visit London and see things for himself.

When I returned to London I met Neil Hadow, told him what I had done and, as expected, he raised all the difficult problems I would meet when I had to deal with the Marsden clinicians. I agreed Bondy was not a cancer man, he was an experienced clinician who had to deal with cancer patients, but he was an outstanding clinician and scientist, I repeated, what was needed was an experienced clinician and scientist, to attract, as Hamilton-Fairley had done, a group of young doctors who would become cancer men, and this is what Bondy would do. Neil saw the point; I had convinced him and knew I could count on his support.

The new professor would need an honorary consultant contract from the Marsden Hospital as, without this, he would not be allowed to take charge of patients. Since the consultant contract was given on the recommendation of the hospital committee, Bondy would be required to appear before them to gain their approval and from previous experience, there was no guarantee this would be given. The medical committee had, as members, a large group of part-time consultants, with between one and four clinical sessions at the Marsden and the rest at other hospitals in London. Nevertheless they regularly attended all meetings of the medical committee and had great influence over any decisions and recommendations made to the Board of Governors. I had had some unpleasant experiences at the hands of some members of the medical committee and naturally was a little apprehensive that my efforts to bring Bondy to the Institute and Hospital might meet with resistance from the medical staff. Fortunately I was mistaken, Bondy met the medical committee and received their approval, his appointment was ratified by the University and the academic division of medicine was established with beds at the Royal Marsden Hospital in London and Sutton. His staff consisted of clinicians who had been attached to the clinical research group, those who had worked with Hamilton-Fairley at Sutton and in time, new young clinicians from the London medical schools. All of those who were attached to Bondy's department of medicine are now leaders in different fields of cancer medicine.

Bondy's division was financed by money I allocated from the Ludwig fund and with grant support from the MRC and CRC. No laboratories were allocated to the division, the research done by the staff took place in Institute laboratories with the assistance of scientists there, and a particularly close

Professor Phillip Bondy. Yale Medical School and Institute for Cancer Research, London, 1974.

relationship developed between the divisions of medicine, biochemical pharmacology and chemistry.

The creation of an Institute division of medicine certainly helped to improve my relations with hospital clinicians. I encouraged them to come and discuss their research interests and problems with me, when I could put them in touch with scientists in the Institute who could help and indeed collaborate with them. This was another way to make use of scientists in the Institute who were supernumerary to the establishment. The academic board had allocated money to a directors' fund which I used to help scientists to initiate a research project and produce results which would help when they had to submit grant applications; it was, as I said, an attempt to prime the pump. I used some of my directors' reserve to help hospital clinicians initiate a piece of research. On one occasion a senior surgeon came to see me, very upset because, as he told me, his application to the CRC for a grant had been rejected. I spent some time reading his submission and to his surprise informed him that I would have rejected it, and proceeded to give my reason. His research project was on breast cancer and he requested support for a young biologist to culture breast cancer cells and a biochemist to work on steroid receptors in those cells.

'As a surgeon,' I asked him, 'do you know enough about the culture of breast cancer cells or of steroid biochemistry to help the young scientists you would employ if things go wrong?' He hadn't thought about that and so I continued,

'After all, you would be shocked if I told you that a scientist in the Institute wished to carry out an operation on one of your patients. Rightly you would say "What does he know about surgery?".' He took the point. We resubmitted his project but added that the study would be done in an Institute department under the guidance of scientists trained in tissue culture techniques and steroid biochemistry. I was relieved when his grant application was approved.

The Institute purchased a computer for use by the departments of radiotherapy and medicine. Clinical details were recorded of each patient along with the histological classification, extent of spread or staging of the tumour, and the treatment schedule that was being used. Those computer facilities I offered to the clinicians in the Marsden.

Now I was developing a much better relationship with hospital clinicians and through the skill, vision and tireless efforts of Dr Jim McDonald and Dr Brem Cameron, past and present chairmen of the hospital medical committee, this relationship was firmly cemented with the creation of multidiscipline clinical units in both branches of the hospital. Dr McDonald was a member of the team at Sutton which was dealing successfully with patients who had Hodgkin's disease and some rarer tumours, and was conscious of the need for a similar multidiscipline approach to the treatment of the common cancers where the outlook was poor. Nevertheless he jealously guarded the 1911 rule that each consultant was responsible for the treatment of every patient under his or her care, and the persuasion of clinical colleagues to become part of a multidiscipline clinical unit needed patience. Dr Cameron had this quality and, allied to his firmness and overwhelming interest in the future of the hospital, the two men, in 1973, introduced steps that led to the creation during the next four years of multidiscipline units whose development was reviewed by Dr Cameron in 1977.

Each clinical cancer unit involved senior and junior staff from medicine, surgery and radiotherapy and received back-up support from the diagnostic departments of the hospital. The units were designated where possible on an anatomical basis and in this way gastro-intestinal, gynaecological, genito-urinary, breast and lung units were created. It was imperative that each unit would undertake the study, care and treatment of *all* patients admitted to the hospital with the particular type of cancer which was appropriate to that unit. This was an important decision which every consultant in the unit had to accept. It was not always possible to designate a unit on an anatomical basis and so units dealing with childhood or lymph gland or blood cell tumours (leukaemia) were established. This approach to patient diagnosis and care involved a reorganisation of ward space and redistribution of medical and nursing staff to the different units. Space was allocated to units and patients with a given disease were assigned to the particular ward area. A suitable degree of flexibility was built into the system for patients who needed intensive or terminal care as well as those who required hostel-type accommodation which is valuable and less expensive.

Ideally most medical staff should be allocated full time to the units, and in the Royal Marsden experiment, junior medical, surgical and radiotherapy staff were full time on one unit while their senior colleagues had responsibilities in more than one. Junior clinical staff were rotated through different units to ensure a comprehensive training in the management of most forms of cancer.

The role of the medical records departments had to be redefined to provide secretarial services, data processing and computer facilities which in time would help to assess the success or otherwise of treatment by the individual units. Previously a consultant could treat a patient as he or she thought fit and was not subjected to any internal or external assessment of their results. The new scheme provided a forum where members of the unit could discuss each patient, the histological classification of the tumour, the extent of the spread in the body (stage), the investigations to be carried out and the detailed treatment protocols to be followed. The use of new drugs or more complex combination of drugs could be agreed, large scale clinical trials discussed or initiated and the results of treatment better assessed. The establishment of multidiscipline clinical units helped to forge a closer link between the doctors who encountered clinical problems requiring clarification, and the Institute scientists with the expertise to tackle them. Those clinical units effectively shaped the structure and function of the Royal Marsden Hospital and the applied research of the Institute of Cancer Research. Likewise, the unit provided clinical training for young doctors who wished to make a career in cancer medicine (oncology); and the varied departments of the Institute gave those so disposed an exposure to the scientific approach to clinical problems.

While the hospital was reshaping its clinical units in 1973 the Institute had completed the retraining and redeployment of senior scientists and relocated them to a division. It was now time to resubmit applications for grant support and begin to justify the funding which had been guaranteed until 1977. Two and sometimes three divisions were reviewed yearly and this gave me the opportunity to scrutinise the grant submissions and ensure they followed a format which would allow the application to be assessed easily by the review committee. Dr Richard Carter was a great help in preparing the applications. He was an experimental pathologist whom I had seconded to work for two years to the Department of Health, and during this period we edited a book, the *Scientific Foundations of Oncology.* Richard returned to the Institute to continue his research on head and neck tumours and together we discussed the grant applications with the head of the division and senior and middle-grade scientists. We insisted that a divisional application for a five-year programme should be limited to about twenty pages and should answer three questions. What research has been done and what papers have been published on the subject? What research is now proposed? And what staff, equipment and running costs are needed to carry out the proposed work?

There was no limit to the number of appendices that could be used to expand on points raised in the application. An appendix might describe in detail the reason for requesting one specific piece of equipment rather than a cheaper model, or give a detailed account of a new technique the applicant had devised. It could be used to summarise the author's relevant research publications, copies of which could also be enclosed with the past achieve-ments and future proposals easily submerged in a mass of papers. It takes a great deal of time and effort to produce a grant application and present it in a form that every member of the grant committee can understand without the need to refer to the appendices. They will be read and assessed by those members of the committee who are experts on the subject and by external advisers to whom the application will be sent and whose reports will be available to the members of the grant committee when the application is considered.

Carter and I took a particular interest in middle-grade and younger members of the staff who were preparing for their first grant submission. Their applications once more, had to answer the three basic questions — What have I done? What do I wish to do? And what equipment and staff do I need to do it? Usually the applicant had spent a few years as part of a team financed by the division programme, or had been supported initially from my directors' fund. Now they felt able to run a small group and win support for it. If their application requested junior scientific and technical staff they were expected to detail the role the staff would play in the project. If animals were to be used they should refer to the facilities in the animal house for the care of the animals and the cost of their upkeep. This I felt was important if in the future they left the Institute and had to set up animal facilities elsewhere when they would have to include projected running costs in any grant applications. Miss Allen, my secretary, would advise them on the need to apply for finance to cover secretarial help and to include funding for National Health Insurance and superannuation for scientific technical and secretarial staff as well as administration costs. If their project involved patients it should have the approval of the hospital ethics committee and this should be notified in a covering letter to the grant agency.

About two months after the divisional application was submitted, we would receive a site visit from selected representatives of the grant committee when senior and grade I scientists discussed their research and were questioned on it. At the end of the meeting, which lasted all day, I met the committee in private and had the opportunity to add my comments on the day's proceedings and clear up any points they raised, after which they met in private to draft a report with their recommendations for the main grant committee.

The divisions in the Institute of Cancer Research were reviewed and assessed by external audit. By 1977 all had won financial support for their programmes and only three of the forty-five senior scientists I inherited failed to have their research financed. An external audit by an independent group of specialists is the only way to obtain a satisfactory assessment of work being done and the finance and staff required, and this applies equally to a research institute, a university or to hospitals in the National Health Service.

Since retraining and redeployment of senior scientists can pose problems it is best to try to avoid them, and to do this I had to pay attention to the selection and promotion of the young men and women who were brought into the Institute and who, in the future, would be responsible for its destiny. Young male and female doctors and scientists with a first class or upper second honours degree from a British university were recruited into Institute departments on scholarships awarded by the MRC, the Marsden Hospital or the Institute itself. They were attached for three years to one of the staff in the basic science departments of the Institute and at the end of this period were expected to gain the degree of Doctor of Philosophy (PhD). A yearly report on their work and progress was made to the academic board and the Dean of the Institute, Professor Lamerton, would see any students whose progress was giving cause for concern. Once they had taken this degree, the young post-doctor fellows, as they were called, had to compete in open competition with other fellows who had obtained this degree at one of the British or overseas universities. Successful candidates were given a three-year temporary appointment at Grade II level, and there was no limit to the number of those appointments in the Institute since they would be financed from successful three-year projects or five-year programme support. Toward the end of the second year, their work was assessed by an Institute committee and about three out of every ten were selected for their research potential and given a limited contract for five years, still at Grade II level but with annual financial increments. This selected group was encouraged and expected to develop their own line of research and I helped them prepare and apply for their own grant support.

Towards the end of the third year of their five-year contract the young scientist prepared a progress report on his or her work, detailed the junior scientific and technical staff in the group, the research they directed and their ideas for the future. The Institute and candidate would each nominate an external assessor who received a copy of the progress report and gave, in confidence, an assessment of it and an opinion on the research potential of the candidate. Both external opinions were read at a meeting of a committee which I chose from the basic science and clinical divisions of the Institute. The role of this internal committee was to ensure a uniform standard of excellence in the candidates who were promoted from the different Institute divisions. At each meeting of the committee the head and one senior scientist from the candidate's division were invited to be present at the candidate's interview. This lasted about one hour, at the end of which both senior scientists were given the opportunity to express an opinion on the candidate's suitability for promotion. The assessment committee would now decide on the value of the candidate's research and whether he or she was capable of directing the research project and winning financial support for the staff involved. Some candidates had already won grant support and the finance required for his or her promotion was available. It was expected that two out of every three candidates interviewed would be promoted to a Grade I appointment and those who failed had two years to find an alternative post.

Scientists who obtained a Grade I appointment would, if so desired, have a career in the Institute and eventually could take control of a division. Undoubtedly some would achieve academic excellence elsewhere, but the time would come when promotion to a Grade I Institute appointment would need to be open to external competition. Either way, the rigorous assessment that was used would produce in the Institute a group of talented and creative scientists, who would be able to hold their own with outside competition. The aim to have between one and three Grade I scientists per division was now possible, the Institute had a proper pyramidal structure and a career path in the Institute was available for young scientists.

During this period the Ludwig scientific committee continued their yearly visit to discuss the work of the Ludwig fellows, and in time they were accompanied by some very senior American tax lawyers. Their role was to ensure that the Ludwig agreement with the Institute and the placing of Ludwig fellows into different divisions of the Institute did not infringe the tax free position: and to safeguard this they wanted the Ludwig fellows to be centred in one department which could be designated a Ludwig Unit. This I felt was the kind of thing that could happen if an administrator was running the Health Service and I frankly refused to agree to this request. At any rate, the fellowships were coming to an end and I was able to fund each one from the grant support won by the divisions. If for tax purposes all Ludwig paid staff had to be present in the same department, the answer was for Ludwig to take over financial responsibility for a floor in the Chester Beatty laboratories which housed my MRC group on tumour markers. The group had been enlarged considerably by the redeployment of senior and junior chemists and biologists who were at that time dependent on Institute funds for support. This was agreed. The Ludwig Institute was formed and accepted financial responsibility for all of the staff. I passed over control to Dr Neville and the name Ludwig Institute appeared in large letters on the outside of one of the floors of the Chester Beatty laboratories.

The arrangement suited the MRC since my grant money from them could be used to support research in other parts of the country, and it suited the Institute since more of the scientific staff were financed by Ludwig. It was at this time we received a visit from Mr Ludwig himself, about whom his business associates spoke with bated breath. As I was told, he had begun life by borrowing a small sum from his father to raise a sunken ship which he then sold for $15,000. Later he dredged the Orinoco river and was able to take large cargo ships into the centre of Venezuela and bring iron ore directly to the large industrial towns of the American seaboard. He became involved in oil, and hired, but never owned, oil tankers to transport the oil. When I met him his business interests were worldwide and he was said to be one of the richest men in the United States. At the meeting we had with him at the Surrey branch of the hospital, he said very little and made no comment as I detailed my ideas on the Ludwig development, but he became extremely agitated when I described new plans to build a Ludwig Institute on a site in the grounds of the Surrey branch of the Marsden Hospital. He banged his fist on the table, looked at his unfortunate associates, and in front of some of my senior colleagues, who had come to meet him, announced,

'You know I will put no money into bricks and mortar.' There was a deadly silence and since no-one looked like speaking, I replied, 'Surely you want to know what we are doing with your money? Indeed, we are not asking you to pay a single penny for the building. The Institute will provide £1 million to construct the Ludwig building and we'll rent it to you.' Later that afternoon when we were alone in my office he said,

'You Scotsmen are like Jews, you say what you think.' I never saw him again.

In 1976 the financial position of the Institute had improved, legacies and endowments increased markedly and the divisions were winning grant support. At my request the finance committee of the Institute set aside one million pounds to build laboratories, offices and a lecture room at Sutton which the Ludwig Institute would occupy and equip as well as taking responsibility for staff salaries and running costs. The Ludwig Advisory Committee would never guarantee to stay permanently in the Institute but indicated a tenure period of ten years. Accordingly I rented the building to them at a cost of £90,000 per year and in ten years the Institute would recoup most of the million pounds and have available to them a fine new building if and when Ludwig chose to leave. In retrospect it is incredible that the first Ludwig Institute should have its origins in October 1971 when two young businessmen should walk unannounced into the Royal Marsden Hospital. Yet this chance encounter contributed a great deal to the recovery of the Institute of Cancer Research and could in future rank as one of Ludwig's real achievements.

CHAPTER 15

Visits to some World Cancer Research Institutes

Toward the end of 1972 I was invited to join the International Union Against Cancer ('Unio Internationalis Contra Cancrum', UICC) which was founded in 1933 as an independent association of 254 member organisations in 84 countries throughout the world. Membership is open to voluntary cancer organisations, cancer research and treatment groups, and in certain countries Ministries of Health. It is a non-profit, non-racial organisation run by a small professional staff from office headquarters in Geneva, Switzerland.

It is supported by membership dues, national subscriptions, contracts and grants for specific projects and programmes as well as donations from foundations and corporations. The annual budget for 1986 was $25 million. Every four years it organises a large International Cancer Congress in a different country in the world. It runs international symposia, workshops and training courses on selected topics of cancer research, control and treatment, all of which are held in the laboratories and lecture theatres of member organisations and run by their staff. It publishes the *International Journal of Cancer*, as well as a number of technical reports and monographs on different aspects of cancer. It conducts a series of active programmes which cover a wide field of cancer activities such as cancer detection and diagnosis, smoking and cancer, cancer treatment and tumour biology. Each programme is co-ordinated by a chairman, and may have within it a number of projects, each one led by a project chairman and committee.

When I became a member of the UICC I made the acquaintance of two American surgeons who introduced me to the concept of a comprehensive cancer centre, which strengthened my resolve to see basic scientists and clinicians working in unison to tackle the problems of human cancer. Dr Gerald Murphy was Director of Roswell Park Memorial Institute in Buffalo, USA, which is believed to be the oldest cancer institute in the world;

225

and Dr R. Lee Clark was Director of the MD Anderson Tumour Institute and Hospital in Houston, Texas which, he told me, was the first cancer institute in the USA where the Director was answerable to the President of the university and not to the Faculty of Medicine. Both men had been actively involved in the negotiations which led to the National Cancer Act (1971). Murphy had organised a meeting at Roswell Park to explain to Congressmen the concept of cancer centres, while Lee Clark was a member of the influential Yarborough Committee whose report 'Conquest of Cancer' laid the foundation for the Act, which allocated a vast sum of money to the cancer programme. Both men had been associated with the UICC for a number of years and through them grant contracts became available to the UICC to service the newly created Committee on International Collaborative Activities (CICA). I became chairman of this programme and had a committee of eleven members, all directors of large institutes in Canada, Europe, the United States and South America. The following projects were developed.

The International Cancer Patients Data Exchange System or International Data Bank was intended to provide relevant information on all cancer research institutes and hospitals in the countries represented in the UICC. At the first meeting I attended, Lee Clark produced a number of books which resembled a series of telephone directories with the address and phone number but without the name of the subscriber. The volumes had been compiled by a private consultancy firm commissioned to do the work. The results were so unsatisfactory that the CICA committee decided Lee Clark's Institute in Houston should be financed to undertake the work. At the 11th International Cancer Conference held in Florence I explained the role of the Data Bank and informed the delegates that a comprehensive format had been prepared. This listed the name and address of the institute, hospital or organisation, the number of technical, scientific and medical staff employed, the annual finance involved, the different divisions within the organisation and an indication of the type of research carried out, with a note of recent publications. When collected the information would be made available to all UICC members who would learn where and what lines of research were being undertaken. The response was very encouraging. Most member cancer groups co-operated and in a short space of time Lee Clark had produced the first volume of the Data Bank. This exercise was a valuable, if expensive, lesson on the use of private consultants for a planning role in science and medicine.

Fellowship and Personnel Exchange. The second project involved one of the three fellowships administered by the UICC. The American Cancer Society funded the prestigious Eleanor Roosevelt International Cancer Fellowship which allowed senior scientists to work abroad on experimental or clinical problems for a period of up to one year. The candidates were assessed and selected by an international committee of distinguished scientists who had to be assured that successful candidates would return to suitable research facilities in their own countries when their fellowship period ended.

The Yamagiawa-Yoshida Memorial was provided in 1974 by the Japanese National Committee to honour the two scientists who had opened up the field of chemical carcinogenesis which led to the discovery by Kennaway of the first chemical carcinogen. This fellowship enabled senior scientists to spend up to three months abroad in a laboratory to undertake collaborative studies. My committee felt there was a need to create a new fellowship which would enable scientists early in their career to spend up to twenty-eight days in a laboratory abroad, to learn some newly developed technique or start some collaborative studies. This fellowship was funded by a United States National Cancer Institute contract to the UICC and was called the International Cancer Research Technology Transfer Fellowship (ICRETT). It proved very successful and in the passage of time the number of fellowships was extended by financial support from cancer organisations of UICC member countries in Britain, Canada, Norway and Sweden.

Comprehensive Cancer Centres. This was the third project discussed in the early days of CICA, and focused on the help that could be given to any country planning (and financially able) to develop a centre. Both Murphy and Lee Clark had been active in convincing the United States Congress of the importance of cancer centres, and their institutes had been recognised by the National Cancer Institute of America as comprehensive cancer centres even before the National Cancer Act was passed in 1971. It was through my contact with both men and later with Dr Edwin Mirand, the Associate Director of Education at Roswell Park, that I would learn how the centres were created in the United States and efforts made to encourage basic scientists and clinicians to work together on cancer problems in patients. This was the very problem I was trying to resolve at the Marsden Hospital and Institute of Cancer Research in London.

Initially the aim of the United States Institutes of Health at Bethesda, Maryland was to provide financial support for research in the hope that discoveries would bring benefit to mankind. Most of this support went to basic research units in their institutes and the extra-mural funds they administered were allocated for basic research in the universities they supported. However, in the United States and in Britain, scientists who worked in basic science departments were reluctant to become involved in research applied to human problems and genuinely believed that, in doing so, they were prostituting their science which they felt should be directed to understanding the basic problems of life. Undoubtedly there was a need to support this form of pure research, but equally there was a need for another group of highly talented scientists to collaborate with clinicians and study the problems of human disease. The stimulus to create such a team came from those American congressmen who insisted that any increased federal funding should be dependent on the ability of basic scientists to demonstrate that the new emerging knowledge could be applied quickly for the good of patients. This indeed meant bridging the gap between clinicians and scientists and to achieve it the National Institutes of Health needed clinical facilities where well-designed clinical research could be undertaken.

The National Institutes of Health decided in 1953 to create a clinical centre at Bethesda, Maryland and a massive building was constructed in which scientists and clinicians could work together. Basic research laboratories were sited on one side of the building and clinical wards on the other. Connecting corridors joined the two sides of the building so that the exchange of information encouraged planned clinical investigations. Each one of the National Institutes involved in this dual effort was assigned a certain number of beds and laboratory space for clinical and basic research. Close proximity of scientific and clinical departments does not guarantee successful collaboration, yet the Bethesda experiment, as I found on my first visit to the United Sates in 1955, was a resounding success. The new scheme attracted a high quality of medical staff, eager to learn the language of science and the new emerging technology which would allow them to bridge the gap between basic science and clinical problems. For many years after the Second World War, young medical graduates in Britain and the United States had to spend two years on National Service and in the United States they could apply to the National Institutes of Health for the service to be done there. As a result, many of the country's best graduates who were successful in their application found the experience so stimulating that they remained after their period of duty ended.

Each institute within the National Institutes of Health complex carried out clinical and basic research and the studies were funded from each institute's budget. Patients were admitted to the clinical centre only for research studies and at no cost to themselves. The clinical centre was a success and each institute was able to initiate and expand the collaboration between their laboratory and clinical research efforts.

The concept of a clinical centre was well received throughout the United States and the federal government now became a major supporter of clinical research. In 1960 the clinical centre became the pattern used in the National Institutes of Health in their extra-mural grants programme to create, develop and run general clinical research centres in American universities and medical schools to improve the quality of clinical investigation in medical institutions. This was distinct from the patient care which was provided by the regular hospital facilities. Grant guidelines were drawn up and naturally stipulated that each clinical centre must have a director who would establish policy and the necessary procedures for allocating beds. The grants made provision for finance to help build new premises and enlarge or modernise existing facilities. When the centres were established and functioning, site committees were organised by the National Institutes of Health to visit them and review the work. The appropriation for this imaginative programme in 1960 was $3 million and by the late 1970s it rose to $50 million and covered nineteen universities and medical schools. The United States was now financing the most highly nationalised research in the world to produce a class of clinicians and scientists who could collaborate successfully in studies of clinical problems.

Naturally I was interested to learn what was happening about cancer since the National Cancer Institute had one of the largest programmes in the clinical centre at Bethesda and controlled its own bed and research space in the facilities allocated. When clinical centres were developed in University Medical Schools most of the research was devoted to illnesses other than cancer or cancer-related problems. It was difficult for cancer clinicians to participate in clinical trials organised by the National Cancer Institute, since they could not find the necessary bed space in many general hospitals. Accordingly, the National Cancer Institute decided to establish its own cancer centre project and in 1961 was able to announce the grant support programmes designed to extend the cancer facilities in the country.

The *Cancer Research Facilities Grant* was created to meet part of the cost of the new buildings required exclusively for clinical and non-clinical cancer research in universities and cancer research institutes. Dr Lee Clark's MD Anderson Tumour Institute and Hospital was one of the six recipients of this award. Initially the *Programme Project Grant* was the second funding system and used to support broadly-based, multidisciplinary cancer research with a specific major objective in mind. This could be orientated to the laboratory, the clinic, or both. The third system, the *Cancer Clinical Research Centre Grant*, was essentially the same as the second, but with the express purpose of creating comprehensive cancer research centres. A fairly well-defined programme had evolved in 1963 at twelve major institutes in the United States that included Roswell Park Memorial Institute (Buffalo) and the MD Anderson Tumour Institute and Hospital (Houston), and both were designated by the National Cancer Institute as Comprehensive Cancer Centres.

As more federal money became available, staff at the National Cancer Institute tried to organise and extend the cancer centre programme to universities and medical schools throughout the country. At that time the definition of cancer centre was rather flexible. Some centres were devoted to

radiation therapy, medical oncology, or surgical research. Others were essentially a collection of basic research units grouped together for grant purposes
and labelled as cancer. Indeed it was quite common for universities and
medical schools to resist any attempts to establish a separate comprehensive
cancer research centre under a director; since surgeons, physicians, radiation
therapists and gynaecologists all claimed responsibility for cancer patients and
had their own treatment programmes which were never subjected to any
assessment or review.

If a comprehensive cancer centre was established under a director, the staff
would need to work as a multidiscipline team. Patients would be grouped in
hospital wards on an anatomical disease basis and there would be a forum to
discuss diagnosis and assess both the extent of the disease and the treatment
which should be given. The success of this agreed method of treatment could
be assessed statistically over a five-year period. Despite opposition from some
universities and medical schools, many medicine schools showed an interest
and requested the help of the staff of the National Cancer Institute, who in 1968
found it necessary to define what was meant by a cancer centre. Guidelines
were drawn up and published by the National Cancer Advisory Council.
Planning applications were expected to conform to the guidelines, whether
they were directed to the creation of a new centre or the extension of an
existing one. The objectives of the programme had to be defined — how it would
develop, the staff and facilities required, as well as the cost of any specialised
equipment. Details should be given of the source of any available local funds
that could be used. A comprehensive cancer centre was expected to become
involved in cancer control and education, as well as the care of cancer patients
in the community. It was expected to enlist the support and participation of
doctors in the community who were in some way involved with cancer. They
were encouraged to evaluate the financial resources of the community and
how this money could be brought into the programme. In many instances a
wealth of unsuspected medical personnel and available finance came to light.

As the concept of a comprehensive cancer centre was extended to involve
community participation, the need for careful planning became very necessary, yet many institutions ignored this. Their applications were unsatisfactory
and only when they were rejected did the applicants realise the need for
proper planning. The National Cancer Institute now introduced a novel, but
modest, planning fund of $800,000 to help institutions explore the ground
and prepare a proper funding application for a comprehensive cancer centre.
On occasions the institution planners enlisted the help of professional consultant agencies and it was only when those agencies understood the concept
and needs of a cancer centre that they made a significant contribution to
planning; indeed, the staff of the National Cancer Institute emphasised the

need for all participants from the institution and community to be involved actively in planning the application. New cancer centres were created and federal funds from the National Cancer Institute were augmented by support from sources in the universities, state and local funds and from private benefactors. Once the cancer centre had been created and funded, the National Cancer Institute accepted a commitment to add additional support for at least five years, after which its success or failure would be assessed.

When the National Cancer Act was passed in 1971, thirty-nine different varieties of cancer centres were actually in operation and funded by the National Cancer Institute. Now the vast sum of money generated by the new Act allowed for an extension of the scheme to create more comprehensive cancer centres throughout the country. The Cancer Centre Support Grant, now used by the National Cancer Institute as the central funding mechanism, gave the director of the centre the financial flexibility needed to develop a cancer-related programme within the parent university. In the ensuing fifteen years, forty-two centres were created in universities throughout the United States. The federal funds used to develop the centres provided the environment for scientists and clinicians to work together and ensured that maximum use was made of endowments, reserve funds and internal private support from the parent body.

Basic research scientists, financed by the cancer programme, have made important contributions to our understanding of oncogens (cancer genes), the role of viruses and the immune system in cancer. In time scientists can lose their creativity and fail to win grant support. The cancer grant programme allows the director of a comprehensive cancer centre the necessary flexibility to redeploy such individuals into a group controlled by younger active scientists or to a clinical team working on a broad spectrum of cancer research.

Inevitably the public will judge the clinical cancer programme a complete success only when a cure is found for the common cancers. The difficulty of achieving this will be appreciated when it is realised that cancer is not a single entity but is, in reality, about two hundred and fifty different conditions, each presenting a different problem in biology. Accordingly the cancer programme can be considered a success only when there is a significant reduction in the mortality statistics for the common cancers of lung, breast and colon, as we have seen in patients with Hodgkin's disease and some childhood tumours. Community programmes organised by the comprehensive cancer centre on cancer education will become effective when the public becomes aware that many cancers of lung, bowel and cervix can be prevented. Undoubtedly the comprehensive cancer centre programme is improving the standard of care and treatment of patients within those established centres. Patients do not feel abandoned to an undignified end of rejection and the pain of terminal illness. I feel more can and should be done for those patients by developing hospice facilities and care for them in their own community.

Whereas patients are admitted to clinical research centres for research purposes only and at no cost to themselves, comprehensive cancer centres have a responsibility for research, education, patient care and treatment, and this involves the community as well. If the centre is state-supported, as many are, treatment is free, although in some such centres as we will see, provision is made for paying patients. My association with Lee Clark and Murphy not only clarified the concept of comprehensive cancer centres and the problems involved in trying to create them, but reinforced my conviction of the need to develop multidiscipline treatment units at the Marsden Hospital and the role institute scientists could play in them.

In time the International Union Against Cancer (UICC) initiated a project on comprehensive cancer centres and published guidelines based on the experience of the United States National Cancer Institute programme which was backed by large sums of money. Whether UICC would ever have access to the type of funds needed to initiate cancer centre programmes is doubtful, but they have available, in different member countries, experienced clinicians and scientists who could develop such programmes. They would need a modest sum to help with planning applications which would involve the medical and scientific staff of the institution and interested representatives of the community. The experience of the National Cancer Programme was that many hidden resources in the institution, the community and private sources would be discovered and contribute to the 'core' or seed grant needed initially for any successful programme. Even before any institution, in any country, reached the stage of making an application it would have to convince surgeons, physicians, and radiotherapists who deal with cancer patients, to accept a director of the centre, a redistribution of beds to deal with cancer patients on an anatomical basis and a multidiscipline approach to each type of cancer. This, as I found, is not easy to achieve.

It would facilitate matters if a sum of money was made available to UICC to build new premises for the centre or to update, modernise and equip old ones. Where was the money to come from? During the time I was Director of the Institute of Cancer Research, the Ludwig officials extended their activities to create or support clinical research institutes in a number of countries in the world. No doubt these institutes will become centres of excellence. However I am convinced that one of the great contributions the Ludwig associates could make to the problems of cancer is to help the UICC develop their comprehensive cancer project by providing the finance needed to establish those centres in countries who are members of the UICC organisation. Cancer centres in the United States led to an improvement in the standard of care and treatment of patients and a Ludwig contribution, which would result in a similar improvement in the cancer care of patients in other countries in the world, is surely a prize worth winning. Perhaps even now it is not too late for the Ludwig associates located in Zurich to make this invaluable contribution to the activities of the International Union Against Cancer.

My Institute responsibilities in London limited the period I was able to spend at the UICC, and after I resigned I maintained my interest in UICC activities. The Institute of Cancer Research held a workshop on tumour markers and later the staff ran a course for young science and medical graduates from abroad who wished to make a career in oncology. I maintained a close link with Lee Clark and Gerald Murphy and other members of CICA, visited their institutes and learned about the circumstances that led to their creation.

I visited Roswell Park Memorial Institute in Buffalo for the first time in February 1973, and during the next ten years I took part in a number of site visits and attended and spoke at conferences there. I met most of the scientific and medical staff, discussed their work and was invited to give the Clowes lecture. During this period my wife and I developed a close and friendly relationship with Dr Murphy and his wife Bridget, and with Dr Edwin Mirand, the associate director of education who had written a concise and informative history of the Institute, which I found had much in common with the Marsden Hospital in London. Both were created by surgeons and, while Marsden, in 1851, developed the first hospital devoted exclusively to the care of cancer patients, Roswell Park created the first institute directed to cancer research.

Roswell Park was a distinguished Professor of Surgery from Chicago, appointed in 1883 to the University of Buffalo Medical School. He was very concerned at the lack of any organised national support to investigate the nature and cause of cancer and find ways to improve treatment. Although tuberculosis and infective diseases were the real killers at that time, the incidence of cancer in patients was rising and Roswell Park set up three small rooms to study cancer in the University of Buffalo Medical School. In 1898 with the help of a local paper magnate, he induced the New York State Legislature to pass a Bill which provided a grant of $10,000 to establish a laboratory devoted to the study of cancer. It was called the *New York State Pathological Laboratory of the University of Buffalo.* Since that time New York State has continued to support the Institute. Funds from private benefactors and very considerable federal support through the agency of the United States National Cancer Institute have also helped to create an impressive and world-famous institute.

As Roswell Park's programme expanded, the space available became too small and the imposing new Gratwick Research Laboratory was opened in 1901 financed by a wealthy benefactor. Sir William Osler visited the laboratory and was impressed by the research being carried out. He records his appreciation of the need for large expensive equipment and a staff of thoroughly trained men who should devote years to the work. From humble beginnings the New York State Pathological Laboratory was created and, while Roswell Park retained his connection with it until his death in 1914, the pressure of his many activities induced him to resign as director in 1904 and his successor Dr Harvey R. Gaylord remained in office until 1923.

During those highly productive years, Gaylord drew attention to the role of immunity in cancer, followed Osler's advice and brought into the Institute scientists like Dr George H. A. Clowes who carried out extensive chemical studies and initiated the first cancer chemotherapy programme in the United States. Later Clowes joined the staff of a pharmaceutical company and was involved in the commercial manufacture and clinical use of insulin, which he supplied for trials to the clinicians at the institute. Gaylord travelled abroad and, when in Prague in 1922, induced Drs Carl and his wife Gertie Cori to come to Buffalo where they began studies which contributed to an under-standing of the main glycolytic pathway in glucose metabolism. This study won them the Nobel Prize. They joined, in this work, an illustrious group of Nobel Laureates like Myerhof and Warburgh whose research and teaching did much to make biochemistry the science it is today.

Gaylord, along with Clowes, was influential in founding and developing the American Association for Cancer Research, but his consuming interest was in trying to identify the parasitic cause of cancer. In a memorandum of 1911 he writes, 'After three years' state support (1898–1902) the cancer laboratory came out solidly for the parasitic theory of cancer and has consistently supported this view.'

Indeed Plimmer, who in 1889 became head of the pathology and cancer research department of Marsden's cancer hospital in London, also was an ardent supporter of the parasitic theory of cancer. After leaving the Marsden in 1903 to become Director of the Lister Institute (London), he wrote an article in the *British Medical Journal* in 1911 describing round ovoid bodies as the possible causal organisms. He refers to Gaylord in this article It is now possible to look more objectively at the claim 'the Roswell Park Memorial Institute is the oldest cancer research facility in the world', keeping in mind the developments in the Marsden Hospital and the Institute of Cancer Research in London.

When, as I recounted earlier, Marsden created his cancer hospital in 1851 and occupied the new 78-bed unit in Fulham Road in 1862, he had a pathology and cancer research department. He appointed as pathological anatomist Dr Robert Knox, who had to leave Edinburgh because of his association with the notorious resurrectionists, Burke and Hare. There is no evidence that either Knox or Marsden contributed to our understanding of cancer and when Knox died in 1862 and Marsden in 1867, no appointment was made to the pathology and cancer research department until 1889 when Plimmer took over. Bearing in mind his research on the parasitic cause of cancer, it is difficult to conclude that the New York State Pathology Laboratory of the University of Buffalo was the first facility in the world dedicated specifically to cancer research. Nevertheless it certainly led the world when the Gratwick Research Laboratory was opened in 1901.

After Plimmer's resignation from the London Cancer Hospital in 1903, some medical staff there were unhappy about the research being done and felt there was a need for better research laboratories and equipment. I suspect there would have been someone from the cancer hospital in London among the many representatives of institutions in Europe who visited Buffalo and returned to establish facilities modelled on the lines of the Gratwick Research Laboratory. At any rate, in London, the Cancer Hospital Research Institute was built to replace the old department of pathology and cancer research and in 1909 the first director, Dr Paine, was appointed and the Institute of Cancer Research was born. Whereas in London almost sixty years elapsed between the creation of Marsden's cancer hospital and the birth of the Institute, Roswell Park in Buffalo began with a research institute. Within a few years his successor Gaylord saw the need for hospital facilities to apply to patients the scientific principles learned by experiments in the Gratwick Research Laboratory, which at this time was not a state facility, although it was funded by the state. In 1911 things changed. The Gratwick Research Laboratory became the *New York State Institute for the Study of Malignant Disease*, and from then onwards it was called the Institute. Research covered the preparation and action of vaccines, a search for cancer-producing bacteria, transplantation studies of mouse and fish tumours and a study of the relationship of the immune reactions to cancer.

In 1913 Gaylord built a thirty-bed hospital, the Cary Pavilion named after one of the original trustees, and in the same year developed the Springfield Biological Station on a farm thirty miles from Buffalo. He appointed a director who, with Gaylord, carried out research on thyroid tumours in trout and bred mice in which to study the role of hereditary cancer.

Over the years, the biological station was expanded and its role and research activities changed by subsequent scientific directors. In 1946, the Institute altered its name, in honour of its founder, to the *Roswell Park Memorial Institute*, and unlike the Marsden where the hospital and Institute of Cancer Research became separately administered, all directors of Roswell Park Memorial Institute have since then had control of basic and clinical research as well as the hospital care of patients.

After Gaylord's death in 1924 the new director, Dr Burton T. Simpson, placed more and more emphasis on patient care. Patient numbers increased and in 1927 when the Institute came under the jurisdiction of the New York State Health Department, a new hospital, the Gaylord Building, was constructed to accommodate the increased patient load. The state of the economy affected the Institute, its funding was reduced to a minimum and the staff took a voluntary reduction in salary to keep the Institute functioning. Major and minor surgical treatment of patients kept increasing and without an increase in staff, a system of patient referral replaced the old one where the hospital had operated an open door for patients to come at any time. In the early 1940s things improved, a new hospital – the Simpson Building, named after the third director – was occupied and all staff in the Institute became full-time, but because of the Second World War, shortage of staff was now a problem. Over $7 million was allocated from the New York State Reconstruction Fund to improve facilities for better patient care and develop closer links with the University of Buffalo Medical School.

New surgical specialities such as thoracic and plastic surgery were added to existing ones. A blood bank was formed and basic and clinical research programmes were expanding so much that the director at that time, Dr Louis C. Kress, appointed Dr Joseph G. Hoffman, a distinguished biophysicist, as director of cancer research. Hoffman had been a member of the Manhattan team project which led to the development of the atom bomb. He was interested in the biophysical properties of cells and was one of the first to study the effects of atomic radiation on man.

Dr Kress died suddenly in 1952 and the fifth director, Dr George E. Moore, was only thirty-two when appointed. During his period of tenure (until 1967) there was great expansion in patient care, clinical and basic research and education, as well as growth in the number of staff and facilities. Over a period of forty years the Institute grew from a building with thirty beds to a large clinical research complex which could accommodate 227 patients.

The Institute was developing as a major cancer research and treatment centre at the time when the Clinical Research Centre was built at Bethesda in 1953. However, as a state facility, Roswell Park Memorial Institute could not accept private funds. A non-profit-making organisation was formed to receive gifts from grateful patients and relatives and grants from federal organisations such as the National Cancer Institute, the United States Public Health Service, the American Cancer Society among others. In time a very substantial sum was raised each year and used, with financial support from New York State, to construct or extend the many fine clinical and basic science buildings I saw on my first visit to Roswell Park Memorial Institute.

In 1960 the original Gratwick Research Laboratory, which had been the

The Author with Dr Gerald Murphy and Sir Alistair Currie
at Roswell Park Cancer Institute.

model for so many cancer research institutes throughout the world, was demolished and replaced by the new Gratwick Basic Science Building. The West Seneca Laboratories, opened the following year, were used to breed mice for institute research under satisfactory hygienic and genetic standards. In 1962, during this period of activity the Institute, following the lead of the National Institutes of Health, constructed a Cancer Clinical Centre on the fourth floor of the hospital. This consisted of a sixteen-bed ward and adjacent laboratory space, and was an attempt to bring together basic scientists and clinicians who were studying the effects of diet and drugs on patients with leukaemia. This expansion of facilities continued under Dr Moore until he left in 1967. A cell and virus building with programmes in virology, cell culture, biochemistry and germ-free biology, as well as a crystallographic centre was built in 1965. This centre was used by scientists to study the arrangement of atoms in a compound and it was hoped that information on its structure might help predict its carcinogenic potential.

During his tenure of office Dr Moore had a profound effect on Institute developments and when he left for another appointment, he was succeeded by Dr James T. Grace Jr, who died tragically three years later in a car accident. Nevertheless, he left his mark on the Institute and with his successor, Dr Gerald Murphy, planned additional important facilities and introduced a number of administrative changes. The Institute now was a very complex organisation. The new facilities that had been and were being created could not be managed by one individual, and Dr Grace appointed associate directors in clinical affairs, basic and applied science and education, with whom he could discuss those matters. Although he never lived to see it, Dr Grace, along with Dr Murphy, had planned the Research Studies Centre, with funding of $3.5 million from the New York State Legislature. The centre, opened in 1970, housed a fine five hundred seat auditorium, a computer centre, conference rooms and a well-equipped medical and science library. Two years later the Cancer Cell Centre, funded jointly by the National Cancer Institute and New York State at a cost of almost $8 million, was built and provided space for basic research on cancer cells in the departments of molecular immunology, experimental pathology, genetics, endocrinology and radio-biology.

Drs Grace and Murphy had secured funding for a cancer drug centre and when it was opened in 1973 it was named after Dr Grace to mark the contribution he made both as a director and earlier as a member of the staff of the institute. The centre, staffed by senior scientists and clinicians, provided a complete pre-clinical programme of anti-cancer drug development and testing within the same building.

Roswell Park Memorial Institute had been involved for many years with cancer control and education. In 1936 a Bill in the New York State Assembly established a cancer survey commission to study the cancer problem in the state and the need to reorganise the Division of Cancer Control in the State Health Department. The commission gave priority to developing cancer control and to achieve this they broadened the operating scope of the Institute. The new clinical facilities being created at that time allowed the Institute's education programme to be expanded and lectures on cancer were given to students from the University of Buffalo Medical School. Local hospitals sent doctors for training in cancer medicine and young clinicians could undertake research and learn research techniques in the basic science departments.

Dr Mirand joined the Institute officially in 1951 as director of the Springville Biology Station and biology department at the main campus. He became associate director of education in 1967 and he played a vital role in developing and expanding the broadly based programme on cancer education firstly within the Institute and eventually to the public in New York State. In 1953 he established the Institutes Research Participation in Science, a summer programme funded by the New York State and the National Science Foundation. This was designed to interest young college and high school students in a career in science and cancer medicine. In time Mirand became Dean of the Roswell Park Division of the University of Buffalo Graduate

School which was established in 1955, and since then more than six hundred advanced degrees have been awarded in science. Medical students from the State University of New York at Buffalo, as the University of Buffalo is now called, could work in the out-patients clinics and wards of the Institute whose staff provided relevant seminars for them. Doctors came from hospitals in the United States and abroad for training: postdoctoral research training in basic and clinical sciences is given to about eighty individuals a year and intensive courses in oncology nursing offered to nurses from many parts of the country.

It is not surprising that Roswell Park Memorial Institute was one of the first institutions in the United States to be designated a comprehensive cancer centre by the National Cancer Institute, even before the adoption of the National Cancer Act in 1971. Indeed the Institute had strengthened its links with the community when in 1968 it established a wide area telephone service programme. This made it possible for doctors and dentists in New York State to telephone, free, staff members about patients who had been admitted to hospital or to seek assistance concerning others.

In 1973 Roswell Park Memorial Institute introduced a public telephone cancer information system, CAD-DIAL, in which an individual could call the Institute and listen to tape-recorded messages on a variety of cancer-related tapes. Initially the facility was restricted to the counties around Buffalo, but the scheme was so successful in the first year that it was expanded and made available to all residents in New York State through a toll-free number. A Spanish language tape was also added.

Cancer is an illness that can have a devastating effect on the patients and their relatives and often the latter need as much help as the patients. Where patients have to travel long distances to hospitals for treatment, often there are no facilities to house relatives who may need to travel with them. This applies particularly to parents of young children who are undergoing therapy and to the elderly husband or wife who may be on their own. The Garvey Foundation in Roswell Park dealt with this problem. It purchased and equipped the Kevin Guest House Complex which was sited on land near the Institute and used it to provide low-cost housing for ambulant patients under treatment, and their families.

It was through the efforts of Roswell Park himself in 1898 that the New York State became committed to cancer research. Over a period of seventy years his successors skilfully used the allocated state money and supplemented it with substantial federal support thus providing funding to produce the imposing new research and hospital buildings which make up the Roswell Park Memorial Institute. Whereas the MD Anderson Tumour Institute and Hospital also began as a cancer hospital, supported by Texan State funds, its rise to international recognition can surely be attributed to the efforts of one man, Dr Lee Clark.

In the summer of 1974 I was invited by him to be the Mike Hogg Visiting Professor at the MD Anderson Tumour Institute and Hospital in Houston, Texas. I lectured on the role of the basic scientist in clinical research and illustrated the importance of this co-operation with reference to my adrenal research. I was asked to make a television recording of the lecture which would be made available to the graduate students who were in his training programme. During the week my wife and I spent with Lee Clark, I visited all the basic science departments in the institute as well as the superb hospital wards which, like those in Roswell Park Memorial Institute, were under the director's control. During the week we spent in Houston, Margaret and I had a lovely flat in the Anderson-Mayfair Hotel. Dr Clark and his wife Bertha lived on the top floor of the hotel building and during our visit I had ample opportunity to discuss comprehensive cancer centres, data banks and the involvement of basic scientists in clinical problems.

During a visit to one of the basic science departments I learned from one of the scientists that he had returned recently from a trip abroad and had had the unenviable experience of being on a plane that had been hijacked. During the long hours of suspense, and realising that his life could be terminated at any moment he wondered how he might gainfully occupy the time. Eventually he decided to go over in his mind all the books he had read and decide, if he could have two books with him now, during this crucial period, which books he would choose. In this way, he told me, he was able to pass many hours, assess the value of each book and what comfort they could be to him at this moment of time. In the end, after hours of useful deliberation he chose the Bible and Sir William Osler's 'Equanimitas' which, as I have already mentioned, was a collection of his articles and named after the valedictory address that he delivered to the students of the University of Pennsylvania when he left the Chair of Medicine there to become Regius Professor of Medicine at Oxford.

A few years later when Margaret and I were flying from Philadelphia to Toronto she found herself sitting next to a very old gentleman. The stewardess came round the plane, handed him the customs form and said she would return later and help him with it. In the interval he began talking to Margaret and in the end she filled out his form which he completed with a spidery signature.

'You are Scottish,' I heard him say, and when she confirmed this he said, 'Is that your husband? What does he do for a living?' When she told him we were both medicals he replied, 'Ask him if he knows my cousin.'

'What's his cousin's name?' I asked.

'Sir William Osler,' was the reply. I told him that his cousin had opened the department of pathology in Glasgow in 1911 where I had been the professor and he was delighted when I told him the story of the hijacked plane.

After my lecture at the MD Anderson, Dr Clark and his wife invited us to spend the weekend with them at their ranch at Rokansky in Texas. We set out early on Saturday morning and stopped for breakfast at an attractive wayside coffee house, then drove on to the ranch. On the way, Lee talked about his family who had been teachers for many generations and had established seminaries in many parts of the United States. He was a tall, well-built, muscular man and I was not surprised to learn that in his college days, he was a national amateur wrestling champion, had read widely on the subject and learned about the large number of holds and counter-holds used in this sport.

The ranch house, originally a scout hut, had been extended by them and was now L-shaped. It was situated in the centre of 1500 acres of land on which they grazed a large herd of Brangus cattle. They had started in a small way, acquiring scrub land which they cleared and over a period of years the ranch was extended to its present size. Lee Clark developed the ranch as he would deal with any medical research project; he experimented with twenty-two different types of grass before he settled on coastal Bermuda which, he told me, had roots that went six feet into the ground. His experiments were so successful that his fellow ranchers now used coastal Bermuda. Margaret and I drove in the ranch truck with Lee and his farm manager around the ranch, saw the herd of cattle lying in the shade of the single large trees he had preserved for their protection against the sun, and paid a visit to the village store. Here was the President of one of the biggest and most prestigious cancer institutes in the world, whose picture hung on many corridors in the hospital he had created, a man who had played a leading role in establishing the National Cancer Act signed by the president of the United States in 1971. It was indeed the same person who met, talked and behaved in such a friendly manner to the village folk in the little store. On the way back to the ranch we stopped to inspect the six beautiful quarter horses on which his wife had won many prizes and rosettes which hung in the sitting room of the ranch. Quarter horses, I was told, could run very fast over distances of a quarter of a mile.

After dinner we sat in the lounge and Lee told us about his career and how he became involved with the MD Anderson Cancer Hospital and Institute. Dr John Spies had been on the staff of the Memorial Hospital which was a large cancer hospital in New York, attached to the Sloane-Kettering Cancer Research Institute. It was highly regarded throughout the world for its treatment of cancer patients, training of physicians and surgeons in patient care and research into the cause of cancer. I had given a lecture there on my adrenal research when I visited the Memorial Hospital in 1955 and was interested to hear about the role one of its staff had played in the development of the MD Anderson Hospital and Institute in Houston. Dr Spies moved from New York to become Dean of the University of Texas Medical School in Galveston and helped to write the Texas Legislature Bill which created a cancer hospital for the state. The Bill was passed in 1941 and rather wisely, as it turned out, put the cancer hospital and research laboratories under the University of Texas Board of Regents and not the medical school. It was left to the regents to decide on the location.

About the same time the MD Anderson Foundation purchased an estate in Houston and donated it to the University of Texas as a temporary home for the State Cancer Hospital and research laboratories until permanent accommodation could be built. In addition the trustees matched the state legislature's allocation of $500,000 and the MD Anderson Cancer Hospital was born and located in an old home in Houston where it remained until 1954. A temporary director was appointed in 1942 and Dr Lee Clark took over in 1946.

Lee had taken a degree in chemical engineering and worked as a chemist with Du Pont Chemicals in Newark New Jersey before entering medical school in Virginia, where he met and married a fellow student, Bertha Davis, who was a great help and inspiration to him in his medical work and helped him develop the ranch. She was an anaesthesiologist in one of the Houston Hospitals at the time we visited them. Lee took up surgery and gained experience in that speciality in the American Hospital in Paris before returning to the United States and a career in surgery at the Mayo Clinic in Minnesota. In 1942 he was a Lieutenant Colonel in surgery in the United States Airforce; later in Jackson, Mississippi, he helped to set up a medical school.

When he was appointed Director of the MD Anderson Cancer Hospital, he was a talented and experienced surgeon with a consuming interest in cancer, a capable and shrewd administrator, and above all, a charismatic doctor. He gathered together a team of talented doctors and scientists and in time built one of the most imposing cancer hospitals and research institutes in the world.

At the time of his appointment there were a number of cancer hospitals with an international reputation in the United States, but none was in Texas. I knew some of the senior doctors who had been interviewed for the post in Houston, but none of them wished to tackle it and in the circumstances many wondered why Dr Clark considered it, since the salary offered was a fraction of what he could earn as a surgeon.

'It was,' he told me, 'the challenge and excitement of building the first cancer hospital in the United States which was part of the University, not the medical faculty.' However, he insisted on certain terms. He must be entirely independent and responsible only to the President of the University of Texas, have control of his own budget and be responsible for the clinical and research building programme. While the hospital, as state supported, would have a major responsibility for cancer patients who could not pay, he insisted the hospital must be made available to those who could pay; and it was this source of income that would help him attract some of the best clinicians in the country and yet build up a full-time university staff.

During the first few years he brought no pay patients into the hospital but gained the confidence of the private doctors in the area by developing a free consultation service for their patients. Gradually he admitted a small number of private patients to the hospital and in time built up a Patient Referral Service (PRS). The funds from those private patients he used to supplement the university salary of the full-time clinical staff. He provided health benefits and retirement pensions for them and was able to attract and keep first-class medical staff. His plans were approved by the university regents and the Inland Revenue, and his creation of the patient referral service is a tribute to his administrative ability and vision for the future of the hospital. He arranged for members of the Board of Regents to be trustees of the fund, along with representatives of those who earned the money; and a yearly budget on expenditure was submitted for the board's approval. I was interested to learn that the fund was supervised by the manager of the Anderson-Mayfair Hotel where we were living. The hotel was built by money from the PRS fund and used to provide an ambulatory care facility where patients could be treated under medical supervision. We had the opportunity to meet and talk to some of the patients and their relatives during our visit, and all agreed the hotel made their stay there much easier. Undoubtedly the facility was a valuable investment and in time would repay the outlay from the PRS fund. I could only reflect on the need to have an Anderson-Mayfair type of facility at the Marsden Hospital in London, and at Sutton there was plenty of space to build one.

While the PRS fund allowed Dr Clark to attract the best medical staff to the hospital, how did he fund the yearly salary increments? He told me the basic salary of all members was approved yearly by the University Board of Regents and based on faculty rank; then he established six criteria on which he based salary augmentation. The first was service given to patients, whether they were paying or non-paying, and great emphasis was laid on patient care since it is the main reason for having a hospital. The other criteria used to grade the individual was their contribution to teaching, research, administrative duties and length of service as well as general value to the institution. On the basis of these criteria each staff member was graded one to five and salary augmentation applied accordingly. Dr Clark graded the head of each department and decided on salary augmentation, then in consultation with each department head, decided on the salary of members of their departments. It was an ingenious concept which allowed him to recruit and keep excellent clinical staff and retain bright young men and women who had been trained at the MD Anderson but might otherwise leave. He could also, by refusing any salary augmentation, induce those staff members he did not wish to retain to look for a post elsewhere.

In the early days of his stewardship the function of the laboratory was to provide a service in tumour diagnosis (pathology), clinical chemistry and haematology, which would help the clinical care of the patient. Those essential laboratory services would always be required but Dr Clark saw the need to establish a laboratory for basic science to look at the nature of the cancer cell and how the disease was caused. When we discussed this phase of its development, I reminded him that the Royal Marsden Hospital in London was my MD Anderson Hospital and he was going to tell me how he developed something like my Institute for Cancer Research. He thought this analogy summed up the position. He wanted his cancer hospital to be in a university campus where there were in existence academic departments of basic science. Naturally they felt the MD Anderson should restrict its activities to clinical research and leave them to carry out basic work. However Dr Clark, like myself and many congressional leaders, saw the need for basic scientists to become involved in applied cancer research. The university agreed with him and in 1963 the *Texas Graduate School of Biomedical Sciences* was established within the MD Anderson and given its own allocation of funds. The graduate school prospered until there were a number of divisions which dealt with problems in genetics, environmental health, and dental science with a role in fascio-maxillary surgery, tumour research and carcinogenesis. Some were similar; others were different from the divisions I had reorganised at the Institute of Cancer Research in London.

In 1954, at a cost of $9 million, Dr Clark built and moved into the new hospital he helped to plan. He raised money from the Texas State, the National Cancer Institute and from private sources, to realise the dream of his undergraduate days. At dinner that evening at his ranch, he told us his story. In the summer of 1930 he worked at the wheat harvest in Texas to earn enough money to help support his studies at medical school in Virginia. He and a friend had walked from Texas to Atlanta, Georgia and camped in the grounds of Emory University. In the morning he woke up to bright sunshine and while gathering his camping equipment together happened to look through an opening in the trees and was struck by the reflection of the sun on the pink marble buildings of Emory University. One day, he decided, he would build his own hospital of pink marble but was brought back to reality when he discovered a mongrel dog had invaded the privacy of his camp site and was proceeding to use his knapsack as an alternative to an adjacent tree. The dog was dismissed hastily but he never forgot the decision he made on that summer's day in 1930. In 1954 his ambition was realised when the new MD Anderson Cancer Centre was built and clad in pink marble like Emory University.

I visited him in the autumn of 1976 when the budget for the MD Anderson was a massive $33 million, most of it from the Texas State Legislature, a large amount from grants he attracted from the National Cancer Institute and the American Cancer Society and a sizeable sum from the patient referral service fund he had created. Unfortunately I was able to spend only a few hours with him as I phoned home to find my son's condition was deteriorating and I returned immediately to London.

My numerous visits to countries behind the Iron Curtain were interesting and enjoyable for many different reasons. While in Glasgow I had developed a close link with the medical school in Szeged in Hungary; and over the years a number of Hungarian scientists and doctors had come to work with me. The Franz Josef University moved from Transylvania to Szeged in 1921, and in 1971 when the University celebrated the fiftieth anniversary of the move, I was one of a group awarded their honorary degree of Doctor of Medicine. In 1977 I visited cancer hospitals in Warsaw in Poland and prior to this visit was approached by a golfing friend from the Walton Health Golf Club in London and asked to take a letter to a Polish officer who had been with him in the Air Force during the war. They had lost touch and he was keen to renew their wartime friendship. I told him I was very willing to take the letter provided I could hand it to the interpreter who would meet me at the airport, and explain the reason for it. He agreed. There was, he said, nothing in the letter to compromise me. When I arrived in Warsaw I was met by a lady doctor who was the wife of one of the University professors. She readily agreed to take the letter and try to have it delivered. My visits to cancer hospitals in Warsaw and Krakow were interesting and enjoyable and I found it fascinating how my medical colleagues talked about their country. I also learned some interesting facts from them about Polish history. I had always believed the Stuka bombing of Warsaw by the German air force in 1939 had destroyed the city, and was surprised to find those attacks accounted for only 20%, the main destruction being carried out by the German army as they retreated before the advancing Russians. Stalin, my friends informed me, encouraged the Polish underground to rise against the Germans and he halted the Russian army for six weeks on the east bank of the Vistula while the underground fighters were annihilated. When the Germans finally left the city the Russians took over. The underground movement and any political opposition no longer existed. Understandably the Polish people felt betrayed and there was great bitterness towards the Russians. In Krakow I visited the university which, like the old university of Glasgow, was built in the form of a rectangle, and I was thrilled to visit the room which had been occupied by Copernicus and see the gleaming, round copper spheres he used to develop his revolutionary theory. In the sixteenth century, Copernicus challenged the accepted view of Ptolemy that the sun and planets orbited the stationary earth. He was a mathematician and astronomer whose belief in the importance of theory and experiment helped him to conclude that the earth orbited the sun; with some modifications his views are accepted today. His theory ran counter to the doctrine which for 1400 years was supported by the church, and for thirty years he did not publish his observations for fear of the Roman Catholic Church who considered his views heresy. Indeed, Copernicus was dying when his book *Concerning the Revolution of the Celestial Bodies* was published in 1543, yet it was another three hundred years before the church accepted his theory. The two young pathologists who accompanied me took me to see the new church built in the shape of a ship whose mast took the form of a cross. The church was packed; hundreds were taking communion and as we walked around my friends pointed out the many alcoves which were used to commemorate important incidents in Polish history. One alcove was empty and when I commented on this, they announced with pride, 'Some day this will be dedicated to Katyn.' When the Polish troops retreated before the invading German army in 1939, they were caught between them and the Russian army which had invaded Poland. Four thousand Polish officers were slaughtered and although the Germans were blamed, the Poles held the Russians responsible and one day they were sure they would admit to this atrocity, and the name Katyn would appear in the vacant alcove in the church.

I returned to Warsaw stimulated by this visit to Krakow and was taken to see the house where Marie Curie was born. My wife and I had represented the University of Glasgow at the Marie Curie celebration in Paris in the 1960s, met some of her family and talked to many old students who had worked with her. In her later years they told us, she always wore white linen gloves and was constantly rubbing her fingers together. It was little wonder she did so, as an auto-radiograph of one of the letters she wrote is in the Marie Curie Museum in Paris and is heavily contaminated by radio-active material. After the war the Polish government began to reconstruct buildings in the centre of Warsaw from old drawings which had been preserved and I was able to see Marie Curie's home in the form she knew it.

As I was preparing to go to the airport for the return flight to London, the lady doctor handed me a letter addressed to my golfing friend at Walton

Heath. During the week I had spent in Poland she had managed to trace the Polish Air Force officer. He had been admitted to hospital where his leg had been amputated for gangrene. His spirit was very low, she told me, and the letter from his friend in London had made all the difference to him; and now I had the pleasant task of reuniting two wartime friends. No doubt 'there is a divinity that shapes our ends'.

During my association with CICA in Switzerland, I met Professor N. N. Blokhin, who was a member of the committee, and visited him in Russian on three occasions. I had been associated with the British Council for many years and a number of young doctors from abroad who worked with me in Glasgow came on British Council scholarships. I maintained a close link with the Council while in London and in 1974 was invited to lead a small cancer delegation to Russia. It was bitterly cold when we arrived in Moscow in February of that year and I was delighted to find we were in accommodation in the large new International Hotel Russiya. There was a reception for us that evening at the British Embassy dacha in the country and the following morning our guide and interpreter, an attractive young lady called Lena, arrived at the hotel and took us to the Ministry of Health where we had some general discussions with officials there.

I would find the Russian visits were never the high pressure scientific affairs I had experienced in America and our routine was very standard. A morning visit to a hospital or research department was followed by an excellent lunch at the hospital or in a nearby restaurant, invariably with a liberal supply of cognac or vodka. The Russians were excellent hosts, although on the occasions when we had breakfast or an evening meal on our own, the service left much to be desired.

Professor Blokhin's All-Union Cancer Research Centre is one of the largest in the world and, as expected, was built by government funds which, in this case, came from an interesting source called a sybbotnik. Every worker in the Union of Soviet Socialist Republics (USSR) worked one Saturday in the year and their wages were given to the government who used the money to build research institutes for studies in science and medicine. In Kiev I visited the Institute of Gerontology which was built with the money from the sybbotnik and Professor Blokhin's Cancer Centre was financed in this way. Like the directors of most of the institutes in CICA, Blokhin was a surgeon and, although responsible for the activities of this large cancer organisation, he was in addition the Member of Parliament for the Volga.

The divisional structure and research conducted in the cancer institute were along the same lines as in centres in the West and in America; each department I visited was a self-contained, enclosed unit. The scientists talked freely about their work and although many were fluent in English, inevitably the discussion was conducted through an interpreter. I was never able to discover how a department was financed or how the work of scientists was assessed. As far as I saw, there was no attempt to integrate the work of clinicians and basic scientists.

In the afternoon our guide arranged for us to see different places of interest in Moscow, which was the capital of the fifteen states that made up the Soviet Union and is one of the oldest cities in Russia with a population of seven million people. It is the seat of the Academy of Science and its imposing university enrols more than 20,000 students. The city has many art galleries and we visited the Pushkin Fine Arts Museum with its excellent collection of West European paintings and the Tretyakov Picture Gallery which is a treasure house of Russian painting and sculpture. On our way to one of the galleries we saw the vast outdoor swimming pool which is open in summer and winter, the temperature being maintained constant in all kinds of weather; it was being well patronised.

We visited the University of Moscow, walked through Red Square, saw the Lenin Museum and visited St Basil's Cathedral and the other churches in the Kremlin. Close to the belfry of Ivan the Great is the large Tsar Cannon, with three massive cannon balls, and the Tsar Bell; a part of the side of the bell broke during casting. The Kremlin churches, like so many in Russia, had been reconstituted as Museums of Christian art. Surprisingly this seemed to cause great distress to some of my Catholic medical colleagues who had visited Moscow, and I was pleased to tell them of the comments made by my friend Monsignor Philip Flanagan who was Rector of the Scots College in Rome. During a visit my wife and I paid to the Vatican, as I admired the marvellous paintings of scenes from the Bible, he remarked, 'This is how the story of the Bible was taught to the people in the days before the printed word.' Maybe, I kept thinking, this is how young Russians were learning the Bible story, for I saw many young and old persons in the churches we visited.

In the evening, on many occasions, we visited the Bolshoi Theatre and the equally impressive Kremlin Theatre which is housed in the imposing white marble building of the Palace of Congresses.

My first week in Moscow coincided with Women's Day which is a national holiday. Lena nevertheless arrived in the morning to take us on a visit to the country home of Count Yussopov. Her mother, whom we never met, had baked scones and biscuits for us, and as a token of appreciation on Women's Day, we sent her a box of Russian chocolates, which incidentally are very good. The Yussopov home resembled one of the stately homes in this country. In Russian it was taken over for the people by the state after the revolution, whereas in Britain stately homes are acquired by the National Trust for the people by a more subtle if less traumatic, but still punitive form of government taxation. I was impressed by the fine display of china which had been created by countless master craftsmen and their families. They spent whole lives as serfs in this creative work. We entertained Lena to lunch at a nearby restaurant and on the way home, laughingly she informed us that the meat we had enjoyed so much was bear steak.

We were due to travel to Leningrad by night sleeper on the Sunday of our first week in Moscow, and we were invited that day for lunch to the home of the science attaché of the British Embassy. In the afternoon he and his wife drove us into the country to visit the grave of Boris Pasternak in the village of Peredelkino where he had a dacha in which he wrote Dr Zhivago and where he died in 1960.

On the way to Peredelkino we were followed by the KGB and as we drew up on one side of the road they did the same; when we crossed the road they followed, always at a discreet distance. We parked the car at the cemetery and walked to the unpretentious grave, which was surrounded by a single rectangular iron rail. I could picture the burial of young Zhivago's father taking place on a similar spot. Meanwhile the KGB simply kept us in sight.

'They will not disturb us,' said our host, 'they don't know who you are but if you are going to pass any secret information or meet someone and receive papers or books, it will be done in the country. As far as we are concerned they will escort us back to the flat,' which they did.

'At times,' he said, 'they can be useful if the car breaks down.' It was an interesting experience and a sobering thought.

That evening we boarded the night sleeper to Leningrad where we spent a few days with Professor N. P. Napolkov at the cancer institute which was the first one formed in Russian and named the Petrov Institute after its founder. I was familiar with Napolkov's research on the experimental produc‹ tion of cancer of the colon in rats and had reason to refer to this study in the legal case in which I became involved. I visited Leningrad a second time in November 1976 to take part in the celebrations to commemorate the fifty years since the establishment of the Petrov Institute. Representatives of cancer institutes from all fifteen states in the Soviet Union were there. Along with colleagues from France, Germany and America I presented a paper which was translated simultaneously into Russian for the assembled staff of the Petrov Institute. This meeting took place in the original town house of Count Yussopov whose country estate in Moscow I had visited on my first visit. Around the walls of his Leningrad estate were pictures of Russian peasants taking part in the revolution. The house had been used for peasant education and in large letters which covered an entire panel in one of the rooms was written '2 x 2 = 4'. This was one of the most interesting visits I paid to a foreign country and I was intrigued to learn it was in the basement of this house that the dissolute Siberian mad monk, Rasputin, was murdered in 1916. On the second day of the meeting, a group of young and old scientists and clinicians from cancer institutes in Russia, Poland and East Germany invited me to lunch at a restaurant in Leningrad, 'to show', they said, 'their appreciation of the help they received from the staff of the Chester Beatty Institute during the year they spent in London, when in receipt of an Eleanor Roosevelt Fellowship'. It was then I fully appreciated the importance these doctors attached to this UICC scholarship.

On my first visit to Leningrad I was privileged to have a conducted tour of the Hermitage Museum which is something I will always remember. On the two occasions I visited the city I asked to see Paul's Palace which was situated outside the city and was in the hands of the German army during the siege of Leningrad. The walls of the palace were pitted from machine gun fire, as were the statues which still remained outside the palace. They had been used for gun practice by the German soldiers. Photographs taken after the siege showed the massive destruction and desolation within the palace and it is a great tribute to the lady curator of the museum that not a single exhibit was lost. In the few days before the Germans captured the palace, she had crated all the exhibits and sent them to Siberia, yet she was almost shot for defeatism by the Russian authorities. Before the vast programme of renovation of churches and museums could start, schools of fine art were created in the country and, when sufficient people were trained in fine art restoration, the churches and museums were restored to their former magnificence.

During my second visit to Moscow in 1975, I was accompanied by my wife, and our cultural visit on that occasion was to the Academy of Theology at Zagorsk which lies about forty miles from Moscow. This is where the Russian priests are trained. We were shown round the churches and museum by the Patriarch, a delightful venerable gentleman with a long beard. Along with the two young interpreters who accompanied us, we had lunch with the Patriarch and the Secretary of Zagorsk Academy who gave us an insight into the origin of the ancient town and its religious background.

Originally it was named Sergiyev Posad, and for six centuries the centre of faith for devout Russians has been the Monastery of the Holy Trinity and St Sergius who is the patron saint of Russia. The Trinity Monastery was founded in 1337 by Sergei Radonexhski who was an active fighter for freedom and enjoyed great popularity in the country, since at that time the country was under the Tartars. The Monastery has played an important role in the history of Russia and was linked closely with the development and strengthening of Russian governments. Monasteries in old Russia had strong fortifications which formed the main points of the country's defence. In addition, they were the original centres of culture, education and architecture, and many of them are the pride of Russian national architecture.

In 1930 the town was renamed Zagorsk after a prominent member of the communist party who died in 1919 and the museum we visited was a rich storehouse of Russian national art, masterpieces of old priceless icons, ancient embroidered church vestments, gold and silver crosses and chalices encrusted with diamonds and other previous stones. Included in the collection were many bibles, all the work of expert calligraphers, some were opened to reveal hand-painted scenes, and most were embellished with gold and precious stones. An item of interest to us was a small replica of the Cross of St John which stands outside the Abbey of Iona in Scotland. It was a stimulating and memorable visit and inspired by the beauty of what we had seen, I wrote in the guest book, those appropriate lines from Keats' 'Endymion'.

> A thing of beauty is a joy for ever:
> Its loveliness increases; it will never
> Pass into nothingness.

As we left the church they rang the bells for us.

While I did not learn a great deal about cancer medicine during my visits to Russia, I shall long remember the elegance of the Russian theatre, the spectacular performances of ballet and opera, the paintings and exhibits in the many churches, museums and palaces of Moscow and Leningrad and our visit to the museum of the Academy of Theology in Zagorsk.

CHAPTER 16

Retirement and the Ayrshire Hospice

THE SUN WAS SHINING through the window of the room when Margaret and Sandra returned. They had scarcely been away more than ten minutes, yet to me it seemed an eternity. Sister appeared. 'Robin,' she said, 'is due another injection,' but it was not required. His breathing was shallow, his pulse not detectable, and in a few minutes he was gone. We went back with Sister to her room, no one talked as we waited while the nurses gathered his clothes and personal belongings and we made our way out of the hospital to the car. I took the keys out of my pocket and tried to open the boot of the car, but my hands began to shake; Sister took the keys, opened the boot and placed the bag with his belongings in it. We thanked her for her help and kindness and drove home. That evening the minister, who had given Robin great support, and a number of friends came to see us. Next day was spent in preparation for the funeral on Wednesday and on Tuesday I appeared before the Industrial Tribunal. Although Margaret had tried to persuade me not to go, I found it concentrated my mind to some extent, and kept me from dwelling on the events of the last few days and of our loss. Like all families we had been sad when our parents had gone, but they, like us, had lived their life, whereas like my father, Robin had been taken from us in the full bloom of youth and at a time when he was beginning to enjoy and make a success in life.

This is the stage when one begins to question one's faith.

'Why him?' we would say.

'Why not us? We have had a good life.' It is the kind of question many people ask during the post-bereavement period, and this is the time when many need and benefit from good counselling and begin to appreciate that God too had voluntarily made the ultimate sacrifice on the cross.

I spent what appeared an interminable period in the witness box during the Tribunal and previously had consulted some senior geneticists in this

Margaret and Author in the garden of retiral home in Troon, Scotland, 1989.

country on the relevance of the claimant's research to cancer. They had given this advice in confidence and it was on the basis of their assessment that I rejected the application for promotion to a senior grade in the Institute. Accordingly I refused the request of the Institute's council to call them as witnesses. It was up to me, as Director of the Institute to accept responsibility for the decision I made. Apparently I did not present my case with sufficient conviction. The Tribunal judged in favour of the lady who was promoted and, since the Medical Research Council did not support her research, the Institute had to provide her augmented salary from reserve funds. It must be emphasised that the lady in question was a well-qualified scientist whose genetic studies, the advisers informed me, were suited more to student teaching and research in a university. In retrospect, as part of the redeployment programme I introduced successfully into the Institute, I should have tried to do this with her and her studies on Drosophila genetics.

The general manager in charge of Robin's company flew from Nairobi to the funeral and afterwards came to see us in our home. It was a gesture Robin would have appreciated as he had spoken of his superior with great respect, and this action meant a great deal to us. Although our son had worked in Africa for little over a year with Minet, they had looked after him, were kind and appreciative of his illness, and through them we learned the future they had planned for him. They earned our gratitude and inspired our thoughts of what he might have achieved if only his life had been spared. This was not to be. He had had many serious illnesses during his short life, but he bore them with great fortitude, and in our minds he would never grow old but remain an active, kind young man who was always helping people. With the passage of time, Margaret and I could talk about him and eventually laugh about some of the things he did, and we always would wonder, had he not gone to Africa that fateful evening, would my colleagues in the Marsden hospital have been able to save his life? We would never know. Yet he enjoyed Kenya so much, loved the visits he was able to make to the game reserves, and the cine films he took of the animals were to sustain him in hospital on the numerous occasions he went for treatment. In the end we decided there was no guarantee, even at that stage of his illness, he could have been cured, and at least he was not denied the happy experiences he had in Kenya.

As so often happens as one life is taken, a new one appears, and six weeks after Robin died our first grandson Robbie was born. In the ensuring years our daughter had another son Andrew, and son Alan had three lovely girls, Emily, Fiona and Nina. The first two are now teenagers and all have been a source of great joy to us. Like grandparents generally we have had the pleasure of seeing them grow up without having the responsibility for them.

I did not have the same enthusiasm for the Institute after Robin died; things were running well, restructuring was complete with the exception of a few scientists whose research was not funded; the divisional reorganisation was complete and the Institute was fully funded. The development of multidiscipline units in the Royal Marsden Hospital was progressing satisfactorily and the links with the Institute well-developed. Both institutions had weathered the trauma of reorganisation and were in a strong position to meet the financial challenge of the 1980s. There was no incentive for me to remain any longer and accordingly I decided to retire in the autumn of 1977 to Troon in my native Ayrshire, where we had many friends. I had retained my membership of the Royal Troon Golf Club which in the next ten years would host two Open Golf Championships. The fog-free international airport at Prestwick was close to our home and many American colleagues who were keen golfers, visited us to play over Royal Troon and Prestwick Golf Club, which was founded in 1851 and hosted the first eleven Open Golf Championships.

'Where else in the world,' my American friends would say, 'could you find a fog-free international airport adjacent to a historic championship golf course?'

Daughter Esther with husband Robert Le Borgne and sons Robbie and Andrew in 2001.

*Grandson Robbie Le Borgne (aged 26) and wife Danielle and our
great-granddaughter Elizabeth, 2001.*

Toward the middle of November 1977 a letter marked 'urgent personal'
arrived from the Prime Minister. I had never met Mr Callaghan and was at
a loss to know why I should hear from him now. As I opened the letter,
Margaret asked what he wanted.

'It's not from the Prime Minister,' I informed her, 'It's from his Principal
Private Secretary,' and handed her the letter which said in strictest confidence
that, 'the Prime Minister has it in mind, on the occasion of the forthcoming

Wedding of grand-daughter Fiona Symington to Mark Buckingham, son Alan and wife Celia with daughters Emily and Nina, June 2001.

Grandparents at Fiona and Mark's wedding.

list of New Year Honours, to submit your name to the Queen with a recommendation that her Majesty may be graciously pleased to approve that the honour of Knighthood be conferred upon you. Before doing so, the Prime Minister would be glad to be assured this would be agreeable to you.' I had read about individuals who had turned down a Knighthood, but it was clear from this letter this was not so. They could certainly claim they did not wish to be considered for the honour, but no one could say they turned it down. Naturally I was pleased to receive the award since it was one honour Margaret could share with me. We heard nothing more until the television announcement of the New Year Honours list, read about it in the morning papers and were surprised at the many phone calls from friends in this country and abroad.

'What is this I hear?' asked the Director of a well-known cancer group in Canada. 'Did you get it for golf or medicine?'

'They don't tell you, Bob,' I replied, 'but I don't think it was for my golf.'

Margaret and I appreciated the numerous letters we received and none more so than the one from Dr J. M. Johnstone who was Secretary of the Scottish Hospital Endowment Research Trust. It awarded my first research grant and provided financial support for the MacFarlane Chair of Cancer Medicine I had initiated at Glasgow Royal Infirmary. He had been, he said, surgical resident at Glasgow Western Infirmary with Sir Kennedy Dalziel when his award of Knighthood was announced. Next morning, during the routine ward visit with his medical and nursing staff, Sir Kennedy stopped at the bed of an old female patient who offered her congratulations with these words, 'Some hae soucht (seek) it, some hae bocht (buy) it, but you have wrocht (work) it,' and, Dr Johnstone added, 'You hae wrocht it.'

In March the following year, Margaret and our son Alan went with me to Buckingham Palace to receive the award, at an impressive and well-organised ceremony which was held in the Palace Ballroom. I had to report to an adjacent room where a number of individuals had gathered. I was not sure what I was supposed to do until I noticed some people had congregated in a corner of the room. Each in turn went forward and rested the right knee on what was a kneeling stool. The man in front of me made no attempt to go forward and on enquiring why, he said, rather sadly I thought, 'I'm not getting a "K".' I had heard the letter 'K' used to describe an antibody dependent cytotoxic cell that could break up or kill tumour cells and knew the K-region of certain chemical compounds was related to its ability to produce cancer, but I was learning another use for the letter. When he said, I thought with surprise, 'If you are getting a "K" you had better go and see the fellow at the kneeling stool.' I was pleased to seek advice on what was to happen and was told, 'When your name is announced, you enter the hall and turn left. When you

At Buckingham Palace, March 1978.

are in line with Her Majesty, bow, approach her and place the right knee on the kneeling stool. The Queen will touch you on the shoulder with the sword. You will rise and she will hang the Knight's Bachelor badge over your head and say a few words to you. When she has finished she will shake hands and this is the sign for you to retire backwards, bow to her, and turn right out of the ceremony room.'

During my army service, on parade in Malaya outside the British Military Hospital, I had been known to turn the wrong way on the command to dismiss, and find myself face to face with a colleague, much to the amusement of the Chinese workers at the hospital who were watching the ceremony. It worried me what would happen if I turned the wrong way after the Queen had dismissed me. Fortunately everything went well, and I could only surmise Her Majesty might have enjoyed the spectacle of one of her Knights making a wrong turn to face an oncoming recipient of an award.

It surprised me to find the people in the small mining village of Muirkirk looked on the award as a tribute to the village and in the summer of 1978 they organised a dinner for Margaret and me, and invited Sandra, my sister Ina and her husband, Jim Hodge.

I was presented with a suitably inscribed champagne salver, which I treasure, and Margaret received a large bouquet of flowers. I was sorry this should happen after Robin died, for he had attended other village functions in which we had been involved. My mother had died ten years earlier, but all her old friends were there and I brought the medal presented by the Queen and the letter from the Prime Minister's Office for them to see. Maisie, a close family friend handled the medal with great care and interest, pointed to the sword, the spurs and the laurel wreath and asked about each one.

'Your father and mother would have been so proud if they had seen this,' she said, and added, 'So would Uncle Bob.' This afterthought made me wonder. He laid great emphasis on education, and educational achievements would meet with his approval. He had done so much for the young miners in the county, sought no reward or honours for himself, yet no one deserved them more. I was not sure how he would have reacted now; outwardly he would have appeared unimpressed by it all, yet inwardly, I began to think, he would have experienced a little pride that he had made it possible.

We settled well into retirement in Scotland. Margaret carried on with clinical work in one of the Ayrshire hospitals. I did some part-time work in the University of Edinburgh, became external examiner in pathology in the University of Belfast for a few years, and undertook some site visits to cancer institutes and hospitals in North America and Canada.

It was the autumn of 1978 when I received an invitation to give a talk on cancer to members of the Women's Rural Institute at Millport, on the small holiday island of Cumbrae which lies off the Ayrshire coast. After the lecture, Margaret and I would spend the evening at the home of two school friends I hadn't seen for many years, and so we looked forward to this visit. It is interesting to think it was this talk that convinced us of the need to establish a hospice for the people of Ayrshire, a task that would keep us busy for the next eight years.

The President of the Rural Institute was concerned at the small audience who had turned up to hear my talk and said many members would like to hear what I had to say but had vivid memories of the pain and suffering experienced by members of their family who had died of cancer. Their experience with the 'Big C', as the disease was called, was too recent and my lecture, they felt, would only make them relive those unhappy memories. It was the type of challenge I had not anticipated. I had a few lantern slides to illustrate my talk and decided to use them to get the ladies to feel at ease and thus make them understand what cancer was, how it was produced, and what attempts were being made to 'cure' the illness. The time might come when cure was unlikely, but at no time should the patient be made to feel cure was impossible. It was at this stage the efforts of doctors and nurses should be directed to *care* for the patient and deal with symptoms such as pain, which many patients experience during the terminal phase of the illness. It is the lack of care shown to patients during the terminal illness that lingers in the memory of relatives and makes them frightened of the disease.

'I do want to make it clear,' I said, 'that patients with cancer are not infectious and you won't get the disease visiting them in their homes. Indeed in most instances a visit from friends, provided you don't tire them, can be beneficial.' I pointed out there was no need to burn the patients' clothes as some people do, when the end of the illness has come.

I knew many of the ladies collected for cancer charities and asked them about this; did they know how the money was spent or indeed think or ask about it? Most of them said they contributed to one of the cancer charities and understood the money was for research. They never doubted it would be put to other than a good use. I was able to assure them this was the case, and the main cancer charities like Cancer Research Campaign, Imperial Cancer Research Fund and Leukaemia Research Fund all had scientific committees made up of doctors and scientists who scrutinised applications for research grants. The recipients of those grants had to submit progress reports and some would receive site visits from members of the committees.

I talked to them about some of my research and told them that most changes are caused by chemical, viral or radio-active environmental factors to which we are exposed in the air we breathe or the food we eat. Strangely enough, I said, it is quite difficult for those factors called carcinogens to gain access to the cells of the body and produce cancer. The cells of the body have developed techniques to render the agents inactive and it is only when the carcinogen escapes from the body's defences that cancer is produced. I said it may take many years before the tumour reaches a size to cause the symptoms which make the patient consult a doctor. If the tumour occurs on a site like skin or cervix it can be seen and treated at an early localised stage, and the doctor can assure the patient the cancer will be cured. When it occurs in most other sites and can't be seen easily it becomes more difficult for the doctor to say it is localised and predict the outcome of treatment. I illustrated this point by drawing their attention to the five year survival rates of some common cancers shown below and asked them to comment.

Type of Cancer	Localised	Regional lymph glands involved	Distant spread of tumours to bones, liver, brain, etc.
Breast	85%	58%	10%
Colon/rectum	71%	44%	8%
Lung	33%	11%	1%
Bladder	72%	21%	4%

They could see the survival rate was markedly improved if the tumour was treated when it appeared localised. The outlook was bad when the tumour had spread to the lymph glands and worse when it had spread to distant sites. One perceptive lady noted the poor outlook, even with so-called 'localised' tumours of the lung and made the comment that all tumours in the localised category therefore could not be truly localised. This was the point I hoped they would make and I explained how difficult it was for the doctor with the techniques available at present, to be sure, as he could with skin and cervix, that the cancers in other sites were localised and curable. There was a need for more research to help clinicians determine the extent of the disease. Nevertheless, the ladies understood the importance of finding a tumour when it was early and localised, and naturally one of them asked about breast self-examination. I took the opportunity to encourage this but to allay a sense of fear, if a swelling was found. I stressed that five out of every six breast swellings found were not malignant. While this information might be comforting, they said they would go through a worrying period until they could be seen in hospital and the nature of the swelling determined.

'This factor alone,' I said, 'should make early diagnosis and treatment by the surgeon a priority.' I reminded them that cancer develops slowly over a number of years and a delay of one or two months before treatment would not affect the outlook for a woman with breast cancer. I agreed the pressure of waiting was so tremendous that early diagnosis and treatment of the condition should be a priority. If the swelling is simple, as most are, the woman can get on with her life; if unfortunately it is malignant, she will face up to treatment with determination and the desire to see her family grow up and reach the stage in life when they can look after themselves.

In hospital, I told my audience, cancer teaching for medical and nursing students is directed to cancer *cure*. When the outlook for the patient deteriorates and the terminal phase of the illness is reached, there is no attempt to enlighten students on either the measures needed for the *care* of the terminally ill patient or the problems faced by relatives during this period. Yet this is what motivated William Marsden in 1850 to establish the world's first cancer hospital.

My audience could see from the survival studies I presented that there was a need to deal with the terminal cancer problem, and so we discussed what happened at present to those patients. During the last six months of life, terminal cancer patients will spend twenty-eight days in the surgical, medical or geriatric wards of a large acute general hospital. Seventy per cent of them will end their days in this environment, where the medical and nursing staff are busy dealing with acutely ill patients and unable to provide the type of care the terminally ill cancer patient requires. Likewise, there is a lack of proper facilities for relatives who wish to spend as much time as possible with the dying patient.

The 30% of cancer patients who die at home are cared for by the primary care team of family doctor and nurse, and often the relative is left with the responsibility of caring inadequately for a patient suffering severe pain and lack of sleep. It is this lack of care and help which has devastated many relatives, caused them to dread and fear the illness, and made them ask the question 'when will it all end?'. When it does, they feel guilty and believe they did not do their duty and willed death on someone dear to them.

'What can we do to help the patient and family during this difficult phase of life?' I asked them, and raised the question of the hospice and its function. My audience had heard about such places where patients went to die, and this disturbed them.

'I would like to tell you some stories about cancer patients and the hospice, and let you judge for yourself the role a hospice can play,' I said. During the years I spent in London, I told them, I became friendly with Dame Cicely Saunders of St Christopher's Hospice, and took part in the training classes she ran for doctors, nurses and social workers. During my first visit to the hospice, Margaret and I were talking to Dame Cicely in her office when matron came in to announce that the ambulance with a new patient had arrived.

'It is my custom,' she said, 'to go to the ambulance with matron and welcome the patient. Would you like to accompany us?' I was intrigued to see a bed had been taken to the ambulance in which was an old man who moaned and complained about the severe pain he was suffering and the lack of interest shown him. He had lung cancer. Dame Cicely introduced herself and the matron, then my wife and me, and told him she had brought the bed for him. She said that he would be taken to the ward to receive something for the pain and we would see him later. When we saw him one hour later in the well-equipped wards, where some visiting children were talking to the patients, he looked quite different. He was relaxed, the pain, he said, had gone. Later Dame Cicely told us that much of his pain was the pain of rejection; now he was in a caring environment he would still have it, but that the pain would be anticipated and he would receive treatment before a further attack was due. She said many doctors feared terminal cancer patients on morphine would become addicted, but this wasn't so and frequently, once the pain had been controlled, the dose required could be cut down. Although the old man died a few days later, he died with dignity and free from pain.

The ladies were interested but still apprehensive, as I was to discover.

'You said the hospice was *not* a place where you go to die, yet that is what happened to the old man,' said one of them.

'I will try to deal with this point by telling you about another patient who went to St Christopher's,' I told them. 'A friend asked me to see a man who had had an operation for bowel cancer in a private hospital in London. Unfortunately he had developed extensive secondaries and as you will see from our figures, he had only an 8% chance of a five year survival. He had been told nothing more could be done for him and he was left on his own, with a wife and young family. He realised the seriousness of his condition and the effect the illness was having on the family. I told him he must never give up. He must get back to the literary work he did and look on every month as a year, every week a month and every hour a day. I brought one of my colleagues who worked weekends at St Christopher's to meet him. When he felt ill, had pain or needed attention for some other clinical problem, he went to the hospice, had a few days' rest, got his medical problem dealt with and returned home. In this way his wife got a rest and the family could carry on normally. One evening his wife rang to let me know he had died in the hospice, and said they had been out having lunch together the previous day. St Christopher's had allowed him to live a full life within the limits of his disability, and he had died with dignity. The fact that people die in a hospice is not a failure. What *is* a failure is death without dignity'.

The ladies were beginning to appreciate the role of a hospice and how the existence of such a facility would have helped them. They were not, I told them, the only people who were ignorant of its function, and proceeded to tell them of the time my wife and I were on a visit to the Cancer Centre in Moscow. During the flight on a sparsely filled British Airways plane, a man asked if he could sit with us and began to talk. He had had a distinguished career in science, was paying a scientific visit to Russia and was very apprehensive. During the last visit he had been accompanied by his wife who had died recently, and on learning we were visiting the Cancer Centre in Moscow, he told us his story. His wife, a very beautiful lady, had developed a very malignant cancer which spread rapidly throughout her body, draining her strength and her good looks. Eventually, after treatment, the doctors informed him they could do no more and he was left on his own to deal with the problem. As he watched her die in agony, he decided he would commit euthanasia then kill himself. He managed to get the necessary intravenous drugs for the purpose but in the end, he said, his Christian faith prevailed, his wife died with no dignity and he had a mental breakdown from which he was recovering. When I told him about the terminal care ward in the Royal Marsden Hospital, where the type of tumour his wife had was dealt with regularly, he was aghast. No one suggested she could go there or to a hospice. What a difference this would have made to his life, and it certainly would have erased the bad memory he would have forever.

I felt the hospice was no longer a death house in the mind of my audience and I ventured to ask if any of them had ever visited a hospice. None of them had, but one lady told her story of a friend on the mainland, who had stayed with her sick brother in a hospice in the North of England. Many years ago her friend's mother had developed a brain tumour and died rather tragically. Her brother, a drunkard, had not attended his mother's funeral and the rest of the family stopped speaking to him. Eventually he disappeared and there was no contract for thirty years. One day her friend received a phone call from a hospice in England. Her brother was dying of cancer and he wanted to see her. She went to England and lived in a room in the hospice where she helped with the patients, was reunited with her brother and was with him until he died. The hospice had allowed him to die with dignity and had reunited a family, a not uncommon occurrence.

Equally, I told them, the hospice has on occasions, helped to share the load of an illness and keep a marriage intact. The young man whose wife developed cancer, and the young wife whose husband has a terminal brain tumour or indeed any form of terminal illness, both require hospice support. The young couple with a child who has terminal cancer need help; the hospice may not save the life of the child, but it can save the parents' marriage and the future of the other children.

The meeting went on much longer than expected. More questions were asked and in the end I was stimulated to think of the terminal care facilities in Ayrshire and the need to do something for the people. On the way home next day, Margaret and I talked things over and in the end decided we would start working for a hospice. There was an obvious need for one and it was something we could do together. Later that year I met Sir David Cuthbertson, one of my former university teachers who had retired to Troon.

'I hear you were giving a lecture in Millport,' he said. 'Were you at the Marine Biology Station?' which he knew well.

'No,' I replied, 'I talked to the ladies of the Rural Institute on cancer; and Margaret and I have decided there is a need to establish a hospice for the people of Ayrshire.' A few weeks later he called me, 'I have been to dinner in London and sat next to Her Highness The Duchess of Kent who is very interested in the hospice movement. I told her you and Margaret are going to try and get one in Ayrshire. She's very interested and is going to write to you.'

It would be necessary to raise money by public subscription and we had no experience of this. Since Ayrshire is a county with a number of large towns, a large scattered rural area of small villages and a number of island communities, the development of a terminal care programme could present many problems. Many people I talked to had had a bad experience with relatives who died of cancer and, like the ladies at Millport, regarded the hospice as a house hidden in the woods where cancer patients went to die. It would be necessary to convince them that the hospice is a place of caring for the terminally ill cancer patients and their families, and was a way of dying rather than a place to die. Central to this concept, they would be told, is the management of terminal disease so that patients can live comfortably until they die and afterwards their family can be helped to live a normal life. We would spend many years trying to put over this philosophy to the people of Ayrshire.

I talked to a friend who was an active member of the multiple sclerosis group. He encouraged me to go ahead with the project.

'There might be occasions,' he said, 'when some of our patients would benefit from hospice care.' I realised this was so. Whereas 94% of patients who would use a hospice were terminal cancer patients, the remaining 6% who would benefit from hospice care were those suffering from forms of chronic nervous and muscular diseases. I learned something else from my friend about the multiple sclerosis group; only a part of the money they raised locally was sent to the central committee and used to fund research; the rest was retained locally to provide benefits for the patients in the region. They purchased invalid chairs which were used by the patients to visit some of the beauty spots in the area. They provided portable home telephones which kept the patients in touch with the outside world, and held Christmas lunch for patients in one of the local hotels. This was an example of money being raised locally and the public could see that it was being used for the benefit of patients with the illness.

The large cancer charities raised considerably sums locally. Could some of this money be used to help provide a hospice so that the public would see some tangible evidence for their contributions? I had served on the Scientific Committee of the Cancer Research Campaign, and wrote asking for help to develop a hospice, only to be told it was not their policy to be involved in this field. I was disappointed, because a large, well-equipped house, ideally sited on the shore at Troon became available; it had been used as a holiday home by the County of Stirling. It was about this time I received the letter from the Duchess of Kent who expressed interest in my endeavour and referred me to the National Society for Cancer Relief, who had helped develop the hospices in Aberdeen and at Strathcarron in Stirlingshire. Cancer Relief had matched the sum raised locally in both instances. Once built, the Aberdeen hospice was handed over and run by the Health Board, whereas Strathcarron received a grant from its Health Board and the hospice was managed by a local committee and supported by local fund-raising. Unfortunately when I contacted Cancer Relief in London, their policy had changed; they were not giving support for new hospices, but were providing home care services for patients in the form of nurses who would work with the patient's own doctor and district nurse.

This has proved to be a valuable and enlightened move, and over the years Cancer Relief has developed home care services in many areas in Scotland by financing for two or three years what are called Macmillan nurses. They are highly qualified and specially trained nursing sisters for whom the Health Board or hospice eventually must accept financial responsibility. The duties of Macmillan nurses were defined clearly by Cancer Relief. They should not be used simply as an extra pair of hands, but could be called to a patient by the general practitioner or community nurse, and support a family caring for a cancer patient at home. The Macmillan nurses keeps a check on pain relief and disturbing respiratory or intestinal problems, like constipation, and makes sure the latest aids are available. Above all, they give the family confidence to cope with the illness. The use of a Macmillan nurse may obviate the need for patients to go to a hospital or hospice, and creates a better quality of life for the patient at home; and by providing support for the family, makes them feel what they are doing is of real value. A third of terminal cancer patients die at home and a further third of this group will have severe pain. By dealing with this problem Macmillan nurses relieve relatives of the worry that occurs and prevent much of the post-bereavement reaction which inevitably follows. Each Macmillan nurse can provide support and advice for fifteen to twenty families at any one time. It is important to understand their role is to co-operate with the home-care team of general practitioner and community nurse and not be used as an extra pair of hands, as some Health Board nursing officials wished.

There was no way I could apply for Macmillan nurses and start a home-care service, since the National Society for Cancer Relief would make the award only to a hospital or hospice which in time would be able to accept financial responsibility for the nurses. I met the Chief Medical and Nursing Officers of the local Health Board, who arranged for me to talk to the Medical Committee and senior nursing groups, when I put the case to them for a hospice, how it could react with consultants in hospital and the relationship that could develop with the Macmillan home-care service.

Our attempts to establish a hospice were attracting considerable public interest, and I was invited to talk to most of the Round Table groups in Ayrshire. Margaret and I visited Women's Circles, Rural Institutes and meetings of Church Guilds. We talked to schoolchildren and Church leaders, and on two occasions I was invited to give the Church sermon on the hospice. People who suffered bereavement would phone or come to our home with donations, but since we had no organisation to accept gifts, we had to refuse and suggest, until a hospice fund was established, they should send the donations to some cancer charity. Other groups were showing an interest and in time Margaret and I were invited to become part of the hospice sub-committee of Age Concern (Ayr). Since 85% of patients who would benefit from a hospice and home care programme were over the age of sixty, it seemed logical for Age Concern to be interested. At first I had difficulty convincing them that the hospice was not a hospital in which old people could spend long periods. Based on the size of the Aberdeen hospice which served the same half million population as Ayrshire, I calculated that only sixteen beds would be needed, particularly if Macmillan nurses were used to work from the hospice and develop the home-care service.

Two years had passed since the Millport talk, and in spite of the time my wife and I spent with different groups throughout the country, little real progress had been made. Then toward the end of 1981 the Chief Administrative Medical Officer invited me to produce a paper for the Health Board on 'a terminal care programme' and in it I reviewed the arrangements which existed for the cure and care of cancer patients in the Health Service, the need for a hospice and a home-care programme. I recommended the Health Board should liaise with a voluntary organisation in a public appeal to raise money for an Ayrshire Hospice. Since Age Concern (Ayr) had already established a responsible hospice sub-committee which was raising funds, I suggested the Board should liaise with them. Further I recommended that until the hospice was built and functioning, a cancer support group should be created from existing hospital staff and be provided with two hospital beds. The support group would, on request, act as an advisory body to consultants on problems related to terminal cancer patients under their charge, and organise a day care service for them. The Health Board should make a request to the National Society for Cancer Relief for two Macmillan nurses who would be part of the hospital cancer support group and have access to the designated hospital beds. They would liaise with the primary care team on the home care of cancer patients. Such a scheme would bring immediate help to terminal cancer patients and their relatives, and provide a stimulus for the public support that would be required to raise funds to build and run a hospice in which I hoped the Health Board would play a major role.

About nine months after I submitted my proposals, the Board established a small working party to review possible options for the care of dying patients in Ayrshire. It was a reasonable decision by them, since they had responsibility for the care of all dying patients, but cancer patients presented a more difficult problem. At the request of the working party, their remit was extended to the care of the terminally ill and their families which covered the cancer problem. The working party carried out an extensive review, visited hospices in this country and invited my wife and me to meet them when we had a comprehensive discussion on the document I had submitted. In March 1983 they published a clear incisive report which recommended the 'development of an integrated terminal care programme for the people of Ayrshire'. The report recognised the hospice philosophy of care which offered special skills and facilities superior to those which existed in acute medical and surgical wards. The report further emphasises 'the essential role of skilled home-care nurses and the need to employ two home-care nurses as part of a developing and integrated terminal care programme'. The report accepted the need for a sixteen bed hospice and suggested the Board should enter into discussions with local voluntary organisations and national charities and review their role and contribution they might make to a hospice development.

While awaiting the Board's response to those recommendations, I was invited by the University of McGill to go with my wife, to Montreal and receive the award of Honorary Doctor of Science This allowed us to visit old friends both in Canada and the United States of America, and discuss the hospice project which interested them. I shall always remember the comment made by one colleague, 'If you create a bandwagon, it will never run until you put wheels on it, and once you have done that and it is going, everyone will want to jump on. This,' he said, 'is the dangerous stage. If you don't hold on tightly, you'll be pushed off.' At the time I wondered why he said it to me. I would learn later.

Margaret and author with Professor and Mrs Duguid to receive the Honorary DSc of McGill University, Montreal, Canada, 1983.

During the rest of 1983 I met representatives of the different groups who had invited me to talk on the hospice, and tried unsuccessfully to get them to join and broaden support for the Age Concern Hospice sub-committee. I realised if the hospice had any hope of success it must be representative of Ayrshire as a whole. In the autumn of that year the Age Concern hospice sub-committee was terminated and, with public support, the Ayrshire Hospice was formed at a meeting in Craigie College, Ayr in November 1983. It was estimated that £400,000 would be needed to build and equip a hospice, but representatives of the Health Board working party, present at the meeting, put the figure at £600,000, which in fact proved to be a more realistic figure. It was a vast sum to try and raise but no-one seemed in doubt that it could be done. A fund-raising project was initiated and in preparation for this I had prepared and handed to the audience at the inaugural meeting, a one-page document calling for the creation of a Friends of the Hospice Group in every town and village in Ayrshire. The role of the Friends was to raise money in their areas and at the same time, when the hospice was functional, organise voluntary help to run it. The Ayrshire Hospice was launched that evening by a generous donation of £20,000 from Age Concern, which indeed was the catalyst which sparked off the fund-raising effort. After the meeting I was interviewed on Radio Clyde, when I was able to announce to the people of Ayrshire that the hospice had been suitably launched by this donation, and expressed the hope that Friends of the Hospice would be established in every town and village. The Ayrshire Hospice Trust was formed and a lawyer became Chairman. During the next two years my wife and I visited numerous towns and villages throughout the county, talked about the aims of the hospice and the need to raise money by creating Friends of the Hospice. The Chairman drew up legal documents pertaining to the Trust and the Friends Groups. One lady on the Trust became responsible for overall fund-raising, while another arranged for hospice collection boxes to be distributed throughout the county. The Ayrshire Post reported different hospice fund-raising projects and, in time, when it was decided to have a hospice logo, the paper organised an art competition for the schools of the county and agreed to donate a computer to the successful school. The response was magnificent, and a panel of local artists chose the design of a young student from Mauchline. His school was awarded the computer, and my wife and a good friend donated a cheque to the winner and runner-up.

As more and more Friends Groups were formed, they had to answer questions from the public about the hospice, and with the help of a London friend, a well-known publisher, I drew up a question-and-answer sheet which could be handed to the public. The public response to the hospice was incredible. My wife and I were invited to receive cheques from large and small groups throughout the county; everyone seemed to be involved, and by the end of 1985, two years after the launch of the appeal, over £600,000 had been raised, including another massive sum of £20,000 from Age Concern.

It was eight years since I had felt the need for a hospice. Money had been raised yet the patients were not receiving any benefit, and I was concerned that public interest might wane. The National Society for Cancer Relief met in October each year to consider applications for Macmillan nurses. Our request for two nurses was approved, a house suitable for a hospice was selected but had to be abandoned because of legal problems, and a new search was made. During a meeting at that time with Ayrshire and Arran Health Board, their Chairman announced they would be putting no money into the hospice and so the Hospice Trust had to accept responsibility for the salaries of the two Macmillan nurses in two or three years' time, when it was hoped the hospice would be functional.

I felt the time had come to plan for this event and the financial responsibility we would be required to meet. Since 70% of the running costs would be salaries, I proposed at a meeting that we should start a Trust Fund and aim to build this up to one million pounds, the interest from which would ensure the salaries of the medical consultant, matron, Macmillan nurses and a senior nurse, and so provide a stable base for the hospice. If a Trust Fund was established we would be able to make an appeal to industry by saying, 'We must be able to meet the salaries of the basic staff needed to run the hospice and we propose to do so by establishing a one million pound Trust Fund, and have put £100,000 of our funds into the Trust.' Earlier my wife had written to Lord Sieff of Marks and Spencer for help, and his reply indicated his interest to hear from her once the hospice was a reality. I had no doubt industry would support a Trust Fund, and did not believe its existence would affect other fund-raising ventures. Unfortunately the Hospice Trust did not approve my scheme.

About this time the Health Board appointed as the Chief Area Nursing Officer (CANO) a man who developed a new nursing structure, including an integrated home-care nurse scheme which would be used for all terminally ill patients. These nurses would receive a short four-day course to allow them to deal with terminal cancer patients. The Health Board was willing to bring the two hospice Macmillan nurses into the scheme and give them a base in hospital where they would be responsible to a senior Health Board nurse. In this scheme the Macmillan nurses would be integrated into the home terminal care programme and carry out the same duties as other district nurses. This was a different use of Macmillan nurses from that laid down by the National Society for Cancer Relief, who viewed the role of their nurses as co-operating with the primary home care team and not simply used as an extra pair of hands, as would happen in the integrated programme. Cancer Relief expected their nurses to spend a considerable time looking to and helping families and it was this activity the CANO failed to appreciate or would not accept.

Nevertheless I felt there was much to commend both programmes, and could envisage a role for an integrated nurse scheme to deal with all terminal problems including cancer in the scattered rural areas of the county and island communities where there were small cottage hospitals run by the general practitioners. If the integrated nurse scheme was to be effective, the nurses involved should undertake not a four-day course, but the full eight-week course taken by the Macmillan nurses. I wrote to my former colleagues, Professor Tim MacElwain and Mr Bob Tiffany, head of nursing at the Royal Marsden Hospital, and sought their advice on a possible three-year clinical trial to assess the relative merit of the integrated and Macmillan schemes. Both men were enthusiastic, such a clinical trial, they felt, would have nationwide value and the diverse requirements of the Ayrshire county was ideal to assess the value of the two schemes. They felt all nurses taking part in the trial should undertake an eight-week terminal care course and, although the three yearly courses they ran were heavily over-subscribed, they were willing to guarantee places for all nurses in the scheme, and help to run and assess the clinical trial. Sadly, neither the Health Board nor the representatives of the Ayrshire Hospice Trust accepted this offer, and no clinical trial was carried out. I had the painful duty of phoning my colleague in London to give them the verdict. They were very understanding. It was unfortunate, they said; the study would have been a useful one.

The finances necessary to build a hospice had been raised, and after eight years I had created a viable bandwagon with wheels. Now it was time for me to jump off, and there were many men and women willing to jump on. Fortunately one of the group induced to do so was a successful local businessman with a genuine interest to see a hospice created and through his drive and enthusiasm a fine hospice was developed in Ayr and actively functioning in 1989. It gave my wife and me great satisfaction to visit the hospice, meet some of the staff and know that at last, terminal cancer patients in Ayrshire had the type of hospice and home-care Macmillan service we had envisaged so many years before.

We could only reflect on what might have been achieved if the clinical trial had taken place.

Our experience with a charity had been an education; on reflection it was gratifying to have the support of our many friends when we began the venture, and we appreciated the cheques, some of them in the four figure bracket, that they gave us. We have many happy memories of the time we spent with the Friends of the Hospice who worked so hard in many different ways to raise the large sum of money needed to make the hospice a reality. Many individuals and other groups can feel a justifiable pride in the contributions they made, as indeed can most members of the Ayrshire Hospice Trust who, in different ways, contributed to its creation; the representatives from Age Concern with their massive infusion of £40,000 can rightly say they were the catalysts in this venture. As for my wife and me, for the friends who joined the Trust at our request, and for those who developed and ran the Friends, the creation of the hospice was our aim, and the help it will give to the people of Ayrshire, our reward.

The creation of a hospice and home care is not the end of the cancer story. In time cancer patients and relatives, as well as the press and television, will demand to know what is being done to cure the condition and what role district general hospitals should play. It is important that everyone should understand and remember that cancer is not a single disease but a large number of conditions, each one presenting as a different problem in biology. The multidiscipline approach to the treatment of Hodgkin's disease by Sir David Smithers and Professor Hamilton-Fairley at the Royal Marsden Hospital led to a dramatic improvement in patients' survival over those who were treated in district general hospitals, and prompted the press to remark, 'It is a case of Russian roulette where you get treated for this disease.' The Marsden clinicians were more successful because they had more experience with the condition and saw more patients than are found in general district hospitals. The same applies to other rare tumours, like testes and childhood tumours, and there is reasonable logic for sending those tumours to centres where the expertise exists.

When we come to the common cancers of breast, stomach, colon, rectum and lung it is the function of research institutions like the Royal Marsden and Institute of Cancer Research as well as comprehensive cancer centres elsewhere in the country to try to understand more about these common tumours, how to assess the extent of their spread and what treatment should be given. The district general hospital will always be involved in treating those common cancers, and those officers in administrative charge, as well as the surgeons, must insist that cancer is recognised as a speciality, so that general surgeons become cancer surgeons. They must become expert in one type of common cancer, be in touch with experts in cancer medicine and be able to use the protocols developed in cancer centres. District general hospitals must provide and establish within them suitable premises designated as oncology units, and I was delighted to find the Ayrshire and Arran Health Board had developed such a unit with beds and a well-trained nursing staff. I visited and was impressed with this unit, which must become a pattern which other district general hospitals will follow; certainly it will provide a fine source of revenue for a district hospital applying for and obtaining Trust status.

Monograph

I HAD BEEN in medicine for close on fifty years, had dealt with patients in general practice in the early part of the Second World War, saw the good side of army medicine in Malaysia and helped to introduce the National Health Service in my position as Professor of Pathology and member of the board of governors at Glasgow Royal Infirmary. During the last eight years of my career I had experience of the Health Service in England when I was Director of the Institute for Cancer Research in London and a member of the board of governors of the Royal Marsden Hospital.

The basic philosophy underlying the National Health Service must always remain care of the patients and since its inception very significant improvements have been made in patient care. A vast amount of money has been and is being spent on the service, which now employs more than a million people. It seems reasonable that every effort should be made to justify this expenditure, the number of people employed in the service and the quality of patient care carried out by the medical and nursing staff in the hospital and primary care service. If this was done and it was shown that more money was required, I have little doubt it would receive public support.

I was in the process of completing this autobiography in 1989 when the Conservative Government's White Paper 'Working for Patients' was published. Many of the proposals in this document emanated from the newly formed Institute of Management and this pointed to the important position that management now held in the health service.

Medicine in Britain
Over the Last 150 Years

A s WE MOVE into the new millennium, the government proposes to spend in excess of 49 billion pounds in the National Health Service. New clinical and financial problems will arise and drastic measures will need to be taken if we are to achieve real clinical and financial accountability in the service. I believe valuable lessons can be learned if we try to understand how medicine has evolved in the past 150 years and the role central and local government, senior doctors and nurses, scientists and management have played in the process and what should be done to maintain, justify and improve the National Health Service in the new century.

Scotland and the Health Service

In spite of the criticism, which the service receives from time to time, there is little doubt that it is still a valued and well-respected part of life, especially in Scotland.

Since the Reformation support for the poor was in the hands of the church and in the mid-nineteenth century, as poverty and disease worsened, the relationship between the two was recognised and doctors campaigned for increased spending on health care for the poor. This resulted in 1844 in a Royal Commission, which recommended that the state should take over from the church. An earlier Act had been established in England. The Poor Law Amendment (Scotland) Act 1845 established Parochial Boards and later Parish Councils to help the poor and establish poorhouse hospitals.

Years of agitation by doctors for medicine reform to protect the public from exploitation by unqualified persons and quacks induced central government to pass the Medical Act (1858). This Act standardised the training of doctors throughout Britain and to ensure a uniform standard of education, students now had to pass an examination before they could be enrolled in a four-year course of medical studies. No doctor could be licensed to practice medicine before the age of 21. Further, the Medical Act induced the London College of Physicians to abolish any geographical limitation to practise medicine as had existed until then. Now medical students were taught in the established universities and in the emerging medical schools in Britain, and graduated with a university degree which involved a training in medicine surgery and midwifery. The Royal Colleges in England and Scotland were allowed to grant a diploma, which covered training in all three subjects. In Scotland those extramural medical schools continued to teach students for the triple qualification until 1948, when the National Health Service was introduced and the Royal Colleges became involved in postgraduate education. The Medical Act (1858) set up the General Medical Council (GMC), which registered the new local qualifications of practitioners, protected the public from unqualified persons, and dealt with misconduct by doctors. The universities and colleges each had representatives on the Council. The Medical Act established medicine as a profession, ended the struggle in England between physicians and surgeons and gave doctors the status of professional men.

Above all, it was the Public Health Act (1867), which helped improve the health of the nation and enhanced the status of doctors and public esteem for them. The Act was designed to prevent the spread of infectious diseases and a Board of Health was set up to deal with epidemics. Medical Officers of Health were appointed in large towns with wide powers to deal with anyone who threatened the health of the community. Sanitation was improved, a good clean water supply installed and attention paid to providing clean food. Overcrowding in houses was prevented, if necessary by force, and the post of Medical Officers of Health (MOH) to large cities attracted men of distinction and the public health measures they imposed improved the health of the population of urban areas.

Role of Medicine Research in the Nineteenth Century

Although the rich industrialists were willing to contribute financial support to existing voluntary hospitals and would help to build new ones in towns throughout the country, neither they nor central government were interested in financing medical research; yet during this period, doctors with no financial support would make outstanding contributions in the field of medical science and pave the way for modern surgery.

When ether anaesthetic was introduced in America, by Morton in 1846 the first step was taken to prevent post-operation shock. A year later in Edinburgh, Simpson introduced chloroform as an anaesthetic and now the limiting factors to surgical progress were control of post-operation haemorrhage and prevention of hospital sepsis caused by fulminating wound infection followed by septicaemia (blood poisoning), the dreaded hospital gangrene.

Joseph Lister, who became Regius Professor of Surgery at Glasgow Royal Infirmary in 1860, had from 1854 been working on methods to prevent fatal post-operation haemorrhage and hospital gangrene and influenced by Frenchman Louis Pasteur's studies and his own experiments, concluded that infection occurred during operation from 'germs' on the surgeon's hands and the surgical instruments he used and from the heavily infected air in the wards.

When he became professor, Lister had no beds in the hospital and no research funds; he was responsible for financing his own studies. Nevertheless the method he used to demonstrate his theory was very simple. He excused himself from the classroom where he was lecturing, passed a specimen of urine, which he divided between two conical flasks and boiled the contents of both. He plugged the neck of one flask with boiled cotton wool and sealed the top so that air could not gain access to the fluid. The second flask he left open on the lecture bench, exposed to the air. Each day as the students came to his lecture they found the contents of the exposed flask became more and more cloudy and the smell reminded them, as Lister intended, of the foul smelling wounds they saw in the surgical wards of the hospital. The other specimen remained clear, and it can be seen today in the Glasgow Royal Infirmary pathology museum along with other Lister exhibits.

Lister discussed Pasteur's work and his own experiments with the Professor of Chemistry at Glasgow University, who told him about a sanitary officer in Carlisle who was using carbolic acid as a disinfectant for drains. Lister, with the help of an engineer, developed a carbolic spray so that a fine mist of carbolic vapour was sprayed into the atmosphere of the operation theatre. The vapour caused such discomfort to the skin and lungs of the theatre staff that the spray was discontinued and instead, at the end of the operation, the wound was covered by a carbolic impregnated gauze dressing so that germs did not come into contact with the operation wound. Later he incorporated an impermeable silk protective between the skin and carbolic dressing. In preparation for surgery, after washing his hands they were immersed in a weak solution of carbolic acid and his surgical instruments were kept in a similar solution until they were required. He solved the problem of post-operation haemorrhage by tying the blood vessels at operation with ligatures made from sheep gut, which he treated with a carbolic solution. The ability to control post-operation haemorrhage and prevent hospital gangrene allowed Lister to deal successfully with such conditions as compound fractures and abscesses which, hitherto, were fatal after surgery. In March 1867, *The Lancet* published his classic paper, 'The Antiseptic Principle in the Practice of Surgery'.

Most advances in medicine are either ignored or rejected initially by the establishment and Lister's discovery was no exception. London surgeons did not accept the antiseptic principle until Lister became Professor of Surgery at the Kings College Hospital in 1876 and even three years later when he opened into a knee to wire the two ends of a fractured patella, leading London surgeons declared he should be sued for malpractice yet the same men acclaimed his results when four years later, he showed them six patients whose patella operations had been successful. Nevertheless, Lister's antiseptic method had defects; carbolic acid was a severe irritant to the surgeons' hands, and older surgeons still unconvinced of the existence of germs carried out his techniques in a very unsatisfactory manner. Lister always insisted his method had to be followed meticulously and only by training a new breed of young surgeons to use the method would advances in surgical technique be possible. Indeed this proved to be the case and while the antiseptic technique was short-lived, it had opened the door to the more scientific approach of twentieth century surgery and helped to allay, but not erase, public fear of hospitals. The new operating theatres that were built extended the scope of surgery and the voluntary hospitals attracted more patients when they opened dispensaries and outpatient departments where patients received a high standard of free treatments.

Whereas the Medical Act (1858) established and unified the profession, the success of the voluntary hospitals in large towns created a class of specialists in medicine and surgery, quite distinct from general practitioners who saw some of their private patients attracted to and benefit from the free treatment now on offer at the voluntary hospitals and their dispensaries. However, in smaller towns general practitioners ran the voluntary hospitals in addition to their practice.

Naturally success of the voluntary hospital service in Scotland and England led to funding problems and as early as 1881 hospitals were faced with the closure of wards. The problem was solved in the two countries in different ways. In London hospitals, consultants induced management to allow them to treat private patients in the wards that were to be closed and since then pay beds have existed in English voluntary hospitals. In Scotland the charter of some old voluntary hospitals prohibited the use of pay beds and the financial problem was met by a successful public appeal; private patients were treated in nursing homes which sprang up in the suburbs of towns where the consultants lived.

Health Services in the early twentieth century

At the beginning of the century, a number of workers and their families received medical care from the many friendly societies that existed. However there was a large group of low-paid workers and their families who could not afford private medicine and were not accepted by the friendly societies. At this time the poor physique of army recruits with a working-class background meant a high failure rate in the army health tests, and the approach of the First World War induced central government to pass the National Insurance

Act (1911). This provided medical cover for families of men in regular work and on low incomes. The worker's contribution was deducted from his wage packet by the employer, who along with the government contributed to the scheme. There was an upper earning limit of £160 per annum above which the worker was ineligible and had to pay privately for the doctor. The worker chose a doctor from a panel of names and in turn the doctor received a fee per patient. Thus, in the industrial towns and villages and in the poorer areas of large towns, doctors were guaranteed a better salary and a more rewarding practice, while the financial limit to qualify for the scheme meant their private practices were largely unaffected.

The Hospital Medical Service (1918–1948) – Teaching Hospitals

A rapid expansion and improvement in health care now occurred in the voluntary hospital medical schools in the twentieth century. Individual units in general medicine and surgery were formed and in time hospital consultants developed an interest and expertise in one of the emerging special branches of medicine and surgery. Separate departments were formed in ophthalmo‐logy, otolaryngology, dermatology, radiotherapy and gynaecology, as well as radiology. A series of laboratory service units were created to support those departments. All medical schools had separate voluntary hospitals, which dealt with midwifery and sick children. It was during this phase of development and later that senior hospital doctors played a vital role in decision making as well as having responsibility for patient care.

In Scotland each clinical unit was run by the chief of wards, an experienced clinician, who received no salary from the hospital. All beds in the unit were under his or her control, and he/she was responsible for the admission and treatment of all patients. Other more junior consultants in the unit, usually three in number, received a stipend of £50 per year. They ran the casualty or reception area and the outpatient departments from which, with the chief's approval, they could admit patients to the wards. However they had no right of access to beds and could not admit patients they saw in private consultation with general practitioners. It was difficult for consultants to build up a private practice and they were usually 40 years of age before they had done so. Accordingly, unless they had private means, young consultants, in addition to their hospital duties, took part time appointments in general practice or became demonstrators in anatomy, pathology or physiology.

The hospital was run by a committee of management whose chairman was usually a lawyer or businessman. Senior doctors were well represented on the committee, four members were university clinical professors and there was an equal number of senior hospital consultants. The lay members were businessmen and a trade union representative. The medical superintendent, matron, secretary and finance officer of the hospital were permanent members of the management committee which received reports from the house finance committee and considered proposals and recommendations from the hospital medical committee for future hospital developments.

The medical superintendent was a doctor with experience in medical administration. Some of them had been senior army officers who had retired from medical service in the armed forces. The superintendent had no clinical responsibility for patient care but exercised considerable authority over the activities of the clinical, domestic and ancillary workers on the staff of the hospital. He kept a close watch on bed occupancy and waiting lists and could and did transfer patients from the waiting list of one surgeon or physician to other clinicians if he felt their waiting list was getting too long. He kept a watch over the activities of domestic and ancillary staff, who in turn always had access to him if they had problems.

The matron was an equally important member of the staff, with responsibility for nurse training, discipline and nursing care of patients in hospital wards, which were run by experienced nursing sisters who exercised considerable authority. Most resident doctors at that time were paid £1 weekly plus board and on many occasions they had reason to appreciate the help they received from sister when they became involved in a difficult clinical problem. Indeed the ward sister was a central and authoritative figure in the unit and although poorly paid many remained in post until retirement rather than seek promotion to an administrative post.

The hospital secretary was an accountant with responsibility for the endowment funds on which the hospital depended. His qualifications and experience, if used in the business world, could have procured him a more lucrative salary; yet like the medical nursing, domestic and ancillary staff of the hospital and the laymen who served voluntarily on hospital committees, the secretary was dedicated to the principle of free patient care, and the open door became an established part of the philosophy of voluntary hospitals. It was this dedication by all members of the hospital staff which was responsible for the informal atmosphere that existed in voluntary hospital throughout the country.

In England, particularly in the London medical schools, there were significant differences from Scotland in the voluntary hospital. Usually the medical superintendent was a practising clinician with access to private beds in the hospital and in competition with other clinicians for private patients. Although there was a chief of wards in administrative charge of a unit he was responsible only for the treatment of patients admitted to the beds under his control. Unlike in Scotland, all consultants in the unit had access to beds and could admit patients seen in private consultation, either to the hospital beds or to the hospital pay beds to which they had access.

Local Authority (poorhouse) Municipal Hospitals

Meanwhile the role of poorhouse hospitals in the early twentieth century was changing. Initially only designated paupers, certified by the parish authorities, were patients in the poorhouses. Towards the end of the nineteenth century, the number of certified paupers fell, while the sick poor increased and the poorhouse became a hospital. The stigma of Poor Law relief disappeared from the patients who needed medical attention.

As the quality of anaesthetics improved, the scope of surgical operation was extended to deal with diseases in most organs in the body, and to gain experience, surgeons in the voluntary hospitals willingly accepted patients from Poor Law hospitals to which they returned after the operation. In time departments of medicine and surgery were established in Poor Law hospitals and a medical superintendent and matron were appointed. Although nurse training began it lagged behind that of the voluntary hospitals and medical students' teaching, which until then was carried out on patients in the voluntary hospitals, was extended to involve patients in the Poor Law hospitals. While they helped to improve their status, those hospital were usually poorly equipped and for many years the training of medical students and promotion of doctors after graduation was in the hands of the prestigious university teaching hospitals.

While the two-tier system of patient care existed between voluntary and most municipal general hospitals, the authorities were making changes which would lead to an improvement in the health care of the population. They withdrew from municipal general hospitals patients who suffered from infectious diseases and mental illnesses and fever, to sanitoria and mental hospitals where patients with those illnesses were treated.

Those specialist hospitals were run by a matron specially trained in the subject and a medical superintendent, usually an experienced wellrespected clinician, who was responsible for patient care and hospital administration. The staff of general and special municipal hospitals were salaried and the appointments made by committees.

The National Health Service (1948)

In the period between the two world wars there were preliminary plans for a more comprehensive health care service for the United Kingdom. The central figure would be the general practitioner, and the family doctors would be grouped in health centres equipped with laboratories, operating rooms, x-ray facilities and dispensaries. No action was taken and health care remained fragmented. Those who could pay, as well as workers who were eligible to pay National Health insurance and their families, received medical attention. However, there remained a group of men and women who had no doctor although some of them paid sixpence a week to a collector for medical attention and drugs dispensed by the doctors. Those patients could receive treatment in hospitals free of charge.

The Second World War delayed the introduction of a centrally directed comprehensive health care service until 1948 when Aneurin Bevan introduced the National Health Service. This is the type of health care older doctors will remember, a service in which many of them had a central role. It was an extension of the National Insurance Act (1911). Now everyone in the country had 'free' service from a general practitioner of his or her choice.

Doctors, in return, received a basic salary and fees according to the number of patients on their list. Although there was no control of doctors by the local authority, the medial profession, as in 1911, was divided and only agreed to take part when Bevan induced the senior hospital consultants to accept the service. He introduced payment for all hospital staff and in addition consultants would be eligible for extra money through merit awards, which would be awarded for distinction, by senior members of the profession. Further Bevan won the support of English consultants by allowing them to retain private beds in the voluntary hospitals. It was his intention to raise the standard of patient care in local municipal hospitals to match that of teaching hospitals by placing them under the board of management of the nearest teaching hospital, which now came under the area health board. While this change took place in Scotland and in the English provinces, Bevan failed with the old established London medical school hospitals, which remained independent and financed directly by the Department of Health, and at the same time retained control of their endowment funds. Indeed it was 1974 before the London teaching hospitals came under area health boards.

Five area or regional health boards were formed to run the service in Scotland. Each one had a chief medical officer and all municipal and teaching hospitals in the area came under his control. A tripartite arrangement of hospital, general practice, and local authority public health services was established and it seemed to function reasonably well. The service was controlled by the five regional health boards through numerous boards of management, exclusive councils and local authority public health departments.

The changes which took place in the hospital services in Scotland following the introduction of the National Health Service are reflected in events which occurred in Glasgow medicine.

In 1948 there were three voluntary teaching hospitals, the Royal, Western and Victoria, and two municipal general hospitals, the Southern General and Stobhill. All came under the Western Region Area Health Board and all were used for medical teaching by the university, who paid the salaries of the senior medical, technical and secretarial staff of the university departments established in those hospitals. The area health board accepted financial responsibility for the salaries of all other medical, nursing, secretarial and ancillary staff that worked in those hospitals. This financial arrangement was worked out by the chief medical officer of the Regional Health Board. Dr Alexander Bowman and the principal of the university, Sir Hector Hether/ington, and since the scheme worked it brought the health board and the university faculty of medicine closer together and made subsequent develop/ments in the service possible.

Each of the five hospitals was run by a committee of management on which senior doctors were well represented and as Bevan intended, each hospital became responsible for the management of the smaller general, fever, tuber/culosis, mental and municipal hospitals in the area of the city allocated to them. Further, the National Service Act transferred the large endowment funds of the voluntary hospitals to the new committees of management who were able to use them to upgrade the buildings and equipment of the old voluntary and municipal hospitals under their control.

In addition, a committee under Sir Sydney Smith appropriated £250,000 from the endowment funds of each large teaching hospital in Scotland to establish the Scottish Hospital Endowments Research Trust (SHERT) with Sir John, later Lord Erskine as Chairman and Dr J. M. Johnstone as secretary. The Trust was advised by an Advisory Committee for Medical Research (ACMR), which consisted of senior university and health board clinical consultants from the four Scottish university medical schools. Financial support for junior and senior doctors and medical scientists in Scotland was made on their recommendations to SHERT who acted on their advice. Medical research in Scotland began to flourish and doctors and nurses were encouraged and assisted to study at medical centres abroad. The committee or management of the newly established group of hospitals used endowment funds to finance extra equipment in all hospitals under their control, and awarded travel grants to medical and nursing staff to allow them to visit hospitals abroad and learn new techniques they could introduce on their return.

Now doctors with full time appointments in academic departments in the medical school could command a good salary, have time and facilities to undertake research and, by winning research grants, employ extra tech/nical and scientific help. The health service had facilitated an era in which the scientist in medicine could evolve. Hospital consultants in medicine, surgery, obstetricians and other clinical disciplines could choose to have a full time appointment, which entailed eleven half-day sessions per week in hospitals, but most of them opted for seven or nine sessions which allowed them free sessions to deal with private patients. Junior consultants, on appointment, could opt for full time sessions for five years. This allowed them to build a working relationship with general practitioners and at the end of this period apply to become part-time when they could undertake private practice. Those were the artists of medicine whose main interest and responsibility was patient care. Once a doctor obtained consultant status he/she became eligible for a merit award, which at the top level could double the consultant's salary. A senior clinician from one of the Royal College visited the medical schools in the country yearly, and met a group of senior consultants from the school. They discussed the merits of every consultant in the area before making the award, which was paid by the area health board. It was easier for those consultants who were trained in research to amass a list of published papers on which they could be assessed. Many artists of medicine did produce and publish clinical work of value and received top merit awards, but many excellent clinicians who lacked scientific training produced publications of little scientific value in the belief it was a case of publish or perish. Whereas the merit award system was able to assess the scientists in medicine, something different was needed to understand and value the artists of medicine whose prime role was in the care and treatment of patients.

Scotland was better prepared than England to extend the benefits of the health service to the population of the counties controlled by the five area health boards. During the Second World War, Emergency Medical Service (EMS) hospitals were built and staffed to accept air raid and battle casualties evacuated from English hospitals. When the expected number of patients did not materialise, the emergency hospitals took patients from the large waiting lists of the voluntary hospitals. After the war the EMS hospitals were retained and funded when the new National Health Service was introduced. They complemented the voluntary general hospitals that existed in county towns and were staffed by general practitioners and visited by consultants from the teaching hospitals. The good relationship which existed between the Western Region Hospital Board and the university hospitals is reflected in their combined effort during the next ten to fifteen years to train consultant staff for the district hospitals and so extend the benefit of medical services to all the counties of Scotland.

All clinical consultants appointed to those district hospitals had charge of beds and this had a profound effect on the young consultants in teaching hospitals who still did not have beds under their control. After much protestation the health board in Scotland agreed to allocate beds to every clinical consultant in the teaching hospitals. They trained the junior staff allocated to them and set their own standard of patient care.

The autocratic chief of wards system now ended in Scottish Teaching hospitals. Divisions of medicine, surgery, obstetrics, radiotherapy and labora, tory medicine were formed and now instead of a chief of wards a consultant was appointed in a democratic manner by consultant colleagues as chairman, for a limited period, in administrative charge of the division, but unlike the old chief of wards, with no responsibility for either the clinical work of the division or the clinical actions of other members of the consultant staff. In those circumstances it was possible for the most junior consultant to be made chairman of the division.

As the chief system disappeared and all consultants in a unit had equal status, the role and influence of the medical superintendent diminished and the post was replaced by a non/medical administrator and in time by a general manager who was also non/medical. It was during this period that the influence of doctors in the health service declined and their role in decision/making taken over by the general manager. A further look at developments in the health service in Scotland gives some idea of the circumstances that led to the appointment of general managers and later, chief executives.

National Health Service Reviews 1970s and 1980s

The Health Service came of age in the 1970s, when the EMS and district general hospitals were adequately staffed and plans laid for building new general hospitals. The tripartite arrangement which existed from 1948 to 1974, for hospital, general practice and local authority public health services, had functioned reasonably well. In 1974 an attempt was made to achieve closer integration of the three services, which had developed and expanded within the different counties of Scotland. The National Health Service reorganisation which took place established fifteen area health boards and each one now embraced within its boundaries hospitals, general practice and community health services.

Each Regional Health Board had a chairman and a variable number of members appointed in accordance with the size and means of the area controlled by the board. The chairman and members of the Board were appointed by the Secretary of State. Each board had an executive group of senior officers, the chief administrative medical officer, chief area nursing officer and board treasurer. Other disciplines involved were the chief admin, istration dental officer and chief administrative pharmaceutical officer. In addition there were board officer posts and departments covering technical, estate, engineering and other work departments. It was not surprising to find the consensus working approach of this multi-disciplinary group was not successful and in the 1980s reorganisation general managers were appointed at health board and hospital level to provide, under the aegis of their board, authoritative executive control and increase the efficiency of management to include financial management and financial accountability. The appointment of general managers was not regarded by the medical profession with equanimity but their influence in the health service grew and became considerable.

An Institute of Health Service Management was formed and many of the proposals contained in the Conservative Government's White Paper (1989), 'Working for Patients' are based on submissions from this Institute. General managers claimed that progress depends on different professions having a mutual understanding and recognition of each other's skills. Courses in medicine were proposed so that managers could understand the language of medicine, the problems involved in patient care, the role of the laboratory in clinical medicine and the use and abuse of modern technology. In return managers believed they could impart management skills to senior consultants, involve them in financial management of the service and make better use of human resources. In spite of objections from doctors and nurses, the British Medical Association and trade unionists that the proposals in the White Paper would return medicine to a two-tier system of patent treatment, the Conservative Government and hospital administration pushed ahead with their efforts to implement the proposals of the White Paper, and create trust hospitals and GP budget practices.

The Health Service after the White Paper (1989)

It was the professed aim of the government in the White Paper (1989) to provide the best patient care by encouraging competition between trust hospitals; those hospitals still managed by area health boards and the private hospitals so that patients would be attracted to the hospital, which provided the best service. This type of competition did not last, but trust hospitals have survived and in Scotland twenty-eight trusts have been created.

Trust Hospitals

Trust hospitals remained in the National Health Service, but were not under the area health board. They were legal entities in their own right and in Scotland were accountable to the Secretary of State, through his advisory management executive. Trust boards employed the staff they need to provide a health care service, and earn through contracts, the finance needed for the service. Their main purchasers were area health boards and the newly formed budget-holding general practitioners. Initially the trusts' income was provided by the area health board and for some time this financial core support was the same as that given to the hospital before it attained trust status. Now trust hospitals are financed by contracts with the area health board.

In the first five years of their existence trust hospital boards recruited into the service a very large number of accountants, business managers, resource managers, accountants, information technologists and computer staff and soon administrative and clerical staff accounted for 17% of the staff of most trust hospitals. Hospital finance was reassessed by the new recruits, existing procedures for costing health care challenged and more effective ones developed to assist management to deal more effectively with their health board purchasers.

Legally binding contracts were drawn up with the health board and general practice purchasing teams, and the quality of care to be provided was expected to be monitored by quality assurance programmes, and regular audits in which the clinical and nursing staff of the hospitals were expected to take part.

In the past doctors had not been accountable for the resources used in their care of patients. Now it was management policy to ensure that senior hospital consultants were involved with the financial and human resources (personnel) staff of the hospital to produce and manage an efficient and economical patient care service. This was done by creating a system of clinical units or directorates in each clinical division, and a senior consultant was made clinical director of the unit. The director had the assistance of a business or service manager and in some instances a nurse manager, and had fully devolved management authority and accountability for the use of the finance allocated to the clinical directorate. In short it was the responsibility of the clinical director to ensure the service to patients was conducted within the finance allocated to the unit. Although he/she had no say in the finance, they were expected to run the unit within the resources. It is not surprising that, in those circumstances clinicians believed patients now followed money and not the reverse. Further, the clinical director had responsibility only for the care of patients he/she admitted to his/her beds in the unit, the other consultants being responsible for the care of patents they admit to their beds in the unit.

Management believed the quality of care provided by the hospital was monitored by the quality assurance programmes and regular audits, which were written into the contracts; but how did they find out if this really happened?

The Management Structure of Area Health Boards

The management structure of area health boards was quite different from the highly unsatisfactory multi-discipline grouping which followed the 1974 and

1980s review, and is the same as that which exists now in trust hospitals. Management of both boards was reduced to a small workable group of chairmen, five executive and five non-executive directors. University trust hospitals have an additional nominee. The general manager of the old hospital and area health boards now became the chief executive who was expected to show leadership strategy, and be responsible for the overall performance of the trust. He/she was supported by the executive directors of finance, human resources (personnel), medicine, and nursing, and by five non-executive directors drawn mainly from business, law and accountancy. Apart from the directors of medicine and nursing, university representatives on teaching hospital trusts and an occasional medical chairman, the membership of trust hospitals and area health boards is non-medical and suited to assess and support the efforts of the large number of recruits who were appointed to reassess hospital finances, challenge existing procedures for costing health care, and develop more efficient ones.

While the steps taken by management to ensure financial accountability could be justified, are the largely non-medical members of trust hospitals and health boards able to assess the quality of care written into the contracts or question the value of the quality assurances programmes that nurses and doctors may use in medical audits? To examine those questions it is necessary to ask what is meant by audit and quality assurance in medicine.

The business members of trust hospitals and health boards understand the triad structure process and outcome, which is used to assess and deal with problems which arise in business or industry. Here a group of trained management consultants (external assessors) visit the premises of a business or industrial firm. The *structure* of the plant is examined and the state of the equipment used to produce the final product assessed, as well as the size and calibre of the workforce employed. The *process* by which an improved product can be made with fewer mistakes and better use of equipment and manpower is examined and recommendations made. The *outcome* should be a better quality but cheaper product which is more saleable to a satisfied customer at a lower price.

Management of health boards believe this approach can be successful in the health service, and expect the audit of medical services contracted from trust hospitals to be a critical evaluation of the methods used to assess, control and ensure or improve the quality of care given to patients. It should take into account the proper use of available human, financial, and structural resources of the hospital as well as the outcome or response of patient to the treatment received. Surprisingly this business approach has been used and there is a voluminous literature on quality assurance in medical and nursing care. Many published papers acknowledge the influence of Donabedian

(1966) who regarded quality assurance as having the same three components used to improve industrial effort, and believed they form a sound basis with which to assess the quality of patient care. The Donabedian triad structure examines and assesses the quality of the material, financial, human and organisational resources of the hospital or clinical services. This should be the area in which management has a major role and in which senior clinicians are now expected to be involved. Naturally, clinicians will deal with the process stage, when they investigate the patient's reason for seeking help, decide on the methods to be used to reach a diagnosis and the form of treatment to be given. The effect of treatment on the health of the patient would be assessed in the outcome phase, which should reflect the degree of satisfaction of the patient with the treatment received.

Undoubtedly the effectiveness of a quality assurance audit will depend on how it is done and who is selected to do it. Specific clinical challenges will arise and their solution by modern scientific methods doubtless can bring universal benefit. Unfortunately some of the excellent scientific contributions described in a recent authoritative review of quality assurance in medical care are complicated.

At present those contributions are unlikely to capture the attention, interest and enthusiasm of those medical practitioners who need to be convinced of the value and importance of making an objective assessment of quality assurance in medical care. However, there are, in the volume, useful clinical reviews which demonstrate what has been and should be done to assess and improve clinical care, and some of them will be examined as they apply to different clinical services.

Surgery

Most surgeons would agree they could learn from ward and grand rounds, or from the clinical pathological discussions which occur during an autopsy demonstration. Those simplistic forms of audit, by peers, can be educational and help to maintain a standard of excellence, but they do not necessarily improve patient care and are not accepted as a basis for quality assurance.

However, surgery is one of the clinical disciplines which lends itself to medical audit and some interesting observations have been made. Surgeons use well-established operation techniques to deal with clearly defined clinical problems and the retrospective studies done have drawn attention, in many instances, to poor documentation in case notes and the need for a structured documentation set.

The three mortality studies in 'The Confidential Enquiry into Preoperative Deaths' (CEPOD) are based on contributions from surgical and anaesthetic mortality and point to the important role quality assurance studies can play in improving patient care. The conclusions drawn and recommendations made are constructive and revealing. The first report found most clinicians were very cooperative, although many surgeons did not hold regular audit meetings. In some regions there was inadequate supervision of junior staff, and examples of surgeons operating outside their specialty. In some instances undue haste to operate led to incomplete assessment of the patient's illness and failure to institute adequate resuscitation. The report recommended that audits should be carried out at local and national level. Clinicians should be encouraged to show greater involvement in care assessment and resuscitation particularly with elderly malignant patients who are unlikely to be assisted by operation.

The second CEPOD report on paediatric surgical practice found most, but not all consultants had expert training in the field. Consultants were not always trained in the subject and junior staff sometimes operated unsupervised. The third report drew attention to the need for adequate staffing of essential services such as recovery room and intensive care units and the need for an increase in support staff.

In Scotland the working party of the Scottish Mortality Study was established by the Royal Colleges. It is based on the initial Lothian pilot project study and was extended to cover four other regions. While the study design was different from CEPOD, the results and conclusions were similar, with some exceptions. There was a higher level of consultant involvement in decision-making and operating, but the report noted the same common errors in surgical deaths. It is clear that surgical audit can improve the service to patients. A wide range of surgical specialties have been assessed by audit and the poor performance of some trauma units, in Britain, noted.

Nevertheless an audit should not be a witch-hunt to uncover incompetence and mistakes, and when they are found there is a compelling need for understanding and sensitivity to improve the situation. Unless this is done there will be resistance to audit by members of the profession.

Medicine

In medicine, unlike surgery, definitive outcome measures which would justify the value of a medical audit are more difficult to identify. This has led to the introduction of specific medical problems as topics for quality assurance, when the audit must have a defined objective if it is to improve the quality of care in general medicine.

Once satisfactory case note documentation has been achieved, the management of special medical problems of national or local importance can be reviewed and assessed and one of them selected as a topic. The use of thrombolytic therapy in the early treatment of acute myocardial infarction was accepted by the Scottish Clinical Resources and Audit Group in 1991 as a suitable topic for quality review. The national guidelines recommended by the expert panel were the clinical indications for thrombolytic therapy, the early treatments of choice and the different care professionals who would administer treatment. They recognised that those clinical guidelines would require to be modified for use in a provincial or district general trust hospital so that patients with suspected myocardial infarction would be assessed and treated with minimal delay. Thus guidelines are needed for the general practitioners, district nurses and para-clinical ambulance staff who deal with the patients initially as well as advice for the medical staff and nursing staff of the general medical or emergency wards to which the patient may be admitted.

There are other members of a district general hospital who should be involved in a topic review. Initially the local audit committee, along with the nursing and clinical services, should be consulted on the feasibility of the topic and indeed may be the group who initiates and develops it. Since the audit might require extra staff and finance, representatives from finance and human resources management would need to be involved. This combination of modified national clinical guidelines and local action provides the type of cover which is necessary for a satisfactory quality assessment for a topic in medicine.

The Laboratory Clinical Support System (Pathology)

Pathology is the term used to define the science of bodily illness and over the years the meaning of the word has changed as more has been learned about the different causes of the disease process and the changes found in deceased organs at post-mortems. Humoral pathology was an apt term used for more than 2000 years to describe the illness attributed to faulty mixing of the body humours. Although the terms morbid anatomy or anatomical pathology were introduced in the eighteenth century to describe the naked eye appearance of diseased organs found post-mortem, the term humoral pathology was retained by clinicians until the early nineteenth century to explain those changes.

In the mid-nineteenth century when suitable sections of tissues were prepared, stained and examined under the microscope, it was found that all organs in the body were composed of cells, which were altered by disease. Humoral pathology was replaced by cellular pathology, and pathologists described the naked-eye appearance of a diseased organ (morbid anatomy), and alteration in a cell pattern seen under the microscope (histo-pathology).

The preparation, examination and identification of a lesion in specimens obtained at post-mortem or removed by surgery required training, and supervision by senior pathologists, of the increasing number of young doctors who were attracted to the discipline. This education and training to recognise disease patterns was the earliest form of quality assurance in pathology. It is little wonder that pathology, during this period, was synonymous with morbid anatomy and histo-pathology. Towards the end of the nineteenth century the scope of pathology widened. The isolation and identification of bacteria as a cause of many infectious diseases led to the creation of departments of bacteriology (micro-biology). When alterations were found in the chemical constituents of the blood and tissues of sick patients, clinical chemistry (chemistry pathology) and later haematology was established (and the term clinical pathology, used to describe the triad of bacteriology, clinical chemistry, and haematology). Later, immunology was added to the series of disciplines which fall within the ambit of pathology.

In the first half of the twentieth century pathology departments in this country were centred in medical schools and consisted of departments of morbid anatomy, bacteriology, clinical chemistry and haematology; young pathologists received a year's training in each department where they were supervised by senior academic staff. The experience gained, especially in clinical pathology, was ideal for young pathologists who served in the Royal Army Medical Corps (RAMC) laboratories during the two world wars.

After the introduction of the National Health Service clinical laboratories were formed in district general hospitals, and there was an obvious need to create and maintain a standard of excellence in those departments. The Royal College of Pathology, established in 1960, played an important role in achieving this. The College, in time, initiated the membership examination which candidates took in two stages. The primary examination involved all four disciplines, and was taken by the candidates after three years' training. Thereafter he/she would select one of the four disciplines, and the final examination taken on that subject after a further two years study. A successful candidate would have at least five years' training under supervision before they could be made a member of the college, and receive the diploma MRC path. Many well-trained pathologists were attracted to the new consultant posts that were created in district general hospitals. In time they applied to the college for accreditation of their laboratories, when they received a site visit by four senior pathologists who represented the four main disciplines and decided which of the departments would receive accreditation by the College. Laboratories which received accreditation, could attract good trainees who in time would be able to take the college examination.

In those early days, quality assurance of all branches of pathology was based on satisfactory training and supervision of medical and technical staff by senior pathologists. During the past twenty years there has been a more business-orientated approach to training and quality assessment, and much of this can be attributed to development in clinical chemistry and to a lesser extend in microbiology and haematology. Three distinct phases can be identified in laboratory quality assurance studies they are pre-analytical, analytical, and post-analytical. The pre-analytical phase is the same for all pathology disciplines. It involves steps taken to ensure the specimen taken from the patient is satisfactory for the examination requested, correctly documented by the ward staff, expeditiously collected and transported to the laboratory, where it is accurately recorded and prepared for the important analytical phase where the real efforts are made to assess and assure quality.

In clinical biochemistry, quality control monitors every aspect of the daily work of the laboratory. Basic equipment such as pipettes, balances and reagents are subject to quality assessment. Expensive instruments are checked, radioactive counting equipment examined for any contamination and a log of users kept for each instrument. Internal quality control of an analytical technique is assessed by adding a sample of known value to the batch of specimens being examined.

When aliquots of the same specimen are sent to a number of clinical biochemical laboratories and the results compared, this type of external quality assessment can improve laboratory performances. In microbiology (bacteriology) external quality assessment is more difficult than in clinical biochemistry. The size and function of those laboratories vary widely. The tests carried out in small departments are limited, whereas large laboratories have to cover a wide range of services in virology, mycology and parasitology, in addition to routine clinical bacteriology.

Unlike in clinical biochemistry it is difficult to obtain specimens, which mimic those obtained from patients and for external assessment of a laboratory's ability to isolate viable organisms. The specimens sent for testing should be freeze-dried. Nevertheless, it is agreed that external quality assessment has improved laboratory performance particularly in antibiotic assessments.

In clinical haematology there is a constant check of the reliability of the tests by internal quality control using control preparations with control charts, duplicate testing, clinical correlation and other tests. An external quality assessment scheme, based on the UK National Scheme (UK NEQAS), uses blood counts and other tests of general haematology, as models to describe the procedures for quality and quantitative tests. Low results are analysed and the performance of the laboratory assessed. This scheme can help to ensure good laboratory practice and the reliability of individual laboratories that take part in the scheme. In turn NEQAS must be able to provide stable material, which is suitable for each test in the programme. Accreditation of clinical laboratories may be granted after external assessment by a professional-led accreditation scheme of the UK Clinical Pathology Association, CPA (UK) Ltd. Beforehand, the laboratory receives an application form and a handbook, which is a guide to the interpretation of the standards expected for accreditation. The standards are very comprehensive and the forty-four headings within six sections cover laboratory organisation and administration, staffing and direction, facilities and equipment, policies and protocol staff education, and evaluation of the service.

The consultant in charge of the laboratory is the applicant who performs in-house assessment against the standard and completes the form to show compliance with or exemption from each section. When the completed form is received by the project officer of CPA (UK) Ltd, an inspection of the laboratory is made by a senior medical laboratory scientific officer. If problems are found by the inspectors, accreditation is not granted until they are resolved to the satisfaction of CPA (UK) Ltd. 'There is no doubt the development of a professionally organised and executed accreditation scheme will improve the quality of laboratory service in the United Kingdom'. Like the three disciplines in clinical pathology which have been discussed, quality control of the pre- and post-analytical phase of histopathology is important and easily assessed. The collection of a surgical or a biopsy specimen from the operating theatre and the time it is received in the laboratory is noted, and a description of the specimen recorded. The time taken for the pathologist's report to be received by the surgeon and the assistance it gives him/her in dealing with the patient may be vital.

However, quality control really begins in the analytical phase when a surgical specimen is processed by the technical staff and the product (microscopic slide) assessed and reported by the pathologist. Quality assurance becomes more difficult when attempts have to be made to assess the value of the diagnostic opinions made by the pathologist. Since histopathology diagnosis is essentially a technique of pattern recognition of the cellular changes found in specific disease processes, young pathologists learn this skill by working at the microscope with senior colleagues who point out the features in the slide that allow them to arrive at a diagnosis. Accordingly, quality assurance of surgical and autopsy pathology is of a high order in academic departments where there are experienced senior pathologists to cover all special branches of histopathology and where peer reviews and opinions are available. The problem of quality assessment in district general hospitals is more difficult, where professional staff may be limited in numbers and consultation difficult when the workload of the department is heavy.

Nursing and Quality Assurance

Nurses have always played a major role in patient care and the quality of good nursing is reflected in the character and personal qualities of the nurse. Education and training is centred on practice issues. Accordingly assessment of nursing skills, though usually very accurate, was nevertheless largely subjective.

In the past thirty years the educational requirements for nurse recruits has been raised and greater emphasis placed on teaching the scientific and technical standards required in nursing. Now it is expected that skilled educated nurses will be trained to provide efficient and sometimes complicated patient care, and at the same time understand, apply and audit techniques which have been developed to assess, objectively, the quality of nursing care. The modern nurse would be trained in the art and science of nursing. The development of standards is central to objective assessment and a number of criteria, which reflect different aspects of nursing, have been selected and developed to produce a series of pre formulated criteria sets. The different criteria used reflect the phases of the Donabedian nursing triad. *Structure* criteria deal with the different aspects of ward resources, equipment and staff training, while *process* criteria should reflect the procedures used by the nurse to produce a quality care service. *Outcome* criteria are those which deal with the patients' well being, hospital experience and satisfaction with nursing care.

Early critical attempts to evaluate the technical and practical skills of nursing and assess how nurses could improve their interactive skills induced the nursing profession in North America to formulate criteria sets for nursing care. The first pre formulated criteria set or audit trial was developed by Phaneuf (1964), and her audit emphasises and reports the monitoring role of the nurse. It is a written appraisal of the quality of nursing service, taken from the case records of discharged patients. This effort was succeeded by QUALPACS, which focuses on the nurse patient interaction and emphasises the psycho social aspect of care.

In this country the pre formulated criteria set in use, Monitor, is based on the problem solving method of nursing. The pre formulated document has 257 questions which relate to the care of patients and the facilities available in the ward. One or two observers or external assessors visit the ward, study the documents which relate to patient care and management, then produce assessments or scores which relate to patient care and ward management. The *patient care score* reflects both physical and non physical care, the planning of care and an evaluation of the care administered. The *ward management score* deals with general ward safety, standards of ward hygiene and the supply of linen, equipment, and disposables. The ward sister is notified of the assessors' evaluation so that any defects can be remedied.

Since 70% of the questions relate to documentation, the results of a Monitor review would be affected by the quality of the ward case documents, the experience and training of the observers, the time taken by them in data collection and their subsequent assessment of nursing care. The amount of data that has to be collected and the potential for observer bias can make Monitor difficult to apply; nevertheless, when properly used this pre-formulated criteria set appears to provide a useful objective evaluation of physical and psycho-social nursing care.

The lack of active participation by ward nurses in pre-formulated criteria assessments of nursing care is a weakness, and the basic problem with British nursing could lie in the confusion which exists between clinical nurses and nurse managers. Pembrey asserts there is nurse management and clinical standards and the latter should be set, conducted and assessed by nurses who are engaged in the daily care of patients. This, she believes, can be achieved in a unit-based quality assurance programme when specific topics such as coronary care are identified and evaluated for improvement. This type of unit-based topical approach enables nurses to describe, audit and if successful, improve the quality of care.

Those studies in surgery, medicine, nursing and laboratory medicine conducted by properly constituted teams show that quality assurance audits can improve patient care, and could provide area health boards with a better understanding of the quality of the health care services they purchase from trust hospitals. However, this will depend on the ability and willingness of the medical and nursing staff of hospitals to undertake a proper self-assessment audit of their activities. This will not be easy to achieve.

In addition there is confusion between management and doctors on the subject of audit. Management feel they should be able to suggest what is audited, and how the audit is carried out. In particular, they see a need for an audit to deal with the outcome phase of medical care, largely ignored by clinicians involved in medical audits. While the Royal Colleges accept that different interpretations of the outcome of care are possible, they maintain control should be invested in doctor's assessments of outcome and based on an examination of the patient's case records.

Williams illustrates the conflict of views by referring to clinical trials of patients tested for hypertension. Whereas a doctor accepts a fall in the patients blood pressure and an increase in lifespan as satisfactory, this may be achieved by the drug making the patient feel ill and listless, a reaction that can influence the life of their family. Management believe those and other studies of patients' views are required and an index of outcomes developed which would involve the patient's own assessment of treatment.

In February 1990, the Department of Health released the draft circular on audit, which declared that each area and every doctor would partake in a regular systematic audit of the activities of the medical teams of which they were members. If the audit committee could not resolve a problem they could ask for a peer review from outside the region.

Since an internal self-assessment audit does not at present provide satisfactory evidence of cost effective and efficient patient care services, external help is required in the form of an independent site visit, carried out by a team of experts to all clinical divisions and all services in a trust hospital. This would provide the trust board with an authoritative assessment of the strength and weakness of all clinical services and the financial and human resources management required to run the hospital. In addition it would give the trust more authority to deal with problems an external visit might uncover. The report of such an expert group would surely meet with the approval of the area health board whose contract with the trust would indicate with greater accuracy the quality of patient care they can expect and the staff and finance they now know is required to run the service. In addition the health board would be better equipped to decide which future developments they may wish to support and those services they may wish to close.

External assessment would give, for the first time, clinical directors the opportunity to request and justify the finance and staff they need to run their clinical directorate. It would provide the Management Executive of the Department of Health with the finance and staff that has been justified and required to run the service. If this is greater that the sum allocated, at present, by government, there is a justifiable reason for government to meet those requirements from taxes. At present, this information does not exist.

In view of the importance to the Health Service of external assessment, it is necessary to consider how an external visit by a team of experts would be carried out.

The Role and Management of an Expert Audit Team on a Visit to a Trust Hospital

This exercise involves a great deal of organisation. The Management Executive of the Department of Health (ME), after consultation with the Royal Colleges and Faculties, the Institute of Health Service Management, health unions and other relevant bodies would prepare a register of individuals to represent the different specialities in medicine, nursing management, health care unions and finance. The members on a site visit audit committee would be drawn from this list.

When the hospital is ready to receive a site visit the chief executive of the trust hospital to be visited would submit to the ME, a document on the service to be examined. In return he/she would receive the names of individ‚ uals selected for the external audit committee and a proposed date for the visit.

As an example, it may be relevant at this stage to describe in detail the preparation of a submission document, the possible composition of a visiting team of experts and the organisation that would be necessary in preparation for a site visit to a hypothetical surgical division of a teaching or large district general trust hospital with five general and nine specialist surgical clinical units or directorates.

Submission Document

The directors of each surgical directorate in the division will prepare a programme of work carried out in their service and to ensure it is understood by all members of the visiting group, the summary document prepared for each surgical directorate should be no longer than three pages and presented under three headings.

The first: *What work has been done in the Unit in the Past Five Years?* This would review the workload, mention the surgical, nursing, management and clerical staff, and deal in particular with the unit's contribution to patient care, training of junior surgical and nursing staff, and where applicable, the undergraduate teaching undertaken by each consultant in the unit. References should be made to the unit's contribution to surgical and nursing audits, minimal invasive and day surgery, the use of operating theatres and an intensive care service, bed occupancy, waiting lists, outpatient appointments, and any special surgical interests and research activities of the staff. Much of this information and other relevant material such as the survival of cancer patients dealt with in the unit could be presented in more detail in tables, graphs, and diagrams or as reprints of articles published in national journals. This relevant information would be incorporated into a series of appendices to which reference would be made in the one page summary.

The second heading would be: *What work is intended in the next five years?* This may be a continuation of present activities at the same or increased level when the reason for the increased request should be given. Here would be an opportunity to identify deficiencies in the service and the need to deal with them. Once more use should be made of appendices to elaborate or enlarge on certain points in the summary.

The third heading in the document: *What staff, equipment, and finances are required to service the work of the Unit?* This should describe the senior and junior medical, nursing, management, clerical and other staff who are involved in the work of the unit and should deal with staff salaries, annual increments and superannuating projections for the next five years. If any new staff or equipment are requested for this period, it should be budgeted and the reasons for the request justified. Since more accurate methods are being introduced to cost the medical, nursing and professional care services of the unit, the business and nursing managers along with other resources and financial management would be enrolled to provide the information required for this section. Again it should be emphasised that in all three sections of the submission document ample use should be made of appendices.

Although the final document with appendices could be quite large the summary document for each surgical unit would be restricted to three pages and for a hospital with fourteen surgical services carrying out general and special surgery, the length of the summary document would be a maximum of forty-two pages. If this routine is followed, every member of the visiting team would be able to understand what work is going on in each surgical service, what is intended in the next five years and what staff, equipment and finance will be required to do this work. The extra information given in the appendices would be assessed by those members of the site visit who are surgeons and experts in the specialities under review.

Careful preparation of the documents for a site visit is time consuming and a period of three or four months should be allowed from the time a start is made to prepare the submissions and copies sent by the chief executive of the hospital trust to the Management Executive of the Department of Health, who should notify the hospital when the site visit will take place and the composition of the external audit team.

External Audit Meeting

The composition of the visiting group will vary with the size of the surgery department and in this instance it might consist of two surgeons to cover the different branches of surgery, an anaesthetist, radiologist and radiotherapist, a representative of the laboratory service, colleges of nursing and general practice, one representative from the Institute of Health Service Management to assess the management and finances of the units and a representative of a health service union.

One of the two surgeons would act as chairman for the visit and would have in attendance secretarial assistance and an audit facilitator as envisaged and now in post. Along with the chairman they would prepare the committee report on the visit. The chief executive of the hospital and the directors of medicine and nursing would be present at all meetings which would consist of morning and afternoon sessions for each service in the surgical division.

At the external audit meeting, the director of each clinical service under review would introduce his/her three-page submission document and respond to any questions from the visiting team. Each consultant in the unit would appear and talk about his or her work and views on aspects of the document that might affect them.

For their part, members of the audit team might use the following criteria to help them assess the consultant's contribution to the unit: his/her care of patients would be given a high priority and the consultant's contribution to training junior surgical staff as well as their role in surgical audits. The committee could consider the consultants administrative experience, his/her length of service and contribution to the hospital, as well as any research in which they are/have been involved. Marks 1 to 5 could be attached to each of those criteria and in a large teaching hospital research and undergraduate teaching would carry a higher assessment than in a large district general hospital. In both cases the external audit committee should emphasise and attach a high mark to the consultant's service to patient care and staff training.

The senior nursing staff attached to the unit and the nurse manager would be interviewed: their role in the wards, theatre or outpatient departments discussed and their views sought on nursing audit and on any other unit problems. Once more the committee's assessment could be based on the contribution to patient care, staff training, administrative experiences and length of service.

In view of the importance now attached to management of the health service, the business manager who is involved with finances of the unit should appear before the visiting committee, explain his/her role in the unit, how the cost of the service is assessed, and how he/she would justify the finances required in the next five years. He/she would be assessed by the committee on his/her performance and contribution to the economy in the service and patient care.

The session with consultants, senior nurses and business management on the unit would take three hours and in the last hour of the four-hour session, the committee should meet privately with the junior surgical, nursing and management staff and listen particularly to their views on training and other aspects of unit activity. If a morning and afternoon session were devoted to each surgical service, a trust hospital of fourteen units would require a seven-day visit.

At the end of each session the chief executive, director of medicine and nursing along with the director of the clinical service which has been reviewed, would have a short discussion with the visiting group when they could put forward any points they thought necessary and answer any questions the visitors might ask. The external audit committee on its own would discuss and assess each clinical service, its strengths and any deficiencies, its contribution to patient care and financial accountability, and the justification made in its requests for staff, equipment, and running costs.

If the committee is satisfied with the work of the service, a five-year accreditation could be recommended. However, if some aspects of the work fail to meet its requirements, full accreditation could be withheld until the deficiencies were rectified. Re-accreditation would be given to the division every five years without a full site visit unless there was reason to believe this is necessary.

Following the visit the chairman and audit facilitator would prepare a report on the surgical service of the trust hospital and send it for comment and approval to each member of the committee. When agreed the report would go to the Management Executive of the Department of Health who would send a copy to the chairman of the hospital trust and one to the chairman of the area health board.

The need for External Site Visits to all Divisions in the Hospital Trust
There are three distinct groups of trust hospitals in Scotland,

1.   trust teaching hospitals linked to medical schools

2.   provincial and district general hospital trusts

3.   community health care hospital trusts.

The visits would be organised to all clinical divisions in the hospital as well as pharmacy and all laboratory services. Visits would need to cover the central services division of general management, finance, planning, information systems and medical records. There would be a visit to the non-clinical support services to cover estates, porters, catering, laundry, transport, telecommunications, and hospital cleaning. A different type of membership of the visiting group, with a different set of criteria, would be required to evaluate these different disciplines, and the length of each visit would vary with the discipline to be assessed. While nurses and business managers would be involved in the site visit to the clinical division in which they were involved, nurse administration and management would be examined and assessed in a separate visit. In all probability, site visits would take about six weeks to cover all the services in a teaching or large district general hospital. However, the series of visits would be spread over a five-year period so that there would be minimal disruption of hospital activities. Accordingly in the first year, surgery with anaesthetics and later in the year nursing administration and pharmacy might be the disciplines chosen for review. In the second year, it could be medicine and the central services division to include general management, planning, information systems and medical records. In the third year all laboratory services and the non-clerical support services could be reviewed. Radiology and radiotherapy could be assessed in the fourth year and obstetrics, gynaecology and paediatrics would complete the review in year five. The review of a large and a smaller division and spreading the visits over a five-year period will make it easier for submission documents to be prepared, the site visit planned and the eventual recommendation of the external review body discussed. If they were accepted by the area health board, they could be written into the contracts drawn up with the trust hospital board. While the assessment of quality is not a precise process, the method described gives a good indication of quality of service to be provided, a critical assessment of it and of the requests made for the staff and financial support needed to carry out the work. In addition this type of external visit can draw attention to services that need to be improved and the means by which this can be achieved.

Ten years ago this exercise would not have been possible. Contract planning models have been developed to assess more accurately, the cost of the service, and this information can now be supplied by management, while clinical directors prepare the submission documents on their service. Thus external site visits by experts is a realistic means of achieving both financial and clinical accountability in the health service.

No doubt it will be said that this exercise must be a long-term measure which could extend well into the present century. While this may be so any measure designed to achieve financial and clinical accountability in the health service must be long-term. However, if a feasibility study based on all twenty-eight hospital trusts is carried out in Scotland, this study could be concluded in five years.

During the five-year period each hospital would have only two visits per year, and each site visit committee would visit four hospital trusts per year. The community health care trust hospitals, about eight in number administer a number of small hospitals, health centres, community clinics, day hospitals and residential properties and over 60% of staff are nurses. A separate site visit group would deal with those trusts, and its work could be completed within the five-year period.

A New Management Complement would be required now for Hospital Trusts and Area Health Boards

If this scheme was acceptable, the structure of both boards would be satisfactory and the existing arrangement of chairman, chief executive, directors of medicine, nursing, finance and human resources along with five non-executive directors should be retained. There would be, however, a need to alter the composition of the five non-executive directors to include individuals who would understand and support the proposals the external assessors may recommend. Accordingly two senior consultants from the clinical directorate and one senior nursing officer should be appointed as non-executive directors. The two remaining places should go to representatives of management and trade unions.

Likewise the composition of the non-executive directorate of the area health boards should be changed in a similar manner. Two non-executive directors positions could be filled by retired, but not politically motivated doctors, dentists, scientists or teachers, one place by a retired nurse, one by a representative of the health care union and management. A health board so constituted would be in a better position to appreciate the measures that would need to be taken to achieve clinical and financial accountability in the service.

There is an urgent need to change the status and role of the directors of medicine and nursing. The medical director must have complete authority for the efficiency of the medical services and where necessary, deal with the press in all medical matters. He/she would be expected to develop a close relationship with the clinical directors of service units and the hospital consultants who have clinical responsibility for the patients they admit to the unit. In many ways the duties of the medical director would resemble those of the old medical superintendent, but to perform those duties he/she would require to be a well-respected, experienced clinician or clinical scientist of between 50 and 55 years who would look on the appointment as a challenge during the last ten or fifteen years of his/her professional career. *This appointment, to be effective, must be full-time and to attract a suitable person it must be suitably rewarded.* Most clinicians would not be willing to withdraw completely from clinical practice but this would be essential if the medical director were not to become like the old medical superintendents of English medical schools, who could compete unfairly with other clinicians for private patients.

Some consultants, with the required clinical status, might not have the personality for the post or be acceptable to colleagues as director. Nevertheless in most hospitals in the country there is likely to be a clinician who would fit the job description and accept the challenges. Where no one is suitable it may be necessary to advertise.

While care of the simple needs of patients should always be an essential part of a nurse's role in hospital, they now perform many of the complicated measures used in modern hospital medicine. Their training is now more scientific and this prepares them for duties, which, in the past, would have been reserved for doctors. The present government is conscious of this and no doubt the directors of nursing, while exploiting this good relationship, will see fit to advise on the cleaning services which in many hospitals in the country leaves much to be desired.

While the Labour government and its supporters have an empathy with the nurses and their aspirations, the important role I see for senior hospital consultants is unlikely, without persuasion, to find favour with the present administration. They feel part-time consultants do not spend the necessary time in hospital in favour of private practice and believe the autocratic senior consultants view their activities as beyond question. This government view was strengthened recently when the General Medical Council removed, from the medical register, two senior surgeons, one of whom was medical director of the hospitals. They performed, repeatedly and unchallenged, paediatric cardiac surgery for which they were not trained, and with tragic consequences. If the audit which health boards insist is included in their contracts with hospital trusts had been carried out conscientiously and the CEPOD recommendations noted those senior surgeons would not have been allowed to operate on children.

However, senior consultants are a highly skilled and talented group of men and women whose active participation is necessary for the continuation of a well-directed National Health Service. Bevan made sacrifices to get them to cooperate, and was sufficiently astute to realise that without their help he would not be able to introduce the type of health service he did.

An important first step now is to restructure trust and health boards, and introduce senior consultants to positions as non-executive directors. If external site visits by experts are used, the activities of junior and senior consultants in all clinical hospital departments could be assessed and defects remedied on the spot, without the need for public embarrassment as at present.

Health Service Waiting Lists and Private Medicine
These are inevitably closely linked, yet the private sector in medicine does not improve the health care of the community. Its staff are drawn largely from doctors trained in the National Health Service, and 85% of medical management are health service consultants. Further, the private sector makes only a small contribution to training doctors and nurses. In most instances private medicine is carried out in nursing homes that lack the facilities and medical night cover of health service hospitals.

Patients are attracted to private medicine because treatment can be carried out at their convenience and without the long waiting period that exists in most health service hospitals. The development of high technology medicine has widened the horizons of health care and successful treatment of patients with osteo-arthritic hip and knee replacements, lens implants for cataracts, and successful bypass surgery for cardiovascular illness, has improved the lifestyle of the geriatric population. However, it has lengthened the waiting period for patients who need hospital treatment for those and other conditions and encouraged many to seek help in the private sector.

A successful health service will always generate waiting lists, and it must be recognised that clinicians who wish to practise private medicine will always be with us. Most of them have part-time sessions in NHS hospitals and this allows them to see and treat private patients in nursing homes that are quite separate and often distant from their hospital. Those consultants develop a more personal relationship with their patients, and regard private practice as a challenge to their medical skill. Nevertheless, they do not need to justify the success or otherwise of treatment to anyone except themselves, the patient and the general practitioner who refers the patient. There is no doubt the remuneration they receive for the work is a powerful attraction for those engaged in private medicine.

Working as they do at two distinct sites raises the question 'Do clinicians engaged in private medicine devote the time and care they should to patients they treat in health service hospitals?' In a National Audit Office report, accountants believe hospital consultants should be more accountable for meeting their contractual obligations to the NHS, and would like to see them with contracts and precise job descriptions and a weekly timetable. This was considered in an article in the BMJ (1990) p. 147–148, entitled 'Consultants' neglect of NHS duties not proven'. If clinicians are to meet their health services and private commitments and provide evidence of clinical account-ability, they should become geographically full-time, and be located in trust hospitals with an allocation of private beds which, according to the Tomlinson Report (1992) could be available.

The Tomlinson Committee was set up to examine the bed situation in London hospitals and their report indicated that between 2,000 and 5,000 acute beds should be closed. In Scotland the Management Executive of the Department of Health identified similar trends in hospital efficiency and health care and concluded that 3,000 to 7,000 acute sector beds should close by the year 2001. The money saved would be used to improve health care in the community. Senior hospital consultants must not simply acquiesce in their closure and to do so they must be fully committed to work in hospitals. Whereas senior academic clinicians are located permanently in hospitals, clinical consultants who are engaged in private practice would never agree to full-time appointments, and it would be disastrous to try to persuade them to do so. However, if surplus beds were available and if private bed facilities were created in all trust hospitals, those consultants could retain their part-time status and become geographically full-time. This move would be beneficial to hospitals, consultants, and the private patients who would have available the hospital medical support and back-up facilities that exist at present only in a few of the private nursing homes.

An agreed number of private beds could be allocated to each clinical unit in a division and like other hospital beds, they would be administered by the clinical director of the service unit. All private beds in hospital would come under the control of a board of trustees consisting of representatives drawn from the board of the hospital trust, consultants responsible for bringing in private patients, representatives from general practices who supply the patients, the private health insurance companies like BUPA, and from health service unions. Since health service hospitals will always have waiting lists, it is important that an acceptable level of waiting list, for health service patients, is agreed for each unit that has been allocated private beds. If this figure was breached all private beds in that service would be closed and used for health service patients until the level of waiting list in the unit was restored and to ensure this the chief executive and directors of medicine and nursing should be members of the board of trustees.

This scheme would make good use of any excess acute sector hospital beds and bring all consultants into close contact with hospital activities and problems. It would be necessary for the board of trustees to agree with the hospital trust, a level of financial support to cover the cost of junior medical nurse and ancillary hospital staff required to service the private patients in the wards and operating theatres, as well as the cost of providing any diagnostic, radiological or radiotherapy service.

The private facilities would be reviewed during the external site visit to the unit and the contribution made by each consultant to the care of health service and private patients assessed and recommendations made on their behalf to the local merit award committee. In such a scheme consultants would become more committed to the hospital, have more time to train junior medical staff and provide more security for their private patients who would benefit from the 24 hour medical cover.

Consultants would have existing health service cover, a better opportunity to present themselves for merit awards and a private practice remuneration. In return, trust hospitals would have a good financial and clinically account‐ able reason for using the surplus acute sector beds. If, for some reason, those beds were no longer available, private beds should still be designated in each unit and used by health board and trust hospitals to deal with accidents or influenza‐type emergencies such as occurred over the period of Christmas 1999. Indeed this temporary use of designated private hospital beds is an economical method of reserving beds for the period of an emergency, when private practice would end until the emergency was over.

The Primary Health Care Service
(General Practice)

A FTER THE First World War the Dawson Report for England & Wales, the MacAllister Report and later (1936) the Cathcart Report for Scotland, recommended that general practitioners should be the central figures in any developing health service. The reports suggested that family doctors should be grouped together in health centres, supported by a small laboratory, a dispensary, a physiotherapy department, a small operating theatre, and an x-ray facility.

It was a great disappointment to general practitioners when the National Health Service was introduced in 1948 and the emphasis placed on hospital medicine. Young medical graduates were attracted by the developments and prospects in hospital medicine and general practice was in danger of disappearing as an attractive career. The fact that general practice became an attractive branch of medicine is, I believe, due to two factors: the creation in 1952 of the Royal College of General Practitioners, and the 1966 Charter Contract won by doctors from the government.

The Royal College of General Practitioners was created to restore the status and confidence of doctors and the publications which emerged judged good practices by the care provided by the doctor, the development of satisfactory surgery premises, and good practice management. A group of doctors, working with a psychoanalyst (Balint) began to examine the doctor/ patient relationship. They drew attention to new aspects of patient care and some of the problems encountered by general practitioners. The study showed that the problems were quite distinct from those met by hospital specialists and concluded that general practice should be regarded as a discipline in its own right. In time this was accepted and academic departments of general practice, directed by a university professor, were funded and established in medical schools throughout this country.

The College introduced a three-year vocational training scheme to attract new medical recruits to general practice and train them for the membership examination of the college. After completing the compulsory registration year in medicine and surgery, the medical recruits spent two years in different hospital disciplines seen as important to general practice. In the third year they became attached to the principal of a practice, who had been accredited as a trainer by the college.

In 1980 vocational training in primary care became mandatory for entrance to general practice and in 1985 the Joint Committee for Post-Graduate Training for General Practitioners recommended that each region should establish criteria which would be used for the approval of GP trainers.

A team of experienced advisers make routine visits to trainer practices, and local training standards are examined to ensure they compare favourably with national standards. The ultimate aim of the training scheme is to produce general practitioners who will promote high quality patient care.

The College encouraged further professional development of general practitioners by publishing a series of clinical information folders with extracts from clinical literature, aids to management, and reviews of the care of some important clinical conditions, such as asthma, hypertension, diabetes and terminal care. In 1990 a college audit programme was introduced and general practitioners were offered a training course and literature service on medical audit.

The Charter Contract (1996) on salaries and conditions of service negotiated for general practitioners with the government made the service more attractive, so that when these were coupled with vocational and other postgraduate training schemes, young medical graduates were attracted to a career in general practice. This continued until the publication in 1989 of the White Paper. Since then recruitment of young graduates to a career in general practice has fallen.

In the twenty-three years that followed the Charter Contract, the National Health Service had become a multi-billion pound business and the government decided there was a need to exercise control over spending in the hospitals and primary care services.

The White Paper *Promoting Better Health* set out proposals to review the conditions of service and remuneration of general practitioners and drew attention to the excessive cost of drug prescriptions. It also indicated the need to devolve financial as well as clinical responsibility to general practitioners by creating *fundholding budget practices* and introducing doctors to the need for medical audit of their activities. The development of these changes required a re-organisation of the management structure of primary health care services, and the creation of a smaller and more efficient committee structure to manage the changes.

Management of the Family Practitioner Service

Since 1974, area health boards in Scotland have been responsible for family practice and community health care services. In England it was the *Family Practitioner Committee* which was accountable for the expenditure incurred in delivering the family practice service – yet the committee's main source of contact with family doctors was through doctors' claims for allowances and fees. While this would continue, it would become a small part of the contact which had to be developed in a working partnership with general practitioners.

The large family practitioner committee of thirty members could not satisfactorily manage the proposed new services and a smaller committee consisting of a professional or lay chairman, four professional and five lay members was proposed. All family practitioner committees would have a highly paid chief executive who was expected to supply the necessary drive, develop a new partnership with general practitioners, and bring about the new changes that would be introduced into the new primary care programme.

Those new proposals were introduced in 1990 and the *Family Practitioner Committee* became known as the *Family Health Service Authority* (FHSA). Initially, a representative from the local *district health authority* was added to the committee to assist doctors in improving access to hospitals and treatment facilities for their patients. This link between district authorities responsible for hospital care and the FHSA was strengthened further by legislation introduced in 1993 to allow the two authorities to merge, and in April 1996 they formed one local health authority or *health commission*. At the same time the *regional health authorities* were replaced by eight regional offices of the *National Health Service Executive*.

During this preparatory period, in an attempt to develop a closer link with the general practitioner, raise the standard of primary care and extend the services, the FHSA needed some mechanism whereby a flow of information could develop between general practitioners and the authority. They did this by adding a functional structure to management. This group gathers information on the doctor's activities from a number of sources, and provides help to doctors when required.

General Practice after the White Paper (1989)

The terms of service and remuneration of general practitioners were intended to reflect the requirements of good general practice. Health promotion measures were introduced and fees and allowances altered to make doctors' remuneration more performance-related.

(1) A proportion of the fees and allowances paid since the 1966 Charter Contract was replaced; at least 60% of the income generated was paid now as *capitation fees* and based on the number of patients on the doctor's list.

(2) Some allowances were withdrawn and the terms altered in others:

(a) the basic practice allowance became a *capitation based payment* which was related to the number of patients on the doctor's list, and on the location of the practice. The allowance was enhanced for patients in rural areas and in urban practices in deprived areas.

(b) Since vocational training was now mandatory, the vocational training and postgraduate training allowances were replaced by a new postgraduate education allowance. Doctors in England and Wales would submit evidence to the FHSA that they attended recognised courses for five days training per year. The accepted courses fell into three broad groups: health promotion, disease management, and service management. The principals in a practice were eligible now to apply and use the money to pay course fees, travel and subsistence costs.

(3) *Health Promotion Target Payment*

Initially this was an important part of government planning – to obtain higher levels of cover for childhood immunisation and screening for cervical cancer. In 1993 politicians decided they wanted to standardise health promotion throughout the country. Patients between the ages of 15 and 74 were offered a health promotion examination and their doctors were paid according to the banding they reached. A doctor qualified for payment in Band 1 when the smoking status of 30% of the practice patients was recorded. If the doctor also recorded the blood pressure of 30% of patients, he/she qualified for the higher payments of Band 2. The doctor qualified for the highest payment of Band 3 when his/her results from Bands 1 and 2 were supplemented by details of the body mass index (BMI), alcohol consumption, and family history of coronary heart disease in 20% of their patients. Doctors were expected to increase their coverage levels in each band by 15% annually, to reach a maximum coverage level of 80% smoking, 90% blood pressure recording, and 75% BMI, alcohol consumption and family history of coronary heart diseases. Participation in these activities was not popular with general practitioners and they were discontinued.

Drugs Budgets

An important outcome of the reorganisation of the family practitioner service was the need for a careful study of prescription costs and the development of drug budgets for general practitioners.

The cost of medicines is the single largest element on the family practitioner service's bill and in the year 1987–88 amounted to £1.9 billion. The cost varies in different parts of the country and reflects the population rise and morbidity in an area, as well as the prescribing habits of doctors who in the past have not been accountable for the cost of drugs they prescribe.

Health boards throughout the United Kingdom have been concerned with this expenditure and for a number of years they have been monitoring the prescribing habits of doctors. In Scotland, the *Common Services Agency* has a computerised prescription pricing division and as an adjunct to this a prescribing information system was formed and became operational in 1990. It produces the necessary basic information for health boards to determine an actual drug allocation for those doctors who would later become fundholding budget practices, and an indicative drug allocation for those doctors who remained non-budget fundholders. This prescribing information system is available to help general practitioners audit their own drugs bill, and to health boards who can monitor excess prescribing.

In England and Wales the *Prescribing Analysis and Cost Data*, referred to as PACT, was introduced to provide good quality information on doctors' prescribing patterns and how they compare with one another. Each year since 1991–92 a family practitioner drug allowance, based on PACT findings, is made by government to each regional health authority, which in turn sets drugs budgets for each FHSA – who agree an indicative drug allocation for each non-budget holding practice. The FHSA monitors the yearly budget spending of the practice and may offer a peer review of the drugs budget. Indeed, its aim is to keep the doctor's drug expenditure lower than the allocation so that the money saved can be used elsewhere in the service.

The drug allocation for budget holding practices comes from the overall drug allocation received by the regional health authority when the authority agrees to the practice receiving budget status.

The primary care clinical services were now clearly divided into two groups, and the government believed that the creation of fundholding budget practices was the means by which financial as well as clinical responsibility could be devolved to those general practitioners who would be able to refer patients to hospitals where they believed they would receive the best treatment. Non-budget holders could refer patients only to hospitals with whom the health board had a contract.

General Practitioner Fundholding Budget Practices – General Features

Initially doctors were required to have practice lists of 11,000 patients before they could apply to the health board in Scotland and the regional health service authority in England and Wales to become fundholding or budget practices, and they had to prove to those authorities that they could manage the budget. In time, the scheme was extended so that three or four small practice groups, each with one or two doctors, could work from the same health centre and that a consortium of practices centred in a small local hospital could unite and share a single fund – which would be managed jointly by the different practice doctors.

The budget would cover the salaries of the medical staff and 70% of the practice staff. Assistance would be available to use the cost/rent scheme to improve practice premises, and doctors accepted into the scheme would receive an actual drugs budget. Patients from the practice were provided with a defined range of hospital, community, and mental health services for which the practice could contract with trust, managed or private hospitals. The scheme covered in-patient and day care hospital treatment, as well as the use of diagnostic and laboratory services. Since the practice would contract with the appropriate hospital department for its services, it was hoped the doctors would have more control over the standard of treatment received by their patient and the time taken by the hospital to send them a report.

As time passed the range of services was extended, the services of district nurses and health visitors became part of the scheme and fundholders could contract for the service of practice-based rather than locally based community nurses. Patients who received day, rather than the longer and more extensive in-hospital surgery, needed more home care and the money so released could be contracted by budget holders to provide extra community nurse hours to cope with those patients in their homes.

Fundholders could purchase out-patient support from the community mental health services, and from the community learning disabilities nursing services. Likewise such community services as chiropody, physiotherapy, and dietetics could be provided from doctors' budgets as part of their purchasing remit.

The ability to vire or transfer underspent finance between hospital and community services and between drugs and staff appointments was encouraged by the authorities, and so very significant financial resources could be vired from acute hospital care and used in the primary care service.

Fundholding Budget Practice – The Application
Initially many general practitioners did not apply to become fundholders because they did not understand what was implied. When this was explained many believed the additional burden of management would merely add to their existing workload. Others thought that devolving financial and management responsibility to budget practices would leave non-budget practices isolated and the family practice fragmented, at a time when there

were no concrete guidelines on how to prepare and submit a budget application. Further, many doctors felt a series of practices should have been selected
for a trial and the experiment assessed before the scheme was introduced.
This was not done and it was not until after five years' experience of budget
practice applications that a detailed if rather complicated 'Guide to Community Funding' was published. This instructed practitioners how to proceed
with a fundholding budget application and the government forms that had
to be completed.

When practitioners wished to join the scheme they contacted the FHSA
in England and Wales and the area health board in Scotland, who expected
the initial budget application to contain information on the following points:

(1) Evidence of the willingness of all partners in the practice and those in
    groups or in a consortium to be committed to the scheme, to be willing
    and able to work together to share economically the management resources
    which would be allocated, and to sign the application form to this effect.

(2) Evidence of the quality of medical service provided for patients, the prac-
    tice or consortium's prescribing costs, and of good practice management.

(3) The role and responsibilities of the practice manager, details of practice
    meetings, and any contact the applicants had made with the members of
    board or health authority management groups who dealt with fundholding,
    purchasing computers, and management.

(4) Information that the practice or consortium had collected on their hospital
    in-patients, radiology and laboratory tests, and what use had been made
    of the information, as well as their experience of patient surveys and in
    particular how they viewed medical audit. If the practice had access to
    information on hospital waiting times and waiting lists, did this induce
    them to change their referral patterns?

(5) Whether the practice or consortium's computer system was adequate or
    required additional capacity to deal with a fundholding budget. The name
    of the supplier of the clinical systems had to be recorded and details
    given of any computer links with the appropriate health authority, trust,
    or managed hospital. If it was the intention of the practice or consortium
    to upgrade the computer system, this had to be stated.

(6) Finally, the nominated *Head General Practice Fundholder* as well as a
    practice manager contact, and possibly a contact for computers.

In England and Wales the FHSA accepted the application and advised on
it, but it was the regional health authority which decided whether to accept
or reject it. A successful application was an invitation to proceed to the
next or preparatory phase of a budget application.

Fundholding Budget Practice – Preparatory Phase

This is a time-consuming exercise and the practice or consortium was given a year to prepare and submit their proposals which in simple terms might be expected to deal with three issues:

(1) What patient services does the practice or consortium receive from provider hospitals and how are those services costed? It was the intention in the White Paper (1989) to fund budget practices, like general practitioner salaries, on the basis of a capitation fee and until a suitable formula could be devised for this purpose, payments would be made on what management called the practice's historical activity.

(a) Accordingly the practice or consortium was expected to cost the in-patient, out-patient, and diagnostic services they received from hospitals over a number of years and learn how management cost their services. In the end the main fundholder must agree with the health authorities a standard for collecting and pricing data on all types of clinical services that the practice would receive for its patients.

(b) The main fundholder had to carry out a careful survey of all community services that the practice or consortium received, and how much each item cost. He/she had to find out, from the community provider services, what the practice's establishment would be and the cost of nurses and other community staff, such as physiotherapists, chiropodists, and dieticians they may wish to employ and locate in the practice. If the main fundholder gathered the information requested, the practice was in a stronger position to negotiate the initial budget offer that the health board would make.

(2) *Practice Staff – Cost of the Service*

When a practice applied for budget status the 70% cost of staff salaries claimed was the same as that made by the health authorities to non-budget holding practitioners. However, budget applications were expected to include a supplement for projected staff salary increases and to cover superannuation, maternity, and nurse overtime, as well as payments for relief staff – all of which became the responsibility of the practice.

If a member of staff became involved *purely* with budget funding, the practice was able to claim the full salary of that person. The cost of travel and subsistence for all staff to attend training and education courses had to be included in the application. If a fundholding practice required to rent and cost additional practice space, or include the cost of capital items such as office furniture and photocopier machines, those items must be used for fundholding and could be justified to district auditors. An extra telephone or fax line may be needed and this was allowed to ensure ordinary clerical practice lines were not blocked. It was necessary to

budget for computer software and hardware and a request made for a
drugs budget, based in England on PACT findings.

(3) *Budget Practice – Future Objectives*

Applicants were expected to produce a *strategic plan* of proposed new
developments and a *business plan* explaining how money would be saved
to finance them. While early applicants experienced difficulty with this
part of the preparation, it was said to have the effect of stimulating active
discussion amongst members of the practice staff.

In the *strategic plan* doctors were encouraged to draw up short-term improvements that they believed could be carried out within the year, and a
longer-term plan of change that they would like to undertake at some time
in the future. The need to improve some practice facilities could be included
in the short-term plan. The acquisition of better computer facilities with an
established link to hospitals would enhance the value, to patients, of existing
out-patient and in-patient services. While not required to undertake medical
audits, those doctors familiar with the range and value of methods used to
assess and assure the quality of health care could include examples in their
strategic plan. For example, if PACT data on drug prescriptions showed the
practice prescribed very few anti-hypertension drugs, and a great deal of
sedatives, doctors might be stimulated to review their screenings of patients
with hypertension and reassess their use of sedatives.

Whereas doctors may find it difficult to formulate long-term strategic
plans, management inevitably will see a role for business methods, such as a
SWOT analysis (Strengths, Weaknesses, Opportunities, Threats) to assess the
strengths and weaknesses as well as the opportunities and threats the practice
could face in the ensuing years.

Every application for budget status must contain a *business plan* including
measures to save money by cutting waste and improving the quality of patient
care. It is accepted that there is little scope for savings on the staff budget,
but savings can be made by viring money from hospital in-patient services
and considerable savings can be made on drug bills by prescribing generic
drugs and cheaper alternatives – and from discussions with health authority
advisers on prescribing policy. Finally, the health authority expected the
business plan to outline the savings likely to result which will finance some
of the short-term changes proposed in the strategic plan.

The Role of the Head Fundholder and Fund Manager

In the preparatory year the practice could claim a management allowance for
a variety of practice activities and the National Service Executive issued a
document (HSG (94) 92) which described the type of practice expenditure

that could be reimbursed. The practice could claim for the time that the head fundholder spent preparing the submission. He/she would be involved with hospital and health authority officials in acquiring the information needed to prepare the submission and to negotiate the budget with the regional health board. The partners in the practice or consortium were kept informed on the progress of the application, the problems involved, and their role in formu‚ lating the practice strategy and business plan, developing drug formularies and analysing drugs PACT data.

This was an intimidating experience for most general practitioners and it became clear why the head fundholder needed the assistance of an experienced fund manager. Single, or even small combined practices, found it difficult to attract an experienced fund manager with the type of salary they could pay from the allowances they could claim. However, if a number of practices united to form a consortium, the allowances that could be claimed, collectively, would be sufficient to attract a manager with the necessary accounting and management skills, as well as the negotiating experience required for a successful budget application.

An efficient fund manager provided support for the head fundholder to establish the budget practice. In doing so, he/she was required to establish a good working relationship with the management staff of the different units in the trust hospital, with those in the health board, as well as with the staff of the computer software suppliers.

Once the application was accepted and the budget practice established, the fund manager would need to work closely with the head fundholder of the practice or consortium to keep the partners informed of their spending within the budget and their prescribing habits, as well as monitoring the hospital waiting list.

Clearly it was the intention of government to make general practitioners, like hospital consultants, conscious of the cost of the service they provided.

Without the guidelines, an application for a budget practice must have been a daunting experience for the head fundholder, but once he/she was able to recruit an experienced fund manager the exercise became easier. The amalgamation of a number of small practices into a consortium able to attract an experienced fund manager extended the range of budget practices, and in time every practice in the country could have been involved in and running a budget practice with its own drugs budget.

There is no doubt that doctors who have been successful in the long negotiations with health boards for budget practices are more conscious of the cost of the service they provide, and the need to improve and monitor the practice facilities. They are more likely to be familiar with the many quality assurance studies that have been designed to improve patient care.

Unfortunately the development of budget and non‚budget practices succeeded only in dividing the profession and, with hindsight, it would have been wiser if budget practices had evolved slowly and guidelines developed which every practice could apply.

Although individual budget practices no longer exist, the amalgamation of a number of small and larger practices to form a consortium with an appointed head fundholder, a fund manager, and a common budget could herald the future for general practice in this country.

Primary Health Care in the New Millennium

It is doubtful if the two-, three-, or four-doctor practices, as presently constituted, can continue to maintain the same doctor/patient relationship as was built up in the early years of the health service.

In the period up to and including the Second World War there were many people who did not have a doctor. When medicine was nationalised in 1948 every patient in the country could select a doctor from a list and a good doctor/patient relationship existed in most practices for many years. In time a number of factors began to strain this relationship. The greater availability of the telephone made night calls easier, so that this facility was abused by many individuals and unnecessary night calls made to the doctor's home after he/she had had a busy day. The publicity given by the press and television to medical problems often led to an invasion of the doctor's surgery by over-anxious patients.

Inevitably, doctors have reacted by creating a barrier of receptionists who protect them during surgery hours and an ex-directory telephone number to guard their privacy when off-duty. In the past, patients who called the doctor only on rare occasions with clinical problems were known to the doctor and receptionist and had easy access to them when the need arose. This facility is no longer available in many practices. It is unreasonable to expect doctors to work during the day, undertake night duty, as would occur with one- or two-doctor practices, and still be available for consultation the following day. Yet this *is* expected of them and it is not surprising that many practitioners have joined the deputising service which relieves them from night calls, or the more recent co-operatives when patients who ask for night calls may be seen by doctors they have never met, have no knowledge of their clinical history, and may come from a general practice many miles distant.

In addition, the drug problem which exists today in our society has put doctors on night calls at risk. If small practices are to exist in their present form and provide the night cover that existed in the past, changes in practice arrangements need to take place.

The present Labour administration has rejected the development of budget practices but agrees that large and small general practices can co-exist as a consortium and share a common budget and administration. Consortia, consisting of nineteen and more general practices, have been formed throughout the country and with suitable business management can achieve financial but not clinical and financial accountability. If this is to be achieved and responsibility for night calls accepted by the medical staff, a consortium of not more than ten general practices with a total of thirty doctors needs to be formed from general practices within a circumscribed area in which night calls can be made easily.

Financial accountability would be achieved in each consortium by appointing a fund manager with accounting and management skills and the negotiating experience to deal with the appropriate hospital and health board officials who would be required to simplify the guidelines drawn up eventually for budget holding practices. The fund manager would assist each practice in the consortium to apply for the finance required to run the practice, as well as a drugs budget. As each practice in the consortium was successfully funded, the fund manager would keep the doctors in touch with practice and drugs spending.

The *clinical accountability* of each practice in the consortium could be assessed by a small expert group of general practitioners nominated by the Royal College of General Practitioners and the British Medical Association. The group would spend a day looking at all aspects of the practice and deal in particular with the clinical work problems and interests of the medical and nursing staff. The visitors would have discussions with the practice and fund managers, secretaries, and receptionists and look at the practice facilities and requirements.

Successful practices would be granted a five-year *accreditation* which should be given automatically to existing budget-holding practices and to those accredited as trainee practices. Since the process can be time-consuming, practices which fail to achieve full recognition could be given three-year recognition with their existing financial support and helped to achieve accountability and move to five-year accreditation. There would need to be some financial inducement for all general practitioners to take part. Once a practice attained full five-year accreditation it would receive a financial payment allocated to all members of the practice as a superannuation payment. This would be paid yearly to the practice as long as it retained full accreditation.

Night Cover

The ten practices, i.e. thirty doctors, which would make up the consortium would need to be within a reasonable distance of one another and to the practice with most space and facilities, selected as the centre for night cover. Two extra doctors would be required to ensure adequate day and night cover for patients in the consortium and their appointment made to the practice chosen as the centre for night cover. Once the two doctors were appointed, thirty-two family doctors would be available for night cover but only two of the group would be on duty each night for one week. One doctor would be stationed in the centre to deal with patients who came there, while the other, with a driver escort, would deal with house calls. A nurse and security officer would be required for duty at the centre. This arrangement would be helpful to old people since they would need to know only one telephone number to get through to the centre.

The two doctors on night duty would work on a weekly basis and be free from all daily duties in their practice during that week. When two practice doctors were on night call their daily practice work would be undertaken by the two doctors appointed to the centre who would become known to patients they attended in the consortium practices, and have access to the clinical records of patients they may be called to treat during their spell of night duty. This arrangement would ensure that all family doctors in the consortium were involved in night work only one week in sixteen. They would have time to undertake meaningful quality assurance studies, build a closer relationship with patients in their practice, and deal with many of the clinical problems they encounter.

Cost of Night Cover
The number of general practitioners in the United Kingdom is 31,950 and if ten practices, each with an average of three doctors, constitute a consortium of thirty doctors, 1,065 centres or consortia would be required for the whole of the United Kingdom. If two extra doctors were required for each centre, 2,130 new doctors would be needed and this is the figure the government states it will produce in time. If each doctor were to receive £60,000 per year, £127.8 million would be required to finance the scheme, but once established there would be no need for co-operatives or the payment of doctors who take part in them. In Scotland just over 210 centres would be required at a cost of £25 million.

The scheme would go a long way to create an atmosphere in which a sound relationship can develop. However this will be possible only when the 2,000 doctors promised by the government are produced either by bringing doctors from abroad or training them in the medical schools of this country, or both. In either circumstance there would be a waiting period of eight to ten years but this time could be used to help all practices in the consortium achieve the five-year accreditation. Irrespective of whether or not this scheme is adopted, meaningful quality assurance studies should be examined and, to be successful, it is important to understand what is meant by audit in general practice.

Medical Audit in General Practice

The medical audit of primary care services is a critical evaluation of the quality of care a doctor gives to patients. General practitioners have not been required to undertake an audit of their activities and in order for them to accept that medical audit could be beneficial to their patients and should be standard practice, the nature of the medical audit triad of structure, process and outcome needs to be explained as well as how it applies to general practice.

Practice premises are expected, now, to comply with agreed minimal standards and each health board in Scotland and family health authority in England and Wales has a yearly allocation of funds for *structural* improvement of doctors' premises. In their annual report a general practice is required to inform the authority of any intended improvement for which they believe directly reimbursed funds are required. Naturally funds are prioritised for the most needed patient care premises and in making these decisions the local medical committee would expect to be consulted.

In 1993 Essex Family Health Authority in consultation with Essex doctors and community health councils published a paper: 'Quality in General Practice – Goals for 1995'. This dealt with a number of agreed standards that should be reached. The exercise was designed to improve the structure, facilities and organisation of general practice. It was neither concerned with the *process* or medical treatment of the patient nor the *outcome* of such treatment. Naturally there was no opposition to senior family health managers who would visit the practices and carry out the exercise. Their initial survey was revealing. It showed that few practices achieved the 100% goal and illustrated the improvements that were needed to be made in most practices to reach the agreed standard.

% of Goals Achieved	No. of Practices	% of Practices
100	8	3
75 or more	104	38
70–75	109	40
50 or less	50	19

In the past it was easier to use simple *outcome* measures to assess the value of therapy (*process*) and ensure the quality of care. The introduction of procedures which have reduced infant mortality, the inoculation of children against once-fatal bacterial infections, the successful use of anti-malarial and anti-tuberculosis therapy when allied to good public health measures such as fresh food, clean water, improved housing and good hygiene all made it possible to assess the *outcome* of treatment of those diseases and assure patients of the quality of therapy given to them. Those illnesses have, to a large extent, been replaced by chronic industrial diseases and community illnesses related to smoking, alcohol, drugs and diet abuse, and in the short term it is difficult to assess the outcome of measures that may be used to deal with them.

General practitioners see patients with a wide variety of acute and chronic illnesses. Some are minor, others are serious complaints, and more patients now seek help because of social or psychological problems. Doctors' written records vary widely; some are full, others scanty and may not include a diagnosis. These records are of little value for quality assurance studies, and practitioners who become interested in medical audit appreciate the need for good case records and are interested in the training courses in audit offered by the Royal College of General Practitioners.

Each family health authority in England and Wales has an established *Medical Advisory Audit Group* (MAAG) whose experienced members are expected to visit general practices and assist doctors to plan and undertake some form of medical audit. It remains to be seen how successful this offer of help by the college and health authority will be in stimulating an interest in medical audit on the part of general practitioners. One problem will be to convince practitioners to change their established working practices and make them familiar with the range of methods which can be used to *assess* as well as those which try to *assure* the quality of care. This is fully discussed by Baker and Samuel in their comprehensive review of 'Quality Assurance in General Practice' and doctors who consult this publication and become interested in audit will begin to understand why no single method can be used to assess and assure the quality of care they provide. The methods used for quality assessment are many and varied and a *Review of Practice Records* is the traditional one in use. The information obtained from an appropriate sample of records is transferred either to a paper record or a computer database and summarised. Understandably the collection of suitable information will depend on the existence of satisfactory case records which are often not available. The extraction of suitable information is time-consuming and costly if large numbers of records are involved, although trained receptionists can be a great help. If a record review is intended the training in quality assurance should include information on sampling techniques. Initially many medical records are likely to be useful only for problem-orientated prospective studies. This will lead doctors to pay more attention to recording clinical information which can be used in future studies.

Computers play an ever-increasing role in quality assessment studies and in April 1994 the National Health Service Management Group introduced a process of accreditation for general practice clinical systems. In preparation for this, in 1993, all general practice suppliers of software were issued with specifications for the first set of minimum standards for accreditation. The specifications involve the ability to store records of consultations with patients, data collection on prescribing, health promotion banding, and targets for immunisation and cervical cytology as well as systems to store details of practice staff.

When computers are used by general practitioners to record information on a patient's illness, the potential audit value of the information is limited by the design of the software. Where most of the clinical data has been recorded on paper, the use of practice computers to identify groups for further study will be restricted. Some practitioners with more sophisticated computer programs have formed user groups and carried out multipractice audits; this type of study could be done in the practices which would make up the consortium. As technology improves, more sophisticated assessments of patient care will result. In response to government proposals for health promotion, most general practices with computers have had audits using age/sex registers for new targets set for child immunisation, cervical cytology screening, and the three health promotion bands for patients between 15 and 74 years of age. Those and other registerdriven audits carried out for clinical and administrative reasons are financially remunerative for the general practitioner.

Practice Activity Analysis
Many doctors have been introduced to the more demanding audits which can arise from this. In England the FHSA provides general practitioners with items of service claims as well as the PACT data on their prescribing habits. Whereas management find the PACT data a convenient method to assess and improve resource management, doctors can use it to identify issues and problems that need to be studied.

Methods of Quality Assurance

Standard setting is one of the commonest methods used to try and assure high standards of patient care. Guidelines are developed to manage clinical conditions such as a patient in a convulsion with fever, or one who suffers from asthma. The North of England Study of Performance in General Practice 1992 showed how standard setting can improve performance. Doctors who took part in setting standards improved their care of patients while those given the standards by another doctor did not. It was concluded that general practitioners should be allowed to discuss and adopt standards to suit their own circumstances.

The Dutch Society of General Practice produced eight to ten standards yearly from 1988 and the selected subjects varied from diabetes and oral contraception to the referral letter. While the standards were popular there was no evidence at the time that they improved patient care.

Feedback of Performance

It is the role of Medical Audit Advisory Groups (MAAG) to advise and encourage general practitioners to carry out medical audits. While it is hoped this will occur, it is easier and commoner for the MAAG team of advisers to select a clinical condition, such as diabetes, and carry out the audit in a number of practices. The group visits each practice and discusses the audit with the doctors. They inspect the practice premises and management structure. Groups of practitioners are organised to audit specific areas of care and a standard audit protocol is used by the selected practices to record the number of diabetic patients in the practice. Some would have specific checks for the appearance of the retina and gangrene of the toes. The practice follows the protocol, transfers its findings to a standard form which is returned to MAAG, who collate the data and compare the practices who take part in the audit. Since the protocols have been prepared the general practitioners do not require any special audit skills and MAAG can collect information on the quality of care carried out by different practices in the area. Careful selection of the topic is important; it should be one which interests the practitioner as well as the health authority and the practitioner must receive a report of the audit findings.

The Geriatric Problem

GERONTOLOGY is the branch of biological science which attempts to understand the nature and control of ageing. Gerontologists study how genes regulate the ageing process and how cells age in tissue culture.

It is obvious that animal species age at different rates and whereas the lifespan of mice and rats is about three years, that of primates like the chimpanzee may be in the region of thirty years. If the basic ageing process in man was not adversely influenced by disease or there was a complete cure for all diseases, gerontologists conclude that the lifespan of man would lengthen and the vitality of youth and middle age could be extended above 110 years.

However the average lifespan of a human male in ancient Rome was twenty-two years and this can be attributed to the effects of wars, drought, famine and disease. Throughout the ages medicine and science have evolved continuously to meet those challenges; and in Britain during the nineteenth century there was a continued increase in life survival in man. Some of this must be attributed in a large measure to government intervention through the Public Health Act (1867) which introduced the public to food hygiene and clean water supplies. The Act further reduced the spread of infectious diseases by preventing overcrowding in houses.

In the twentieth century, despite two disastrous world wars, men and women in this country were living well beyond their retirement age and, in this present century, many more will reach the age of 80 years and above. Unfortunately unless something is done now, more and more of this ageing population will suffer from the major debilitating and killing diseases that affect today's geriatric population and cause even greater financial problems for the National Health Service.

Those major diseases would include cancer, diabetes, chronic liver and lung disorders, and those conditions in which cholesterol-rich atherosclerotic plaques narrow the coronary arteries of the heart to cause coronary heart disease, or constrict the arteries of the brain to produce cerebral softening and hemiplegia in some patients; and the very common and distressing mental deterioration with confusion and loss of memory in others. When those plaques occur in otherwise weakened cerebral vessels of a patient with high blood pressure, a fatal cerebral haemorrhage can result.

At present a number of illnesses which afflict the ageing population can be treated successfully by surgery thus allowing them to live a more active normal life. Surgical replacement of osteo-arthritic knee and hip joints by artificial prostheses and lens implants for cataract are outstanding examples of the role surgery can play in normalising the life of old people. Bypass surgery for coronary heart disease not only improves the outlook for many geriatrics but allows cardiac patients in middle age to reach retirement and lead an active life in old age.

The progressive increase in the number of old people who suffer from cerebrovascular disturbances with or without hemiparesis and mental deterioration is a growing clinical and social problem for hospitals, nursing homes and relatives, many of whom are themselves part of the ageing population. If men and women are to progress well beyond the age of retirement, live an active life, and not be a burden on the health service this century, it is important that the government makes plans to try and eliminate the killing diseases and create an environment in which the population can age, remain active, enjoy retirement and not be an extra expensive burden on the Health Service.

In 1992 the government launched its Health of the Nation Strategy and set twentyseven targets for health improvements in England and Wales by the year 2000. In 1996 the National Audit Office reported an encouraging picture for patients with heart disease, strokes, breast cancer and lung cancer, but failed in key areas such as smoking in children, drinking, and obesity. Since many of the killing diseases which occur in an ageing population are the result of tobacco addiction, overindulgence in alcohol and injudicious choice and consumption of food, it is relevant to examine those factors and consider what might be done to help practitioners deal with or prevent the illnesses they cause.

Smoking

Smoking has been accepted as a health hazard for most of this century. The customary morning bouts of coughing in patients was regarded as a smoker's cough, and the chronic respiratory distress and subsequent heart failure that followed was attributed to the cigarettes they called 'coffin nails'.

Cinema news films of the two world wars invariably showed soldiers who were smoking and it was considered an act of great kindness for the padre to carry a packet of cigarettes and give one to the wounded soldiers he attended. Indeed it was customary in Hollywood war films for severe battle casualties to be given a cigarette to comfort them before they died. All this gave smoking a macho image and tobacco companies exploited this image and marketed cigarettes to attract all sections of the public. New and attractively packaged cigarettes were introduced to cover one end of the market and 'wild woodbines' at sixpence for ten became a popular favourite with working men and young boys.

Cigarettes now found a new role in society: young men, and the new group of young women smokers who might feel awkward in company, would now produce a new silver or even gold cigarette case, offer a cigarette to anyone nearby, and light up from a new cigarette lighter. This peer effect ensured confidence in smokers and this image was exploited by the tobacco companies, whose adverts on films and posters showed beautiful young women smoking their newest brand of cigarettes. All types of sporting venues were supported by tobacco companies and it became progressively more difficult for young men and women to resist the peer effect of smoking.

When it became clear that lung cancer and coronary heart disease could be attributed to smoking, addiction to smoking had been established in men and women. As they grew older, many smokers appreciated the serious effects that tobacco could have on their health and managed to break the habit. Others have tried unsuccessfully, and a hardcore accept the inevitability of the illnesses that could follow – but in the expectation that the health service will deal with the problems that arise.

The government's contribution has been to place a health warning on the outside of each packet of cigarettes and raise, with each budget, the cost of cigarettes. This is unlikely to affect the smoking habit of addicted smokers and will penalise those individuals in the low socio-economic groups where severe addiction to smoking is most prevalent. The government opposes an outright ban on tobacco advertising and believes the voluntary code of advertising agreed with the tobacco industry, along with the public health education campaigns used to remind people of the damaging effects of smoking, will prove more effective than the outright ban on smoking adver-tisement used in several countries. The Health Education Board of Scotland tells people that if they smoke they will die but this is backed up by a helpline to assist them to try and deal with the problem.

While tobacco advertisements now do not appear at many sporting events such as football and golf, they are still used by sponsors of international motor racing. Although tobacco advertisements no longer appear on television, it is surprising how often this medium through its programmes, both old and new, continues to provide free advertising for cigarette smoking.

There has been more public support recently for anti-smoking campaigns, since it was recognised that cigarette smoke can affect the lungs of non-smokers by the process of passive smoking. Non-smoking areas have been designated in many restaurants and places of work, and smoking is prohibited in aeroplanes by many companies.

While those measures may be having a beneficial effect on adult smokers, there is a worrying trend in the incidence of smoking in children between eleven and fifteen years of age. In 1988, 8% of children in this age group were smokers and the target set for 1994 was 6%. Instead the number of smokers in this age group rose dramatically to 12%. Here the peer effect is very much in evidence and while this must be targeted in any anti-smoking campaign for children, there is little value trying to warn them of the killing diseases that could affect them in twenty or thirty years' time. However unless something is done now to educate them on the danger of smoking they will become part of this century's population who will not live to enjoy an active old age.

A few years ago I was contemplating this very problem while conducting a tutorial on cancer with a group of university medical students, who were about twenty-one years of age. I asked how many were smokers and to my surprise none of them were. When I asked why, some said they could not afford to smoke, but all agreed it was a dirty habit. As medical students in hospital they had examined old smokers, experienced the habitual bouts of coughing and seen the damage done to the lungs and heart. They were familiar with nicotine-stained fingers and the yellow colour of the hair. They agreed it was doubtful whether the young would accept smoking as a dirty habit unless they heard this point being made repeatedly on films, favourite television programmes or by the lead singer and members of rock bands which attract large audiences of young people to their concerts. It is through those avenues that the government and television programmes could make a significant contribution to the serious problem of teenage smoking. Further, the tutorial group considered that any anti-smoking campaign should empha-sise the importance of sport to the young and suggested an approach motto might be '*Mens Sana in Corpore Sano*'. If well-known athletes in football, rugby, tennis, hockey, track events and swimming were recruited to teach youngsters and interest them in sporting activities, the detrimental effect of smoking on their stamina and ability to compete effectively would soon become obvious.

Alcohol

When used in moderation alcohol can be a pleasant, sociable drink, but in chronic excess a lethal and dangerous drug. It was the aim of the government's Health of the Nation Strategy for Alcohol Consumption to reduce, by the year 2005, the proportion of men who drank more than twenty-one units of alcohol per week, and that of women who consumed more than the sensible level of fourteen units per week. Sadly by 1994 the number of women drinking more than the recommended level had increased significantly and there was no downward trend in male drinkers. While this will be attributed to many factors the role and contribution made over many centuries by Scotch whisky to alcohol addiction is significant. Indeed, whisky has been both saint and sinner, particularly in Scotland, where dependence on malt whisky has been accepted for generations as a fundamental part of life in the Highlands of Scotland. Most Highlanders would agree with the philosophy, 'if a body could just find out the exact proper proportion and quantities that ought to be drunk every day he might leeve (live) forever without dying at a' and doctors and kirkyards would go out o' fashion'.

The events that led to the distillation and consumption of whisky throughout the United Kingdom and abroad is interesting. The ancient Celts appear to have practised distilling, and the word whisky is derived from the Gaelic words Uisge Beatha (the water of life), which was used to describe the liquid which revived 'tired bodies and failing spirits, drive out colds and rekindle hope'. The Highland Scot perfected the art of distilling, used the home-grown barley to make malt and the pure water of the numerous highland streams which 'come off granite through peat' to produce a distinctive taste in the many different whiskies that are produced.

Whisky drinking spread to lowland Scotland after the Battle of Culloden in 1745 but until 1850 it was drunk mainly by Scots. Two events occurred which extended the appeal of Scotch whisky to wider markets at home and abroad. In 1831 the introduction of the coffey or patent still led to the production of grain whisky, which was less intense than the malt whisky produced in the copper pot still. In 1860 grain and malt whisky was blended together to produce a lighter flavoured product. This extended the appeal of Scotch whiskies to the urban population of the United Kingdom.

The second event was in 1880 when the vineyards of France were severely affected by the *Phylloxera* plague and supplies of wine and brandy dwindled. Scotch whisky took the place of brandy, and malt and blended whiskies became the spirits of choice in countries throughout the world.

Malt and blended whisky now became an integral part of all Scottish life. It was present at weddings and funerals, and became the welcoming drink for most visitors to the house, and 'a wee deoch an dorus' to send them on their way home. It is still used to bring in the New Year and the dark-haired man who is the first foot to the house carries a bottle of whisky and a piece of coal as he enters the house to usher in the New Year and bring good luck to the family.

The effect that alcohol has had on the population of rural areas and urban cities of Scotland needs to be assessed against the social and economic conditions which existed there following the Reformation and dissolution of the Catholic Church. At that time much of the church wealth went to the land and property owners, who had paid taxes for the upkeep of church buildings. In return they were expected to build and administer new schools so that in time every man and woman would be able to read the Bible. The property owners, called heritors, were responsible for the salary of the minister and schoolmaster. Some heritors were more public-spirited than others and it was more than 200 years before John Knox's idea of a school in every village would be realised. The old reformers believed that laymen should be more involved in church matters and a Presbyterian system of church government was created.

In the first book of Disciplines (1590), John Knox waged a campaign against moral weakness and this was vigorously pursued by the church throughout Scotland and became the hallmark of the new church for almost 300 years. In villages the minister and lay kirk session used their power over the population to issue strict codes of conduct, which were vigorously applied to supervise the moral behaviour of the people. The alcoholic drink of the lowland Scot at that time was barley ale and drunkenness, swearing, fighting, failure to attend church, sexual promiscuity, and working on Sunday were crimes. The punishment meted out could vary from a fine to castigation by the minister on Sunday before the whole congregation, or of being placed in the stocks at the church door on Sunday as the minister and congregation entered the church.

In the seventeenth and eighteenth centuries the wealthy landowners in villages brought in labourers to build dykes and make hedges to protect the farm animals and crops. They introduced crop rotation into the numerous small farms which made up the different parishes. In spite of this the standard of living of the people was very poor. Money was scarce yet they had to make a contribution to the church. Small farmers who rented their farm from the landowner paid rent in kind and often half the farm produce went to the landowners. In a poor year there would be near-starvation.

The church exercised its dictatorial power to suppress the abuses which followed the rockings, penny weddings and even funerals. *The rockings* were gatherings of people who met in each others' houses, where they played musical instruments, sang songs, and told stories. Ale, and in the late nineteenth century, blended whisky was drunk, and those evenings helped to brighten the otherwise dull lives of the people. *The penny weddings* were so named because the guests had to contribute to the wedding expenses and there, as at some funerals, drunken disorder resulted. In spite of the tyrannical approach of ministers and the kirk session, rockings and penny weddings persisted in villages in Scotland into the twentieth century.

The purely rural existence of villages in the parishes of southern Scotland came to an end at the beginning of the nineteenth century when vast deposits of coal, iron ore and limestone worth millions of pounds were found. This heralded the industrial revolution. The iron and coal masters built houses for the foundry workers and coal miners, who were given work for years to come. Life was hard and dangerous for the miners who worked in the coalmines from 6a.m. to 7p.m. six days a week for a wage of little more than one pound.

Even with this wage, families could buy better food. While the beneficial effect of industrialisation was experienced in once rural areas, the power of the landowners was diminishing and the influence of the Church on the life of the people was no longer menacing. The industrial revolution brought an influx of workers into the towns to work in the steelworks, shipyards, and housing developments, and the towns grew rapidly to produce the large industrial areas of the central belt of Scotland.

Most workers in the new industries had permanent work and like the miners and foundry workers, had to work long hours for a weekly pay packet – which was small but better than the one they had previously. In most homes the pay packet was given to the mother, who provided from it the food and clothing for the customary large families of the nineteenth century. The father was given his weekly pocket money which he used, particularly in the latter part of the nineteenth century, to attend or take part in a Saturday football match. On the way home he might call at the local pub for a drink, usually a half of whisky and a half-pint of beer. Most men were responsible in their drinking habits, many were abstemious – but there were others who used the weekend for heavy drinking and gambling in the local pubs which were spartan and only women of ill-repute ever went to them. The drinking and gambling habits of some men were so great that their wives never received a pay packet and only after a serious argument were they given what money the father could spare from his drinking and gambling to feed and clothe the children. It was not surprising that such men became involved in fights and, on occasions, became wife and even child beaters. The reaction of the children was mixed. Most looked to the mother for support and comfort and were terrified of the father's behaviour; a few regarded the father's drinking and aggression as normal and in time, when they married, behaved in the same way to their own wife and family. Many young men escaped from the father's influence by joining the army and the daughter left home to go into domestic service. It is not surprising that in this environment temperance organisations flourished to help the victims of alcohol abuse. At the same time the Church spoke out against the evils of the devil alcohol, religious groups – like the Salvation Army and the Plymouth Brethren – held outdoor services in front of public houses, on street corners, in towns and at the end of miners rows in rural areas. Often converted sinners would testify to the evils of drink, what dreadful things they had done while under the influence and how they had repented and were saved.

After the First World War (1914–1918) supplies of iron ore ran out. Blast furnaces closed in many areas; and the wages of men, whose jobs in the heavy industries had been secure for many years, were cut. This led to the general strikes of 1921 and 1926, and the depression of the 1930s. It was only in the few years before the Second World War that full-time jobs in the heavy industries became available once more. In those difficult pre-war days the main responsibility for bringing up young families fell once more on the mother; and many, but not all, saw education as the means by which their daughters could escape the drudgery of domestic work, and their sons could learn to cope with the problems of alcohol and insecurity of life in the mines and heavy industries.

When the Free Church of Scotland was formed in 1843 many schools were built and there was a rapid expansion of education throughout Scotland. Parish boards were established to deal with schools and the care of the poor, and now the heritors and kirk session had responsibility for Church affairs only. The Education Act (1872) placed Scottish schools under the Education Department, but at that time education was not compulsory and pupils at school had to pay. Poor children paid one penny per week, while children from better homes paid three pennies. If a child did not bring the money they were sent home to get it and often they did not return. By 1889 education in schools was free and attendance compulsory, and in rural areas of Scotland by the early twentieth century, boys and girls from the poorest families could go to secondary schools and obtain the necessary qualifications to study at one of the four universities in Scotland – with the help of bursaries from the County Education Department and a grant from the Carnegie Trust.

Parents of the inter-war children had all had an elementary education and in most families, when the children came home from school, the mother would sit with them round the kitchen table while they did their homework. Indeed the kitchen table became the focal point for the family, where the day's work and happenings were discussed and the teachers' comments heard. It was during those early meetings that children learned the value and importance of education and experienced the pleasure and delight when reading books and learning about life. It was round the kitchen table they began to appreciate that parents, especially the mother, were there to listen to the problems of the day; and it was round the kitchen table that parents could discuss with them the use and abuse of alcohol.

Sadly, not all children had this help and in many homes the clever eldest son and daughter were deprived of the opportunity to go to university. At an early age they had to work to feed and clothe the younger members of the family. Fortunately, the Education Department in Scotland had established the evening continuation classes where – with their mother's encouragement – young men, after a hard day's work, could attend classes in mining, mechanical, electrical, and marine engineering. Many would qualify for the Higher National Certificate in one of the disciplines, others would pass the entrance examination and become full-time students at one of the technical colleges which were established in cities in Scotland. The role of the mother as a source of encouragement for education has been a significant factor in Scottish family life and this has continued in most but not all families since the Second World War, where there has been a different attitude to alcohol and drinking in general.

The images of pubs has changed radically. They are now well-appointed comfortable establishments where men and women go to spend the evening in social drinking. This would seem perfectly acceptable if they adhered to the recommended alcohol limits – and their children were cared for and school work and home lessons supported. While the kitchen table remains a valuable central point for most family members to meet today this is not always the case. Some children are left to roam the streets or spend their evening watching violent scenes on television – where actors are invariably smoking. Little encouragement is given by the family of those children to support schoolteachers who, on occasions, have to deal with problem and sometimes disruptive children. It is not surprising to find an increase in alcohol consumption in men and women – and this in time could extend to the children of this group – once they can buy alcohol legally. It is through education that children, with support from parents, can learn to enjoy and not abuse alcohol.

Obesity

When cigarette smoking and excess consumption of alcohol are associated with ingestion of the wrong type of food, serious health problems will arise and this will add further to the cost of the health service well into this century. In 1996 the Government Health Authority set a target for England and Wales to reduce obesity in men from 7 to 6% and in women from 12 to 8% – by the year 2005. So far this would appear to be failing and the figure for men has risen to 13 and for women to 18%. In Scotland, where half the population is overweight and half a million are said to be obese, there does not appear to be an obesity reducing target. However, the Intercollegiate Guidelines' Network is to issue guidelines for dealing with obese patients, and three national centres are proposed for people with severe obesity. In addition, the Health Education Board of Scotland has produced a number of healthy eating and pro-exercise advertising programmes. Over the years a number of diets have been published to help individuals deal with weight problems and all successful regimes are essentially high nutrient rich, low calorie diets. A number are designed to extend the functional age of men and women and this is desirable only if the individual remains active during those extra years.

Dieting studies on mice have shown that animals on a high nutrient rich, calorie restricted diet lived much longer than animals on a normal diet and allowed to eat as much as they wish. A 30-month old mouse fed on this anti-ageing diet was as active physically and sexually as a 12-month old animal. Even on a diet with a 50% or even a 10% reduction in calorie restriction, the mice survived longer. However, when young animals were placed on a calorie restricted diet from the onset they lived longer but their adult size was only two-thirds of that of animals fed on an unrestricted diet. In addition, those animals on the anti-ageing diet had a much reduced incidence of spontaneous breast cancer, as well as a diminished incidence of all spontaneous tumours which occur in animals.

Dr Walford was the physician to the Biosphere 2 experiment, which studied the effect on humans of a high nutrient rich, calorie limited diet — to see if the results found in animals would apply to man. If they did, it was proposed to develop an 'ante-ageing diet' so that human beings would live longer, and what is more important be 'younger in form, features, and function than their birthday age'.

Biosphere 2 was a massive, totally enclosed, ecological space built in 1991 near Tucson in the Arizona desert. It contained a rainforest, savannah and agricultural space to house almost 4,000 selected species of plants and animals and comfortable living quarters for eight selected men and women scientists. The experiment lasted two years. All food was grown in the biosphere and for the first six months the daily calorie intake was 1,800. This was gradually increased to 2,200 calories by the end of the second year period. The food was wholesome and consisted of grains, legumes, fruit, sweet potatoes, a little goat-milk or yoghurt, two eggs per person per week, chicken, red meat (goat or pork) or fish once weekly. While the diet was low in calories and nutrient rich it was labour-intensive to prepare and quite limited in variety and quality as judged by computer analysis of the content of vitamins and other essential nutrients.

While the scientists did not enjoy eating the same food combinations for two years, the diet induced remarkable and beneficial effects. In the first eight months there was a gradual but substantial weight loss of 18% in men and 10% in women, and their weight stabilised at low levels in spite of the gradual increase in calorie consumption to 2,200 per day. The body fat fell in men and women and in spite of the dramatic weight loss, the men and women felt better and their general health improved. They were more resistant to infection, could cope with the intense physical work the experiment demanded and, provided the quality of the food was good, experienced no undue hunger at the lower calorie levels.

There was a significant drop in blood pressure of all subjects. Their levels of fasting blood sugar fell and all showed a significant lowering of blood cholesterol. While the animal experiments indicated a lower incidence of cancer in the mice that were fed the nutrient rich, low calorie diet, the biosphere study was short term and not satisfactory as a cancer study.

Walford refers to a Chinese health project carried out by scientists from China, the University of Cornell in the USA, and Oxford University. These research groups studied the relationship of food patterns to disease in 6,500 largely rural Chinese. The composition of their diet was similar to that of the Biosphere 2 in protein, fat and dietary fibre but higher in carbohydrate and calories per day, and 70% of their calories come from complex carbohydrates.

The Anti-Aging Diet Plan presented by Walford and his daughter in their book is not the biosphere diet. It is influenced by the results of the long-term animal experiments, the Chinese health project, and the experiences of the two-year biosphere experiment. Their book gives details of a large number of diet recipes prepared with food from many countries around the world. All diets are low in fat and calories but high in nutrient quality. They state the diets are 'simple, tasty, easily prepared and allow individuals to reduce weight, give them more energy, feel healthier and have a greater resistance to infection'. The recipes for so-called 'mega-meals' such as vegetable paella, salmon quiche, lasagne, moussaka, and pizza all detail the calories per serving as well as the percentage of calories derived from fat, protein, and carbohydrate. In addition the cholesterol content is given and a national profile of the recommended daily allowance (RDA) of vitamins and minerals present in each serving.

The diet programmes were designed with the help of a computer and so most of the 'mega-meal' recipes described by the Walfords have a larger number of ingredients than are found in cookbook recipes. The computer gave a calorie, fat, protein and carbohydrate count, the number of calories which arise from those substances, and the level of cholesterol, as well as the RDA for amino acids, vitamins and minerals in the food. Their investigation showed that most existing recipes were nutritionally unbalanced and vitamin and mineral content would suffer, unless a wide range of foods were added to the recipe.

If for example the diet being planned lacked selenium, vitamin E, vitamin B6, zinc and calcium, a *Search Routine* was initialised. The computer was asked to itemise those vegetables rich in one or other of those substances so that they could be added to the recipe. The computer showed them the food combinations that met their nutritional requirements and, having achieved this, they could alter the recipe so that a casserole could become a quiche by reducing the liquid content and adding a crust, yet the ingredients remained the same.

Weight Reducing Programme

When individuals decide to enrol on a weight reducing programme they are advised to buy a set of scales and weigh themselves once a week before breakfast on the same day each week. If they decide on a gradual weight loss and health improvement only, they could start on a nutrient rich, low calorie diet of 1,800 calories per day, and not restrict themselves to calorie limits but eat as much as they want of the food in the plan. They will still lose weight but be much healthier and enjoy a life span which will be longer if they limit the calories by even 5 or 10%.

If they opt for weight loss, health promotion and a life span extension by eating the *Anti-Aging Diet Plan* with calorie limitations, they may start with 1,800 calories and if necessary reduce it slowly towards their set point body weight. This is the weight that hereditary and childhood eating habits have set for each person and is recognised as the weight reached by an individual between the ages of 20 and 30 years. Individuals on a lifespan extension diet should choose anywhere from a 10% to 20% loss of their set point body weight and the anti-ageing plan sets a limit of 20% reduction for overall well-being. A very slow and steady weight loss is the best way to extend the life span, using the anti-ageing plan with a calorie limitation.

Irrespective of which plan is chosen, the exercise should be carried out with the support of the person's general practitioner, who should advise on the time and type of physical exercise that should be undertaken. It is important that pregnant female patients and nursing mothers should not be on an anti-ageing plan with calorie limitation, and young people should be fully mature before embarking on the plan.

The government should encourage overweight and obesity clinics, where patients are examined by doctors, and their blood pressure, pulse, weight, blood cholesterol, fasting sugar and other biomarkers determined. If this is reported in two to six months, the effect of diet restriction on those markers will be determined.

The creation of budget practices has allowed general practitioners to use funds to appoint dieticians and it is, I hope, clear from this survey that the help by qualified staff to develop and control patients' diets is essential if the problem of obesity is to be dealt with. This facility could be applied more efficiently and economically if general practitioners work as a consortium.

If obesity clinics were established in those facilities with a dietician in post, more overweight individuals would avail themselves of the service.

The problems involved in applying a dietary plan

Most of the present generation of young and middle-aged men and women who, in time, will make up the future geriatric population, have been reared on a diet of refined and processed foods, such as bacon, steaks, hamburgers, fish and chips, buttered vegetables, whole milk, cakes, biscuits and ice cream. Experiments have shown that students given such refined and processed foods require 3,000 calories a day to satisfy their appetite. When the same students were given a high nutrient, low calorie diet made from wholesome food, such as fruit, hot cereals, skimmed milk, soups, pasta, fish, chicken, brown rice, vegetables, wholewheat toast and rolls, they were satisfied with 1,500 calories per day. Although many young men and women are attracted to a diet of wholesome food it will be difficult to induce the middle-aged group to change their eating habits. Yet this is the group who, in later years, will suffer the major degenerative disorders that will add to the cost and could even result in the collapse of the health service in the present century.

If the problem of obesity and the importance of a high nutrient, low calorie diet to the health of the nation is to be brought to public notice, I believe this can best be achieved by educating schoolchildren to understand what is meant by this type of diet, how it can be prepared, and what effect it can have on their life and that of their family.

Although schoolchildren should reach maturity before they embark on a full anti-ageing plan to extend their lifespan, they should hear about it as part of their course in home economics. Such a course could be exciting and devised so as to employ their knowledge of chemistry, nutrition and statistics, a training in and combined with application of computers, to determine the recommended daily allowances of diet recipes. Children so trained would be able to discuss with parents the importance and nutritional value of food they buy in supermarkets and the contribution that a nutrient rich, calorie restricted diet can make to a more active and longer old age.

The universities, food industry and the supermarkets have an important role to play. In Scotland some universities and colleges have created degree courses which lead to a Bachelor of Arts (BA) degree in Consumer and Management Studies. At first glance such studies might not, and indeed have not, attracted the number and quality of students they deserve – particularly when recruits to the courses are learning about food technology, food science and food production development. Graduates from those courses can have an important influence on the nation's diet, the quality and type of food produced, and the effect on the health of the population in this century.

This is the type of course that should attract students with an interest in mathematics, chemistry and biology and is designed to give them a good working knowledge of the food industry. It could be extended a little to give students an insight into the problem of health care and the important role that food and diets can play. If this were done, I believe more first-class students would enrol – as at present, there are not enough graduates to fill the posts that are available.

Future Perspective

No doubt in time today's young and middle-aged men and women, who will be tomorrow's geriatrics, will become conscious of the illnesses which are attributable to smoking, alcohol, and obesity – as well as the cost to the health service that will have to deal with them. At this stage it is doubtful if they are prepared to take the necessary action to deal with this problem. I believe it is to the schoolchildren of today that efforts should be directed – and it is not enough to lecture them on the dangers of smoking, alcohol abuse, and unsatisfactory diet. Only through a positive approach to their education, while at elementary, high school, and college, will they come to appreciate the medical and social problems of an ageing population, its cost to the health service and the role they could play. This will require the co-operation of schoolchildren and their parents, schoolteachers, food manufacturers and distributors, television chiefs, politicians and government.

For the success of this venture a good relationship between children and their parents is essential; unfortunately, for different reasons, not all parents whether rich or poor, see the need or are willing to spend the time to develop this relationship with their children. Single working mothers may be interested in their children's education but many find it difficult to achieve this. Where parents are in conflict or in the process of divorce or separation, the children and their schooling will suffer. The schoolteacher is often the first to notice a change in the child's performance. A problem in schools today is the disruptive, belligerent pupil from a home where neither parent is interested in, or respects, education and who looks on teachers as enemies, spending no time helping or encouraging the child with homework.

This miscellaneous group of unfortunate children is in need of the support and help from dedicated teachers who can function properly only with the support and co-operation of all parents. Since this is not forthcoming, children from this varied background will not learn the discipline installed initially by the school. These children and young adults will watch television uncontrolled, run the streets, and be prey to the abuses of cigarettes, alcohol, drugs and violence. At school, they will hear or learn about the importance of nutrient rich/low calorie diets, but it is extremely unlikely that they will impart any of this knowledge to their families – who will continue on a diet of processed food and in time will fall victim to the degenerative diseases of the heart and brain.

Figures

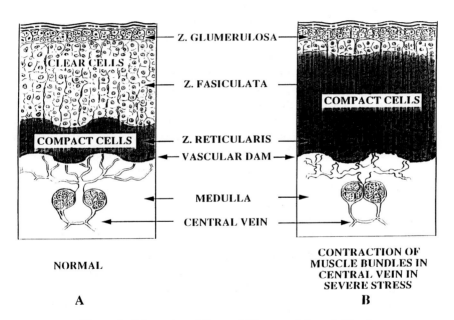

Figure 1. *Normal and Stressed Human Adrenal Glands.*

Some of the main enzymes involved in the steroid assembly line:

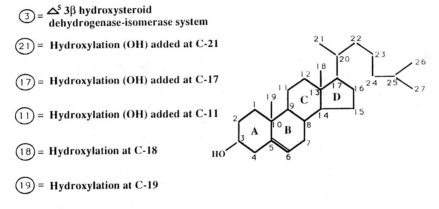

③ = Δ^5 3β hydroxysteroid
dehydrogenase-isomerase system

㉑ = **Hydroxylation (OH) added at C-21**

⑰ = **Hydroxylation (OH) added at C-17**

⑪ = **Hydroxylation (OH) added at C-11**

⑱ = **Hydroxylation at C-18**

⑲ = **Hydroxylation at C-19**

Figure 2. Numbering System used for Steroid Nucleus.

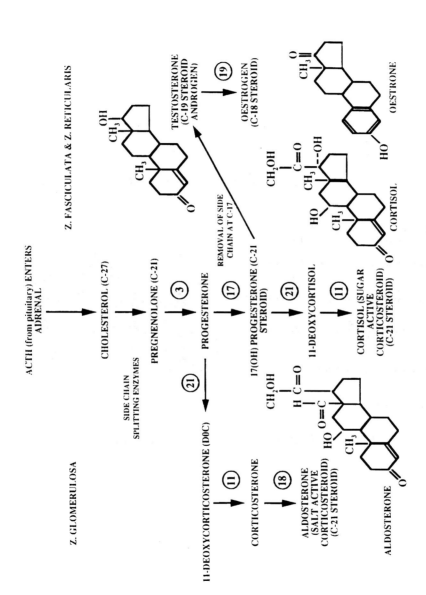

Figure 3. Steroid Hormone Assembly Line.

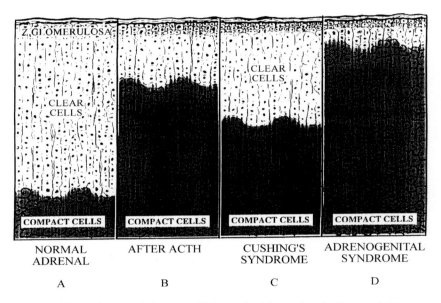

Figure 4. Distribution of Compact Cells in the Normal and Abnormal Human Adrenal Cortex.

References

'Accounting for Consultants' (1990): *BMJ*, p. 149

'North of England Study of Standards and Performance in General Practice' (1992): Medical Audit (1) *BMJ*, 304, pp. 1480–4

Association of American Cancer Institutes News Letter, June 1985

Baker, R. and Samuel, O. (1993): 'Quality Assurance in general practice'. *Proceedings of the Royal Society of Edinburgh*, 101B, p. 135

Balint, M. (1957): *The doctor, his patient and the illness*, London, Pitman

Blacklock, J. W. S., Ferguson, J. W. and Symington, T. (1947): 'Phaeochromocytoma', *British Journal of Surgery*, 35, pp. 138, 179–97

Boucher, I. A. D., Beck, J. S. and Russell, I. eds (1993): 'Quality Assurance in Medical Care', *Proceedings of the Royal Society of Edinburgh*, 101B

Bowman, A. Ian (1989): *Symington and the Charlotte Dundas*, Famous Residents Series

Bowman, A. K. (1942): *Sir William MacEwan. A Chapter in the History of Surgery*, Wm Hodge & Co. Ltd, London, Edinburgh and Glasgow

Boyd, Wm. (1961): *Education in Ayrshire through Seven Centuries*, University of London Press Ltd, Warwick Square, London

Brock, Thomas D. (1988): *Robert Koch – A Life in Medicine and Bacteriology*, Science Tech Publishers, Madison WI, Springer·Verlag Berlin, Heidelberg, New York, London, Paris, Tokyo

Bruce Lockhart, Sir Robert (1951): *Scotch. The whisky of Scotland in fact and story*, Neil Wilson Publishing, Glasgow, p. 21

Buck, N, Devlin, H. B. and Lunn, J. N. (1987): 'Report of a Confidential Enquiry into Perioperative Deaths (CEPOD)', London; Nuffield Provincial Hospitals Trust and Kings Fund

Cameron, Gordon Roy (1956): *New Pathways in Cellular Pathology*, W. M. Clowes & Sons Ltd, London and Beccles

Campbell, R. H. (1961): Carron Company, Oliver and Boyd Ltd, Edinburgh and London

Chadwick, John and Mann, W. N. (1950): *The Medical Work of Hippocrates*, Blackwell Scientific Publications, Oxford

Cohnheim, Julius (1889): *Lectures on General Pathology*, translated by Mackie, Alexander B., with Memoir (p. XIV) by the translator, London. The New Sydenham Society. Printed by Adlard & Son, Bartholomew Close

Comling, E. A., Devlin, H. B., and Lunn, J. N. Report of the National Confidential Enquiry into Perioperative Deaths (CEPOD), London; Royal College of Surgeons of England

Currie, A. R., Grant, J. K. and Symington, T., eds (1962): *The Human Adrenal Cortex*, E. and S. Livingstone, Edinburgh

Donabedian, A. (1966): 'Evaluating the quality of medical care', *Millbank Memorial Fund Quarterly*, 4, pp. 166–206

Ferguson, T. (1958): *Friendly Societies in Scottish Social Welfare, 1864 to 1914*, Edinburgh, p. 335

Findlay, Thos. (1981): *Garan 1631 to Muirkirk 1950*

Fraser, C. G. (1993): 'Quality Assurance in Clinical Chemistry', *Proceedings of the Royal Society of Edinburgh*, 101B, pp. 251–61

Fulton, W. F. M. (2 December 1971): *Seventh Inaugural Lecture. Towards the end of a beginning. Development, implications and prospects of Kenya's Medical School*, Printed by Afropress Ltd, PO Box 30502, Nairobi, Kenya

Glasscheib, H. S. (1963): *The March of Medicine. Aberrations and Triumphs of the Healing Art*, translated from German by Mervyn Savill, Macdonald, London

Glick, D. (1961): *Quantitative Chemical Techniques of Histo- and Cytochemistry*, Vol. I, Interscience Publishers, John Wiley & Sons, New York–London

Glick, D. (1963): *Quantitative Chemical Techniques of Histo- and Cytochemistry*, Vol. II, Interscience Publishers, John Wiley & Sons, New York–London

Hamilton, D. N. H. (1997): *The Healers*, Canongate, Edinburgh, pp. 239, 255.

Kennedy, J. S. (1968): 'The Glasgow–Nairobi Link, 1965–67', *Scottish Medical Journal*, 13, p. 359

Kitson, A. (1993): 'Quality Assurance in Nursing Practice', *Proceedings of the Royal Society of Edinburgh*, 101B, pp. 143–63

Leitch, A. (1922): 'Paraffin Cancer and Its Experimental Production', *BMJ*, 9 December, p. 1104

Lewis, S. M. (1993): 'Quality Assurance in Laboratory Haematology', *Proceedings of the Royal Society of Edinburgh*, 101B, pp. 283–310

Lunn, J. N. and Mushin, W. W. (1982): *Mortality associated with anaesthesia*, London; Nuffield Provincial Hospital Trust

Macon, D. N. (1976): *Clark and The Anderson – A Personal Profile*, published by the Texas Medical Center, Houston

Mant, D. and Phillips, A. (1986): 'Can the prevalence of disease risk factors be assessed from general practice records', *BMJ*, 292, pp. 102–4

Medical Audit (2). *BMJ*, 304, pp. 1484–8

Morrell, D (1988): *Epidemiology in general practice*, Oxford; Oxford University Press.

National Audit Office Investigation (1990): 'Consultant's Neglect of Duties Not Proven', *BMJ*, pp. 147–8

Nixon, S. J. (1993): 'Quality Assurance in Surgical Practice', *Proceedings of the Royal Society of Edinburgh, Proceedings*, 101B, pp. 183–91

Paine, A. (1920): 'The Origin of Cancer', *The Lancet*, 2 December, p. 693

Pembrey, S. (1979): 'Standards in Nursing', *Nursing Times*, 75, pp. 814–15

Phaneuf, M. C. (1964): 'A Nursing Audit Method', *Nursing Outlook*, 12, pp. 42–5

Plimmer, H. G. (1903): 'The Parasitic Theory of Cancer', *BMJ*, 12 December, p. 1511

Prepared by Marshall, A. J., Burton, J. A. G. (1962): *Catalogue of Pathological Preparations of Dr William Hunter, Sir William MacEwan, Professor John H. Teacher, Professor J. A. G. Burton*, University of Glasgow

Qvist, G. (1981): *John Hunter (1792–1793)*, Wm Heinemann Med Books Ltd, London

Robertson, A. J. and Beck, J. S. 'Quality Assurance in Histopathology', *Proceedings of the Royal Society of Edinburgh*, 101B, pp. 263–82

Russell, I., Grimshaw, J., Wilson, B. J. (1993): 'Scientific and Methodological Issues in Quality Assurance', *Proceedings of the Royal Society of Edinburgh*, 101B, pp. 77–103.

Sandwith, Frieda (1960): *Surgeon Compassionate. The Story of Dr Wiliam Marsden*, Peter Davies, London

Saunders C. M., ed. (1978): *The Management of Terminal Disease*, Edward Arnold Ltd, London

Scottish Clinical Resource and Audit Group (1991): 'Thrombolytic therapy in the early treatment of acute myocardiac infarction', Consensus Statement. Edinburgh HMSO

Selye, Hans (1946): 'Adaptation Syndrome', *Journal of Clinical Endocrinology*, 6, p. 117

Snell, J. J. S and Hurley, R. (1993): *Proceedings of the Royal Society of Edinburgh*, 101B, pp. 311–20

Symington, T. (1964): In: *The Scientific Basis of Medicine – Annual Reviews*, University of London Athlone Press, p. 15

Symington, T. (1969): *Functional Pathology of the Human Adrenal Gland*, E. and S. Livingstone Ltd, Edinburgh and London

Symington, T. (1978): 'Cancer, A Challenge to Clinicans and Biomedical Scientists', *Invest Cell Pathol*, 1, p. 263–74

Symington, T. (1980): In: *Cancer, Assessment and Monitoring*, Tenth Pfizer Inter Symp, eds Symington, Sir T., Williams, A. E. and McVie, J. G., Churchill Livingstone, Edinburgh, London, New York, p. 3

Symington, T. (1981): In: *Issues in Cancer Screening and Communications*, eds Mettlin, C. and Murphy, G. P., Liss Ar, Inc. New York, p. 5

Symington, T. and Carter R. L., eds (1975): *Scientific Foundations of Oncology*, Wm Heinemann, London

Symington, T. and Davidson, J. N. (1956): *Scottish Medical Journal*, 1, p. 15

The Concise Scots Dictionary (1985), ed. Mairi Robinson

Tomlinson in Scotland, Health Services Management, July/August 1993.

Tomlinson, Sir Bernard (1992): 'Reports of the inquiry into London's Health Service', Medical Education and Research, London HMSO.

Truax, Rhoda (1968): *The Doctors Warren of Boston. First Family of Surgery*, Houghton Mifflin Co., Boston

Walford, R. L. and Walford, Lisa (1995): *The Anti-Aging Plan*, London, pp. 12, 291, 294.

Walter, W. A., Saunders, J. P., and Putney H. D.: Origins of the Cancer Center Program of the National Cancer Institute.

Whelan, J. (1987): 'Using Monitor, Observer bias', *Senior Nurse*, 7, pp. 8–10.

Williams, A. (1993): 'Quality Assurance from the perspective of health economics', *Proceedings of the Royal Society of Edinburgh*, 101B, pp. 105–14.

Working for Patients (Cm 555)

Index